1962
A GUIDE BOOK
of
UNITED STATES COINS

FULLY ILLUSTRATED

Catalog and Price List—1616 to Date

By R. S. YEOMAN

———————————★———————————

Including

A BRIEF HISTORY OF AMERICAN COINAGE
EARLY AMERICAN COINS AND TOKENS
EARLY MINT ISSUES
REGULAR MINT ISSUES
PRIVATE, STATE AND TERRITORIAL GOLD
SILVER AND GOLD COMMEMORATIVE ISSUES
PROOFS

———————————★———————————

Copyright MCMLXI by
WHITMAN PUBLISHING COMPANY
RACINE, WISCONSIN

9051

CONDITION OF COINS

PF. or **PROOF.** Coins specially struck with mirror-like surface, for collectors at Philadelphia only. Also sandblast and matte proof. See Page 187.

Coins from Branch mints having a mirror-like surface are not proofs but are first strikings of new dies.

UNC. or **UNCIRCULATED.** New. Regular mint striking, but never placed in circulation. Older pieces may be tarnished or "toned."

EX. FINE or **EXTREMELY FINE.** Slightly circulated with some lustre but faint evidence of wear.

V. FINE or **VERY FINE.** Shows enough wear on high spots to be noticeable. Still retains enough lustre to be desirable.

F. or **FINE.** Obviously a circulated coin but little wear. Mint lustre gone. All letters in LIBERTY and mottoes clear.

V. G. or **VERY GOOD.** Features all clear and bold. Better than good, but not quite fine.

G. or **GOOD.** All of design, every feature and legend must be plain and date clear.

FAIR. Coin has sufficient design and letters to be easily identified. Excessive wear.

IMPORTANT: Coins in any condition with defects, such as those which are bent, corroded, scratched, holed, nicked, stained, oxidized, mutilated, or have other imperfections are worth less than if free of these defects.

THE PURPOSE OF THIS BOOK

Coin values listed in the Guide Book are averaged from data supplied by contributors several months before publication. The coin market is so active in some categories that values can easily change during this period. Prices are shown as a guide and are not intended to serve as a price-list for any dealer's stock.

Prices rise because: 1. The trend of our economy is inflationary. 2. The number of collectors is increasing rapidly, while coin supplies remain stationary. 3. Dealers can procure their stock of coins only from collectors or other dealers, who expect a profit over and above what they originally paid.

Prices decline because: 1. Speculators buy and sell in large quantities, drawing in thousands of unwary persons looking for quick profits. When the average collector stops buying, the prices drop. 2. Hoards of coins suddenly are released from estates of deceased collectors or Federal Reserve vaults (as in the case of silver dollars) and the like. Such conditions usually adjust themselves within months or a few years.

Those who edit, contribute to, and publish this book, advocate the collecting of coins for pleasure and educational benefits. A secondary consideration is that of investment, the profits from which are realized over the long term based on intelligent purchases of the best grades of coins.

Neither the publishers, nor the editor, deal in coins; therefore, the prices shown are not offers to sell but are included only as general information.

We thank all contributors to this edition.

R. S. YEOMAN

The Handbook of United States Coins, containing average prices dealers will pay for certain specified coins, is obtainable at hobby dealers for $1.00.

CONTRIBUTORS TO THE FOURTEENTH EDITION
KENNETH E. BRESSETT, Editorial Assistant
GLENN B. SMEDLEY
Co-ordinator, Panel of Contributors

A. E. Bebee
M. H. Bolender
Harry X Boosel (1873)
Q. David Bowers
LaVanch Bercaw
Malcolm O. E. Chell-Frost
Alan R. Cohen
Jerry Cohen
M. R. Cohen
B. M. Douglas
Ben Dreiske
LeRoy (Pete) Foerster
Robert Friedberg

Bernard Gimelson
A. M. Kagin
Paul Kagin
D. W. Karp
Louis R. Karp
A. Kosoff
Abner Kreisberg
Kenneth W. Lee
Bill Mertes
Franklyn H. Miller
Al C. Overton
Earl A. Parker
Richard Picker

Hubert L. Polzer
Elmer B. Ray
James F. Ruddy
F. K. Saab
Earl C. Schill
J. S. Schreiber
Norman Shultz
Arlie Slabaugh
Leonard W. Stark
Maurice A. Storck
R. E. Wallace
Louis S. Werner
Leo A. Young

Credit for counsel and advice is due:

Kenneth E. Bressett, William L. Clark, Alan D. Craig, George Fuld, A. M. Kagin, Lewis M. Reagan, Max M. Schwartz and Walter Thompson for original historical and descriptive data appearing in this book.

Those now deceased, but whose contributions have been a part of this book since early editions, include:

David M. Bullowa, Charles E. Green, Richard D. Kenney, Stuart Mosher, Herbert E. Rowold, Farran Zerbe

ACKNOWLEDGMENT

Selected listings and related material in this edition are from **THE STANDARD CATALOGUE OF UNITED STATES COINS** and are reproduced with permission of **FORD NUMISMATIC PUBLICATIONS**, New York, N. Y. For additional data and comparative pricing information see **THE STANDARD CATALOGUE**.

THE SPANISH MILLED DOLLAR

The Coin of Our Nation's Founders

The Spanish milled dollar valued at eight reals, otherwise known as the "pillar dollar" and "piece of eight," has been given a place in romantic fiction unequalled by any other coin.

This time-honored piece, along with its fractional parts, such as two reals and four reals, was the chief coin of the American Colonists and was the forerunner of our own silver dollar and its fractional divisions, such as the quarter-dollar and half-dollar.

AN INTRODUCTION TO UNITED STATES COINS

Money of the Early Americans

The story of American money, which occupies a period of about three centuries, began when the early settlers in New England carried on their fur trade with the Indians through the use of wampum, which had been fashioned from mussel shells in the form of "beads." Beaver skins, wampum, and in Virginia, tobacco, soon became the common accepted media of exchange for all other available commodities. The immigrants, in fact, had little use for coined money at first, but when traders arrived from foreign lands, coins were usually demanded in payment for goods. Any foreign coins were usually accepted, such as French louis, English guineas, German thalers, Dutch ducats, and various Spanish coins, including doubloons and particularly the Spanish milled dollar, or piece of eight. The coin last mentioned remained as a standard money unit throughout the entire colonial period. Even after the Revolutionary War, the Spanish dollar and its fractional parts continued to circulate in this country with official sanction until 1857. One real equaled $12\frac{1}{2}$ cents and was known as a "bit." A quarter of the dollar thus became known as "two bits," a term still in common use.

England consistently ignored the plight of the Colonists and made no effort to provide gold or silver coins, or a small-change currency for them. Although coins known as "Hogge Money" were provided for the Sommer Islands, now known as the Bermudas, about the year 1616, the first coins minted in America were minted by John Hull in the Massachusetts Bay Colony. The General Court of the colony granted him authority to begin coinage. Starting in 1652 the Boston mint provided the famous N.E., pine tree, and similar shillings, with their fractional parts, for the hardpressed colonists. Other colonies tried similar projects but failed.

As time went on coins and tokens of many types were introduced and employed by the colonists in their daily course of business. Lord Baltimore in Maryland was responsible for a series of silver pieces, which were probably struck in England in 1659. Mark Newby introduced a piece known as St. Patrick's Halfpence into the province of New Jersey in 1682. Coins dated 1722 to 1724, known as Rosa Americana and Hibernia coppers, were produced by William Wood in England and were widely circulated in America. The Carolina and New England Elephant tokens were current in the years following 1694. There were also a few issues of uncertain date and origin, such as the New Yorke Token and the New England Stiver which circulated among the Dutch settlers and were probably sent over from Holland.

Enterprising American individuals were responsible for some of the copper pieces which circulated during the eighteenth century. The Gloucester Token, about which little is known, was one of these. John Higley of Granby, Connecticut, made an interesting series of three pence pieces during the period from 1737 to 1739. J. Chalmers, a goldsmith in Annapolis, Maryland, issued silver shillings, sixpence, and three pence pieces in 1783. In 1787 Ephriam Brasher, a New York goldsmith, struck a gold piece of the value of a doubloon (about $16.00). Standish Barry of Baltimore, Maryland, made a curious silver token three pence in 1790.

Still other tokens, struck in England, reached our shores in Revolutionary times and were for the most part speculative ventures. These much-needed, small-denomination coppers, were readily circulated because of the great scarcity of fractional coins. Included in this category were the Nova Constellatio coppers, The Bar cent, and the Virginia half pennies.

During the period of confederation following the War of Independence, still more English tokens were added to the great variety of coins and tokens employed in the new nation. In 1787 the Nova Eboracs, known as New York Coppers, the Georgius Triumpho, the Auctori Plebis, and later the Kentucky, Myddleton and Franklin Press tokens were introduced.

Another interesting series, important because of their close association with our first president, comprises those tokens bearing the portrait of Washington. They circulated during and after the Confederation.

Coinage of the States

The Articles of Confederation, adopted July 9, 1778, provided that Congress should have the sole right to regulate the alloy and value of coin struck by their own authority or by that of the respective states.

Each state, therefore, had the right to coin money, but Congress served as a regulating authority. New Hampshire was the first state to consider coinage, but few if any coins were placed in circulation. The only specimens known bear the date 1776.

Vermont, Connecticut, and New Jersey, granted coining privileges to companies or individuals. Massachusetts erected its own mint in which copper coins were produced. A number of interesting varieties of these state issues, most of which were struck in fairly large quantities, can still be easily acquired, and form the basis for many present day collections of early American coins.

The Beginnings of United States Coinage

Throughout the Colonial years, Americans had become accustomed to the use of the Spanish dollar and its fractional parts, the real, the medio (half-real), etc. It was only natural, therefore, that when a national coinage was under consideration that the dollar was mentioned most frequently. In earlier years currency statutes in many of the colonies had given first consideration to the Spanish dollar. Connecticut, Massachusetts, and Virginia, particularly, passed laws making Spanish coins a legal tender. The Resolution of June 22, 1775, which authorized the first issue of Continental paper money, offers further evidence that the dollar was to be our basic money unit, for it provided that the notes should be payable in "Spanish Milled dollars or the value thereof in gold or silver."

The Assistant Financier of the Confederation, Gouverneur Morris, proposed a decimal coinage ratio, and his plan was incorporated in a report presented by Robert Morris, Superintendent of Finance, to the Congress, January 15, 1782. Plans for a mint were advanced, and a uniform national currency to relieve the confused money conditions was outlined. Morris's unit, 1/1440 of a dollar, was calculated to agree without a fraction with all the different valuations of the Spanish milled dollar in the various States. Although a government mint was approved February 21, 1782, no immediate action was taken. During 1784 Thomas Jefferson, then a member of the House of Representatives, brought in a report concerning the plan, and expressed disagreement with Morris' complicated money unit. He advocated the simple dollar unit because he believed the dollar was already as familiar and convenient a unit of value as the British pound. He favored the decimal system and remarked that, "The most easy ratio of multiplication and division is that of ten. President George Washington referred to it as 'a measure, which in my opinion, has become indispensibly necessary.'"

The Grand Committee in May 1785 recommended a gold five-dollar piece; a dollar of silver with fractional coins, of the same metal, in denominations of half, quarter, tenth, and twentieth parts of a dollar; and copper pieces valued at one-hundredth and one two-hundredth of a dollar.

In 1783 Robert Morris submitted a series of pattern pieces in silver, which were designed by Dudley to carry out the decimal idea for United

States money. These are known as the Nova Constellatio Patterns and consist of the "Mark" or 1,000 units, the "Quint" or 500 units, and the "Bit" or 100 units. The unit was to be a quarter grain of silver. This was not the first attempt at a dollar coin, for the Continental currency piece of dollar size, dated 1776, had been struck in such metals as brass, pewter, and silver. The variety in silver probably saw limited service as a dollar.

Congress gave formal approval to the basic dollar unit and decimal coinage ratio in its resolution of July 6, 1785, but other more pressing matters delayed further action. Not until the Constitutional Convention had placed the country on firm ground and the new nation had elected George Washington as President, did the congress again turn attention to the subject of currency, a mint, and a coinage system.

The Massachusetts cents and half-cents struck in 1787 and 1788, were the first official coins to bear a stated value in terms of decimal parts of the dollar unit in this country. The cent represented a hundredth part of a Spanish dollar.

The first federally authorized coin was the Fugio Cent, sometimes called the Franklin Cent, as he was supposed to have supplied the design and composed the legends. This piece, similar in design to the Continental Currency dollar of 1776, was privately struck in 1787 by contract with the Government.

Alexander Hamilton, then Secretary of the Treasury, reported his views on monetary matters January 21, 1791. He concurred in all essentials with the decimal subdivisions and multiples of the dollar contained in the earlier resolutions, and urged the use of both gold and silver in our standard money.

Congress passed a resolution March 3, 1791, that a mint be established, and authorized the President to engage artists and procure machinery for the making of coins. No immediate steps were taken, but when Washington delivered his third annual address, he recommended immediate establishment of a mint.

On April 2, 1792, a bill was finally passed providing "that the money of account of the United States should be expressed in dollars or units, dismes or tenths, cents or hundredths, and milles or thousandths; a disme being the tenth part of a dollar, a cent the hundredth part of a dollar, a mille the thousandth part of a dollar . . ."

Denominations specified in the act were as follows:

	Value of	Grains Pure	Grains Standard
Gold Eagle	$10.00	247–4/8	270
Gold Half Eagle	5.00	123–6/8	135
Gold Quarter Eagle	2.50	61–7/8	67–4/8
Silver Dollar	1.00	371–4/16	416
Silver Half-Dollar	.50	185–10/16	208
Silver Quarter-Dollar	.25	92–13/16	104
Silver Disme (dime)	.10	37–2/16	41–3/5
Silver Half-Disme	.05	18–9/16	20–4/5
Copper Cent	.01	11 pennyweights	
Copper Half-Cent	.005	5½ pennyweights	

The word "pure" meant unalloyed metal; "standard" meant in this instance 11/12 fine or 11 parts pure metal to one part alloy, which was mixed with the pure metal to improve the wearing qualities of the coins.

The law also provided for free coinage of gold and silver coins at the fixed ratio of 15 to one, and a token coinage of copper cents and half-cents. Under the free coinage provision no charge was to be made for converting gold or silver bullion into coins "weight for weight." At the depositor's option, however, he could demand an immediate exchange of coins for his bullion, for which privilege a deduction of one-half of one per cent was to be imposed.

Washington appointed David Rittenhouse, a well-known philosopher and scientist, as the first Director of the Mint. A mint building was started nearly four months after the passage of the Act of April 2, 1792. It was located on Seventh Street near Arch in Philadelphia.

The first coin struck at the new mint was the half-disme. Several hundred of these pieces were produced during the month of October 1792 before the mint was completed. Washington supplied some of his own private plate to the value of about one hundred dollars for these first mint coins. Dismes also were probably struck at this time or a short while later. The portrait on these pieces is presumed to be modeled by Martha Washington.

Copper for cents and half-cents was covered in the Act of May 8, 1792 when the purchase of not over 150 tons was authorized. On September 11, 1792, six pounds of old copper were purchased, this being the first purchase of copper for coinage, which was probably used for the striking of patterns.

Planchets with upset rims for cents and half-cents were purchased from Boulton of Birmingham, England from 1798 to 1833.

Several pattern coins were prepared in 1792 before regular mint operations commenced. These included the silver center cent by Voigt, a smaller piece than that of regular issue. The small plug of silver, worth about three-quarters of a cent, was evidently intended to bring the intrinsic value of the coin up to the value of one cent and permit production of a coin of more convenient size. Alexander Hamilton had mentioned a year before that the proposed "intrinsic value" cent would be too large, and suggested that the amount of copper could be reduced and a trace of silver added. This pattern cent with a silver center may have been designed to conform to this recommendation.

The cents by Robert Birch are equally interesting. These patterns are identified by their legends which read "LIBERTY PARENT OF SCIENCE AND INDUSTRY" and "TO BE ESTEEMED BE USEFUL." The cent with an eagle on the reverse side belongs among the early patterns devised before regular issues were struck.

The first depositor of silver was the bank of Maryland, which sent \$80,715.73½ in French coins to the mint July 18, 1794. Moses Brown, a Boston merchant, deposited the first gold in the form of ingots, February 12, 1795, amounting to \$2,276.22, receiving silver coin in payment. The first coins transferred to the Treasurer consisted of 11,178 cents on March 1, 1793. The first return of coined silver was made on October 15, 1794, and the first gold coins were delivered July 31, 1795, 744 half-eagles.

File marks on early U. S. Coins are a mint process of weight adjustment.

Regular Mint Issues

Cents and half-cents exclusively were coined during the year 1793, and by 1799 approximately \$50,000 in these coins had been placed in circulation. This amount proved insufficient for the requirements of commerce, and small denomination coins of the states and of foreign countries continued in use during the first few years of the nineteenth century.

One of the most serious problems confronting the commercial interests during the early years was the failure of the government to provide a sufficient volume of circulating coins. The fault, contrary to popular opinion at the time, did not lie with any lack of effort on the part of the mint. Other circumstances tended to interfere with the expected steady flow of new coinage into the channels of trade.

Free circulation of United States gold and silver coins was greatly hindered by speculators. The silver dollars, for example, were easily exchanged for worn Spanish dollars of reduced weight and value, which meant the export of most of the new dollars as fast as they were minted, and a complete loss to American trade channels.

Gold coins failed to circulate for similar reasons. The ratio of 15 to 1 between gold and silver was close to the world ratio when Hamilton recommended it, but by 1799 the ratio in European commercial centers had reached 15¾ to 1. At this rate the undervalued gold coins tended to flow out of the country, or were reduced for bullion. After 1800, therefore, United States gold coins were rarely seen in general circulation. As no remedy could be found, coinage of the Eagle and the silver dollar was suspended by President Jefferson in 1804 and 1806 respectively. It is generally conceded that the silver dollar was discontinued in 1803, although a few specimens of the dollar bearing the date 1804 are known.

Lacking gold coins and silver dollars, the half-dollar became the desirable coin for large transactions, bank reserves, and foreign payments. Until 1830, in fact, half-dollars circulated very little as they were mainly transferred from bank to bank. This will account for the relatively good supply of half-dollars of this period which are still available to collectors in better than average condition. A senate committee of 1830 reported that United States silver coins were considered as so much bullion and were accordingly "lost to the community as coins."

There was only a negligible coinage of quarters, dimes, and half-dimes from 1794 to 1834. It has been estimated that there was less than one piece for each person in the country in the year 1830. This period has been described as one of nondescript currency, made up of banknotes, underweight foreign gold coins, foreign silver coins of many varieties, and domestic fractional silver coins. Notes of "wildcat banks" flooded the country before 1830 and were much more common than silver coins.

On June 28, 1834, a new law was passed reducing the weight of standard gold, which had the effect of placing our money on a gold standard. Trade and finance were greatly benefited by this act, which also proved a boon to the gold mines of Georgia and North Carolina. Branch mints in Dahlonega, Georgia, and Charlotte, North Carolina, were established two or three years later to handle the newly-mined gold at the source. The Templeton Ried and Bechtler issues of private gold coins were struck in this area.

The law of January 18, 1837, completely revised and standardized the mint and coinage laws. Legal standards, mint charges, legal tender, mint procedure, tolerance in coin weights, accounting methods, a bullion fund, standardization of gold and silver coins to 900 thousandths fine, and other desirable regulations were covered by the new legislation. Results of importance to the collector were the changes in type for the various coin denominations and the resumption of coinage of the Eagle and silver dollar shortly thereafter.

The political and financial elements underwent a crisis at about this time. The familiar "Jackson Tokens" and fractional notes of banks and commercial establishments completely eclipsed the circulation of metallic currency. This was the era of "shinplasters."

The California gold discovery in 1848 was responsible for an interesting series of private, state, and territorial gold issues in the Western states, culminating in the establishment of a branch mint at San Francisco in 1854.

Two new regular gold issues were adopted in 1849. In that year the double Eagle and gold dollar joined our American family of coins. The California gold fields greatly influenced the world gold market making the exportation of silver profitable. For example, the silver in two half-dollars was worth $1.03½ in gold. The newly introduced gold dollars soon took over the burden and hastened the disappearance of silver coins from trade channels. This was the situation when the new three-cent postage rate brought about the bill authorizing the coinage of the silver three-cent piece in 1851. This was our country's first subsidiary coin, for its value was intrinsically 86% of its face value, an expedient designed to prevent its withdrawal from circulation.

The three-dollar gold piece was authorized by the act of February 21, 1853. Never a popular or necessary coin, it nevertheless was issued regularly until 1889.

On February 21, 1853, fractional silver coins were made subsidiary resulting from the fact that the weight of all silver pieces, excepting the dollar, was reduced. As the coins were now worth less than their face value free coinage of silver was prohibited, and the mint was authorized to purchase its silver requirements on its own account using the bullion fund of the mint, and, according to law, "the profit of said coinage shall be, ... transferred to the account of the treasury of the United States."

Arrows were placed at the date on all silver coins except three-cent pieces and dollars, and on the quarters and half-dollars rays were added on the reverse side to denote the change of weight. In 1854 the rays were removed, and in 1856 the arrows disappeared. Production of silver coins in large quantities during this period greatly relieved the demands on gold dollars and three-cent pieces. Consequently for the first time in our nation's history there was a sufficient supply of fractional coins in general circulation.

The law of 1857 was designed primarily to reform the copper coinage. No matter how interesting and valuable the large cents and half-cents may have become in the eyes of the modern collector, they were very unpopular with the people and cost the mint too much to produce.

The new law abolished the half-cent piece, and reduced the size and changed the design of the cent. The new eagle or white cent contained 88% copper and 12% nickel. Several hundred were stamped from dies bearing the date 1856, a quantity considered by many to be too large for a pattern issue. Yet, no authority for the issue existed before 1857. Other important effects of the law were the retirement of the Spanish silver coins from circulation, and dispersal of the new cents in such excessive quantities as to create a nuisance to business houses, particularly in the eastern cities. The Indian head device replaced the Eagle in 1859, and in 1864 the weight of the cent was further reduced and its composition changed to a proportion of 95% copper and 5% tin and zinc. This bronze composition has been standard for our cent except for the year 1943.

Both Jefferson and Hamilton had contended in their day that the currency of money of small value benefits society. The history of our cent and its daily use proves the soundness of this principle.

Abundance turned to scarcity following the outbreak of the Civil War. Anticipation of a scarcity and depreciation of the paper money was sufficient to induce hoarding. The large volume of greenbacks in circulation caused a premium on gold, and subsidiary silver as a result of the sudden depreciation quickly vanished in the North. Resort was soon made to postage stamps for small change. All types of fractional notes were put out at this time by municipalities and the Government. "Postage currency" became widely used, and in 1863 a great variety of tokens appeared to help fill the vacuum. Like the tokens of 1837 they were of two general classes, tradesman's coins and imitations of legal cents. The latter were usually produced at a profit, many of which were political or patriotic in character, with slogans typical of the times.

The Law of 1864, which effected changes in the cent, provided also for the new bronze two-cent piece. The act, moreover, provided legal tender status for these two coins up to ten times their value. The two-cent piece was the first coin to bear the motto IN GOD WE TRUST. The new coin was readily accepted by the people but proved an unnecessary denomination, going out of fashion and being discontinued only nine years later.

Secretary Chase had issued a great many currency notes of three-cent denomination early in 1865. The nickel interests seized upon this circumstance to fight for a new three-cent coin for redemption of the paper money. A law was quickly passed and signed by the president as of March 3, 1865, providing for a three-cent coin of 75-25 copper-nickel composition. Our country now possessed two types of three-cent pieces. The nickel three-cent piece was struck continuously until 1889; the three-cent silver until 1873.

[10]

The new copper-nickel alloy ratio was selected for the five-cent coin, adopted May 16, 1866, to be thereafter known as a "nickel " Again the people had a coin value available in two forms. The silver half-dime, like the three-cent piece, was retired from service in 1873.

The Carson City Mint was established in 1870 as a convenient depository for the miners in that area and operated until 1893.

The Law of March 3, 1871, was a redemption measure and was passed to provide a means for the disposal to the United States Treasury of millions of minor coins, which had accumulated in the hands of postmasters, newsdealers, and others. Small-denomination coins as a result of this new law were placed on an equal footing and could be redeemed when presented in lots of twenty dollars.

There was a general revision of the coinage laws in 1873. Several years study and debate preceded the final enactment. The legislative history of the bill occupies hundreds of pages of the Congressional Globe, and the result was considered by many a clumsy attempt and a failure. The law has sometimes been referred to as the "Crime of '73." One consequence of the bill, which achieved final enactment February 12, 1873, was the elimination of the silver dollar. In its stead the Trade dollar of greater weight was provided for use in commerce with the Orient in competition with the Mexican dollar. The legal tender provision, which unintentionally gave the trade dollar currency within our borders, was repealed the following year.

The charge for converting standard gold bullion into coin was reduced by the act to one-fifth of one per cent. The same rate was imposed on silver bullion for coining trade dollars only.

It may be a surprise to some collectors to learn that the silver dollar had not circulated to any great extent in the United States after 1803. The coin had been turned out steadily since 1840, but for various reasons such as exportation, melting, and holding in bank vaults, the dollar was virtually an unknown coin. The Law of 1873 in effect demonetized silver and committed our country to a gold standard. The silver mining interests came to realize what had occurred a little later, and the ensuing quarter century of political and monetary history was filled with their voluble protests. There was a constant bitter struggle for the return to bimetallism.

From an economic point of view the inadequate supply of gold was responsible for a gradual decline in prices throughout the world. This brought about a gradual business depression in our country, particularly in the South and Middle-West. Private silver interests influenced great sections of the West for bimetallism as a remedy for the failing price level. Authorities have concluded that a world-wide adoption of bimetallism would have improved economic conditions, but the United States alone proceeding to place their money on a double standard at the old 16 to 1 ratio would have led only to a worse situation.

Of particular importance to collectors, however, were those features of the Law of 1873 which affected the status and physical properties of the individual coins. The weight of the half-dollar, quarter, and dime, was slightly changed and arrows were placed at the date for the ensuing two years to indicate the difference in weight. Silver three-cent pieces, half-dimes, and two-cent pieces, were abolished by the act, and the manufacture of minor coins was restricted to the Mint at Philadelphia.

The next coinage legislation was that of March 3, 1875, which authorized the twenty-cent piece. This denomination was purely an experiment, and the coin was short-lived, for the general public complained about its similarity in design and size to the quarter-dollar. The last twenty-cent pieces were struck in 1878, and all were proofs. No logical reason for this coin's existence has ever been advanced.

The Bland-Allison Act of February 28, 1878, gave the Secretary authority to purchase two to four million dollars worth of silver bullion each month to be coined into silver dollars. The coin, never popular, was produced in minimum quantities. This was not a bimetallic law, nor was it a free coinage act. Strictly speaking it was a subsidiary coinage law, called by some "a wretched compromise."

The North and East so disliked the silver dollar that they found their way back to the Treasury, mostly through tax payments. Secretary Manning transferred ownership to the people and removed them from Treasury holdings by the simple expedient of issuing silver certificates in small bills to effect a wide circulation.

The Bland-Allison Act was repealed in 1890 and the Sherman Act took its place. Under this new law 4,500,000 ounces of silver per month could be paid for with Treasury Notes that were to be legal tender, and redeemable in gold or silver dollars coined from the bullion purchased. Important in this case was the fact that the notes were constantly being redeemed for gold which was mainly exported. The measure was actually a government subsidy for the silver miners and as such it was marked for failure, and was hastily repealed. The Bland-Allison Act and the Sherman Act gave a total of 570 million silver dollars to our monetary stocks.

The "Gold Standard Act" of 1900 gave our country a single standard, but re-affirmed the fiction that the silver dollar is a standard coin. It still enjoys unlimited, legal tender, but is as much a subsidiary coin, practically speaking, as the dime, for its value in terms of standard gold, even before the gold surrender executive order, was far below its face value.

The lapse in coinage after 1904 and until 1921 was due to lack of bullion. Legislation authorizing further metal supplies for silver dollars was not forthcoming until 1918 when the Pittman Act provided silver for the new dollars.

The new type dollar issued from 1921 to 1935 was a commemorative peace coin, which might easily have been a half-dollar. The peace dollar, in fact, was issued without congressional sanction, under the terms of the Pittman Act, which referred to the bullion and in no way affected the design.

Before the first world war the value of gold was equal to the value of gold coined into money. In order to encourage a steady flow of gold to the mints the government (with the exception of the period 1853-1873) had adopted a policy of gratuitous coinage. The cost of converting gold into coin had generally been considered an expense chargeable to the government.

In practice the mint made fine bars for commercial use or mint bars for coinage at its discretion. The bars in later years were stored in vaults and gold or silver certificates issued in place of the coins.

On March 6, 1933 an order was issued by the President prohibiting banks from paying out gold and gold certificates without permission, and gold currency was thus kept for reserve purposes. Gold imports and newly mined domestic gold must now be sold to the government. Gold may not be hoarded, and there is no free domestic gold market. The coinage of all denominations above 50 cents was suspended after 1935.

No important legislation has been placed on the books governing the coinage system since the redemption law of 1879. Our Federal Reserve System has withstood all strains of war and economic disturbances. The rate of issue of the one, five, and ten cent pieces has been greatly accelerated during the twentieth century. Cents particularly are in greater demand because of "odd sum" prices, sales taxes, etc.

By the Law of September 26, 1890, changes in designs of United States coins cannot be made oftener than once every twenty-five years. Since that date, there have been design changes in all denominations and there have been many gold and silver commemorative issues. These factors are largely responsible for the ever increasing interest in coin collecting.

COINS AND TOKENS OF THE ENGLISH-AMERICAN COLONIES

★ **Star Throughout Colonial Section Indicates That Facsimilies Exist.**

Copies of certain early American issues were made to provide facsimiles of rare issues that would otherwise be unobtainable. A star has been placed adjacent to such early American coins or tokens, together with the fabricator's name for which corresponding copies are known.

The specimens illustrated are the genuine specimens.

SOMMER ISLANDS (Bermuda)

This coinage, the first struck for the English-American colonies, was issued about 1616. The coins were known as "Hogge Money" or "Hoggies."

The pieces were made of brass or a similar substance lightly silvered, in four denominations; shilling, sixpence, threepence and twopence, represented by Roman numerals. The hog is the main device and appears on the obverse side of each. SOMMER ISLANDS is inscribed within beaded circles. The reverse shows a full-rigged galleon with the flag of St. George on each of four masts.

The islands were named, during this early period, for Sir George Somers who was shipwrecked there in 1609 while enroute to the Virginia Plantation. Shakespeare's "The Tempest" was supposedly based on this incident.

The Bermuda Islands, as they are known today, were named for Juan Bermudez who is believed to have stopped there in 1515. A few hogs which he carried for delivery to the West Indies were left behind. When Somers and his party arrived many years later, the islands were over-run with the beasts, and they served as a welcome source of food for the members of the expedition.

	Good	Fine
Shilling	$150.00	$335.00
Sixpence, Large Portholes	125.00	250.00
Sixpence, Small Portholes	V. Rare	
Threepence	150.00	335.00
Twopence	125.00	235.00

Shilling ★ Dickeson

Sixpence   Large Portholes   Small Portholes

Threepence   Twopence

MASSACHUSETTS
New England

The earliest medium of exchange in the New England settlements was wampum. The General Court of Massachusetts in 1637 ordered "that wampampege should passe at 6 a penny for any sume under 12 d." Wampum consisted of shells of various colors ground to the size of a grain of corn. A hole was drilled through each piece so they could be strung on leather thongs for convenience, and adornment.

Corn, pelts and bullets were frequently offered in lieu of coins, which were almost non-existent. Currency brought over from England, Holland and other countries tended to flow back across the Atlantic for much needed supplies. The colonists thus thrown on their own resources, dealt with the friendly Indians in kind. In 1661 the law authorizing wampum as legal tender was repealed.

Agitation for a standard coinage reached its height in 1651. England, with a civil war between the Puritans and Royalists on her hands, ignored the colonists, who took matters into their own hands in 1652.

The General Court in 1652 ordered the first metallic currency in the English Americas (The Spaniards had established a mint in the City of Mexico in 1535), the silver N.E. shillings, and fractional denominations. Silver bullion was procured principally from the West Indies. Joseph Jenks made the die for the first impression at Iron Works (Saugus, Massachusetts) just outside of Boston where the mint was located. John Hull was appointed mint-master; his assistant was Robert Sanderson (or Saunderson). Mint-master Hull received one shilling threepence for every twenty shillings coined as his compensation. This fee was adjusted several times during his term as Mint-master.

NE Shilling ★ Wyatt

NE Sixpence ★ Wyatt   NE Threepence

	Good	Fine
NE Shilling	$225.00	$435.00
NE Sixpence	450.00	
NE Threepence (2 known)		

[14]

WILLOW TREE PIECES

The simplicity of the design on the N.E. coins invited counterfeiting and clipping of the edges. Therefore, they were soon replaced by the Willow, Oak and Pine Tree Series.

The "tree" coins were minted about thirty years without change of date; Charles II disapproved of the issues, and mintages dated 1652 could not be easily proven to be unauthorized.

The coinage was abandoned in 1682; a proposal to renew coinage in 1686 was rejected by the General Court.

Willow Tree Shilling

Willow Tree Sixpence   Willow Tree Threepence

	Good	Fine
Willow Tree Shilling	$200.00	$425.00
Willow Tree Sixpence	375.00	650.00
Willow Tree Threepence (3 known)	—	—

OAK TREE PIECES

Oak Tree Shilling ★ Wyatt   Oak Tree Sixpence
Various Die Varieties

	Good	Fine
Oak Tree Shilling	$47.50	$90.00
Oak Tree Sixpence	42.50	77.50

OAK TREE PIECES

★ Wyatt

Oak Tree Threepence   Oak Tree Twopence (1662)
Good $35.00   Fine $55.00   Good $27.50   Fine $40.00

PINE TREE PIECES
Various Die Varieties

★ Tatham

Pine Tree Shilling—Large Planchet

The first pine tree coins were stamped on wide thin planchets. The later issues were narrower and thicker in imitation of English coins.

Pine Tree Shilling—Small Planchet

Pine Tree Sixpence ★ Wyatt   Pine Tree Threepence ★ Wyatt

	Good	Fine
Pine Tree Shilling, Large Planchet	$47.50	$97.50
Pine Tree Shilling, Small Planchet	35.00	72.50
Pine Tree Sixpence	30.00	55.00
Pine Tree Threepence	30.00	55.00

GOOD SAMARITAN SHILLING

Although this piece was formerly thought to be a pattern for the 1652 shillings, recent findings show that the known specimens are all fabrications. Three different varieties are known. The most common type was made by Thomas Wyatt, about 1856. The variety pictured here is somewhat older and is probably unique.

Good Samaritan Shilling (Unique).................... ———

MARYLAND

In 1658 Cecil the second Lord Baltimore and "Lord Proprietor of Maryland" began an issue of coinage. These pieces were made in England.

There were four denominations, shillings, sixpence, fourpence (groat) in silver, and the small copper penny (denarium). The silver coins show the bust of Cecil Calvert (Lord Baltimore) on the obverse, and the Baltimore family arms with the values in Roman numeral form and the legend CRESCITE ET MULTIPLICAMINI (Increase and be multiplied) on the reverse. The obverse of the penny is similar, but the reverse has a ducal coronet with two pennants and the inscription DENARIUM, TERRAE-MARIAE (Penny, Maryland). Numerous die varieties and patterns exist in this series.

Lord Baltimore Shilling Fourpence (Groat)

Sixpence Penny (denarium) ★ Idler

	Good	Fine
Shilling...	$100.00	$185.00
Sixpence..	75.00	130.00
Fourpence...	142.50	260.00
Penny (Copper) (3 Known)...........................	———	———

ST. PATRICK OR MARK NEWBY HALFPENCE
NEW JERSEY

Mark Newby, who came from Dublin, Ireland, in November 1681, brought some halfpence pieces believed by Nelson to have been struck in Dublin in 1678. These were called St. Patrick Halfpence.

The coin received wide currency in the New Jersey Province, having been authorized to pass as legal tender by the general assembly in May 1682.

Many of these have a brass insert at the crown so that when the coin was struck it would appear as though it were a golden crown.

There was also a smaller piece known as a farthing. These copper pieces exist in many die varieties. The obverses show a crowned king kneeling playing a harp. The legend FLOREAT REX (May the King prosper) is separated by a crown. The reverse side of the halfpence shows St. Patrick with a crozier in his left and a trefoil in his right hand, surrounded by people. At his left is a shield. The legend is ECCE GREX (Behold the flock).

The farthing reverse shows St. Patrick driving away reptiles and serpents, as he holds a Metropolitan cross in his left hand. The legend reads QUIESCAT PLEBS (May the people be at ease). Numerous die variations exist.

St. Patrick Halfpence

St. Patrick Farthing

	Good	Fine
St. Patrick Halfpence	$13.25	$38.00
St. Patrick Farthing, with Brass Plug on Obv.	8.00	27.50
St. Patrick Farthing without Brass Plug	8.00	27.50
St. Patrick Farthing, Silver	65.00	137.50

COINAGE OF WILLIAM WOOD
ROSA AMERICANA AND HIBERNIA COINS

William Wood, an Englishman, obtained a patent from George I to make copper tokens for Ireland and the American Colonies.

The first pieces struck were undated; others bear the dates 1722, 1723, 1724 and 1733. The Rosa Americana pieces were issued in three denominations, twopence, penny and halfpennies, and were intended for America. This type had a full-blown rose on the reverse with the words ROSA AMERICANA UTILE DULCI (American Rose—the useful with the pleasant).

The obverse, common to both Rosa Americana and Hibernia pieces, shows the head of George I and the legend GEORGIUS D:G. MAG: BRI: FRA: ET. HIB: REX. (George, by the Grace of God, King of Great Britain, France and Ireland). Rosa Americana tokens were not well received by the American Colonists.

ROSA AMERICANA

	Good	Fine	Unc.
Twopence (No Date)	$8.25	$27.50	$80.00
Twopence (No Date) Motto without Label (3 known)			

1722 Twopence, Period after REX	9.00	26.50	75.00
1722 Twopence, No Period after REX	9.00	26.50	75.00

1722 Penny UTILE DULCI	11.00	25.00	50.00
1722 Penny VTILE DVLCI	7.00	17.50	36.50

1722 Halfpenny UTILE DULCI	8.00	17.50	40.00
1722 Halfpenny VTILE DVLCI			

ROSA AMERICANA

	Good	Fine	Unc.
1723 Twopence	$8.75	$26.00	$65.00

1723 Penny	7.00	17.50	47.50

1723 Halfpenny	7.25	17.50	47.50
1723 Halfpenny Uncrowned Rose	18.50	40.00	70.00

1724 Twopence (Pattern).........................

ROSA AMERICANA

1724 Penny.. —— ——
1724 Penny (Undated) ROSA: SINE: SPINA (3 known) —— ——

★ A. S. Robinson

1733 Twopence (Pattern) Proof....................... —— ——

The 1733 twopence is a pattern piece and bears the bust of George II facing to the left. Issued by the successors to the coinage patent, since William Wood had died in 1730.

HIBERNIA OR WOOD'S COINAGE

The type intended for Ireland had a seated figure with a harp on the reverse side and the word HIBERNIA. Denominations struck were halfpenny and farthing with dates 1722, 1723 and 1724. Hibernia coins were unpopular in Ireland, so most of them were sent to the American Colonies.

First Type   Second Type

	Good	Fine	Ex. F.
1722 Halfpenny, First Type, Harp at Left.........	$5.25	$11.50	$22.50
1722 Halfpenny, Second Type, Harp at Right......	6.25	16.50	27.50
1723 Halfpenny................................	3.00	7.25	15.00
1723 over 22 Halfpenny........................	9.50	22.50	——

HIBERNIA COINS

1723 Hibernia Farthing   1724 Hibernia Halfpenny

	Good	Fine	Ex. F.
1723 Hibernia Farthing	$4.50	$ 9.00	$18.00
1724 Hibernia Halfpenny	5.50	10.00	18.00
1724 Hibernia Farthing	5.50	12.00	21.00

COINAGE OF THE STATES

NEW HAMPSHIRE

New Hampshire was the first of the states to consider the subject of coinage following the declaration of independence.

William Moulton was empowered to make a limited quantity of coins of pure copper authorized by the State House of Representatives March 13, 1776. Although patterns were prepared, it is generally believed that they were not approved. Little of the proposed coinage was ever actually circulated.

★ Betts

★ Copley

	V. Good
1776 New Hampshire Halfpenny	$750.00
1776 New Hampshire Halfpenny WM in Center (3 known)	—
1776 New Hampshire Halfpenny, Engraved Type (Unique)	—

VERMONT

Reuben Harmon, Jr., of Rupert, Vermont, was granted permission to coin copper pieces on June 15, 1785. The well-known Vermont cents were first produced in that year.

Harmon's mint was located in the northeast corner of Rupert near a stream known as Millbrook. Col. William Cooley, a New York goldsmith, made the dies.

	Good	Fine
1785 Cent IMMUNE COLUMBIA	$85.00	$200.00
1785 Cent VERMONTS	14.00	36.00
1785 Cent VERMONTIS	14.00	40.00
1786 Cent VERMONTENSIUM	11.00	35.00
1786 Cent Baby Head	$16.00	$50.00
1786 Cent Bust left	16.00	50.00
1787 Cent Bust left	80.00	205.00
1787 Cent (Several varieties)	6.00	13.50

VERMONT

	Good	Fine
1787 Cent BRITANNIA	$6.50	$16.00

	Good	Fine
1788 Cent (Several varieties)	$ 6.50	$ 12.50
1788 Cent VERMON AUOTORI	40.00	125.00
1788 Cent *ET LIB* *INDE	17.50	52.50

	Good	Fine
1788 Cent GEORGIVS III REX	$10.00	$27.50

NEW YORK

There are no records to show that coinage was authorized for New York following the Revolutionary War. The only coinage laws passed were those regulating coins already in use.

A firm composed of ten individuals became associated in 1787 for the purpose of striking copper coins, at Newburgh. The establishment was called a "Manufactory of hardware," but the operations there were conducted in secret and looked upon as illegal.

Members of the firm included Reuben Harmon, Jr., who operated the mint at Rupert, Vermont; James F. Atlee, a die engraver and others.

The articles of agreement offer an interesting sidelight on the trade in tokens of that day. Reuben Harmon and William Cooley were listed as co-partners "in such trades and merchandizing and in the coinage of copper for the state of Vermont, Connecticut and New York, for their most benefit advantage and profit."

Perhaps many of the pieces now classified as Connecticut coins, the Vermon Auctori with the Britannia reverse and the counterfeit George III halfpence were products of this "hardware manufactory."

The Nova Eborac (New York) issues are supposed to have been struck in England as a speculative venture.

Cents attributed to New York during the period of 1786 and 1787 include the following:

NEW YORK

1786 NON VI VIRTUTE VICI

	Good	Fine	V. Fine
Cent	$140	$275	$375

★ Robinson

★ Bolen

	Good	Fine	V. Fine
1787 Excelsior Cent, Eagle on globe Facing Right	$80.00	$190.00	$250.00
1787 Excelsior Cent, Eagle on globe Facing Left	62.50	150.00	200.00

1787 Cent Large Eagle on Reverse

Arrows and Branch Transposed (Ex. Rare) ———

1787 George Clinton Cent

	Good	Fine	V. Fine
Cent	$250	$500	$650

★ Bolen

1787 Indian N.Y. Arms

	Good	Fine	V. Fine
Cent	$250	$500	$650

★ Bolen

[25]

NEW YORK

**1787 Indian Cent
Reverse Eagle
on Globe**

Good..............$300.00
Fine............... 600.00
V. Fine............ 800.00

★ Bolen

**1787 Indian Cent
with George III
Reverse (unique)**

**1787 IMMUNIS COLUMBIA
Eagle Reverse**

Good..................$20.00
Fine................... 40.00
V. Fine................ 55.00
Unc................... ——

THE NOVA EBORACS

**1787
NOVA EBORAC
Reverse Seated
Figure Facing Left**

Good............$ 9.25
Fine............. 20.00
V. Fine.......... 32.50

**1787
NOVA EBORAC
Reverse Seated
Figure Facing Right**

Good............$ 9.00
Fine............. 18.50
V. Fine.......... 31.00

NEW YORK

1787 NOVA EBORAC
Small Head

Good	$100.00
Fine	200.00
V. Fine	325.00

1787 NOVA EBORAC
Large Head

Good	$ 25.00
Fine	75.00
V. Fine	110.00

CONNECTICUT

Authority for establishing a mint was granted to Samuel Bishop, Joseph Hopkins, James Hillhouse and John Goodrich in 1785.

Available records indicate that the Connecticut Cents were turned out under a sub-contract by Samuel Broome and Jeremiah Platt, former New York merchants who operated two mint houses; one at Morris Cove and the other at Westville. Abel Buel was the principal die-sinker.

1785 Cent
Bust Facing Right

Good $6.00   Fine $12.50

LIR Instead of LIB

Good $11.00 Fine $25.00

1785 Cent
African Head

Good $6.00   Fine $15.00

1785 Cent
Bust Facing Left

Good..$11.00 Fine...$37.50

CONNECTICUT

**1786 Cent
ETLIB INDE**

Good............$19.00
Fine.............. 37.50

**1786 Cent
Large Head Facing Right**

Good............$11.00
Fine.............. 30.00

**1786 Cent
Mailed Bust Facing Left**

Good...............$ 5.50
Fine................ 11.00

**1786 Cent
Mailed Bust Facing Left
Hercules Head**

Good............$ 8.00
Fine.............. 22.50

**1786 Cent
Mailed Bust Facing Left
UCTORI**

Good............. ———
Fine............. ———

**1786 Cent
Draped Bust**

Good............$10.00
Fine.............. 25.00

[28]

CONNECTICUT

1787 Cent
Small Head Facing Right
ETLIB INDE
Good..$10.50 Fine..$36.00

1787 Cent
Mailed Bust Facing Right
IND ET LIB
Good..$ 5.00   Fine.$10.00

1787 Cent
Muttonhead
Variety

Good................$ 8.00
Fine................ 29.00

	Good	Fine
1787 Cent, Mailed Bust Facing Left	$ 4.50	$ 9.00
1787 Cent, Similar, Laughing Head Variety	5.50	11.00
1787 Cent, Similar, Hercules Head (see 1786)	10.50	24.00

| 1787 Cent, Similar, Horned Bust Variety | 6.00 | 12.00 |
| 1787 Cent, Similar, CONNECT Variety | 5.50 | 13.00 |

| 1787 Cent, Draped Bust Facing Left | 3.50 | 8.00 |
| 1787 Cent, Similar, AUCIORI Variety | 5.50 | 11.00 |

[29]

CONNECTICUT

	Good	Fine
1787 Cent, Similar, AUCTOPI Variety	$5.50	$11.00
1787 Cent, Similar, AUCTOBI Variety	6.50	12.00
1787 Cent, Similar, CONNFC Variety	5.50	11.00
1787 Cent, Similar, CONNLC Variety	9.00	27.50
1787 Cent, Similar, FNDE Variety	5.50	11.00
1787 Cent, Similar, ETLIR Variety	5.50	11.00
1787 Cent, Similar, ETIIB Variety	5.50	11.00

1788 Cent, Mailed Bust Facing Right	6.00	12.50
1788 Cent, Similar, Small Head	9.50	32.50

1788 Cent, Mailed Bust Facing Left	4.50	10.00

1788 Cent, Draped Bust Facing Left	5.00	10.00
1788 Cent, Similar, CONNLC Variety	5.50	12.50
1788 Cent, Similar, INDL ET LIB Variety	5.50	12.50

MASSACHUSETTS
MASSACHUSETTS PINE TREE COPPER

Nothing is known regarding the origin of the Pine Tree pattern cent dated 1776. The obverse has a crude pine tree with an animal resembling a dog at its base; Inscription, MASSACHUSETTS STATE. The reverse has a figure probably intended to represent the Goddess of Liberty, seated on a globe and holding a liberty cap and staff. A dog sits at her feet. The legend LIBERTY AND VIRTUE surrounds the figure.

1776 Cent (Unique)..

MASSACHUSETTS HALFPENNY

This pattern piece is sometimes called the "Janus Copper." There are three heads facing left, front and right on the obverse with the inscription STATE OF MASSA. ½ D. The reverse shows the Goddess of Liberty, seated resting against a globe facing right, inscribed GODDESS LIBERTY 1776.

1776 Halfpenny, 3 Heads on Obverse (Unique)............

An "Act for establishing a mint for the coinage of gold, silver and copper" was passed by the Massachusetts General Court October 17, 1786. The next year the Council directed that the design should incorporate "the figure of an Indian with a bow and arrow and a star at one side, with the word 'Commonwealth,' the reverse, a spread eagle with the words 'of Massachusetts A.D. 1787'."

A Mr. Joshua Witherle was placed in charge of the mint where he soon began coining the Massachusetts cents. There resulted many varieties, the rarest being that with arrows in the right talon. Half cents with similar devices and legends were also struck in 1787 and 1788.

Most of the dies for these coppers were made by Joseph Callender. Jacob Perkins of Newburyport probably engraved some of the dies.

The mint was abandoned early in 1789 as the venture was unprofitable to the Commonwealth.

MASSACHUSETTS

Obverse   Arrows in Eagle's Right Talon   in Left Talon

	Good	Fine	V. F.
1787 Cent, Arrows in Right Talon (Ex. Rare)			
1787 Cent, Arrows in Left Talon	$4.50	$10.00	$22.00
1787 Cent, Horn (Die Break) from Eagle's Head	5.00	11.50	24.00

1787 Half Cent

Good .... $ 6.00
Fine 12.50
V. Fine 20.00

1788 Cent

Good .... $ 4.50
Fine 10.00
V. Fine 22.00

	Good	Fine	V. F.
1788 Half Cent	$6.00	$12.00	$20.00

[32]

NEW JERSEY

Although many were dated 1786, authority for a New Jersey coinage was granted on June 1, 1787. Walter Mould, Thomas Goadsby and Albion Cox were empowered to coin coppers "of the weight of six pennyweight and six grains." They were directed to strike 10,000 pounds and deliver to the Treasurer of the state "one-tenth part of the full sum they shall strike and coin."

In an operation of this kind the contractors purchased the metal and assumed all expenses of coining. The difference between these expenses and the total face value of the coins issued represented the profit.

Later Goadsby and Cox asked authority to coin two-thirds of the total independently. Their petition was granted November 22, 1787. Mould was known to have produced his coins at Morristown, while Cox (and probably Goadsby) operated in Elizabethtown.

The series offers many varieties. The obverse shows a horse's head with plow and the legend NOVA CAESAREA (New Jersey). The reverse has a United States shield and legend E PLURIBUS UNUM (One composed of many).

**1786 Cent
IMMUNIS COLUMBIA
Obverse**

Good.. ——— Fine.. ———

1786 (No Date) Cent, Washington Obverse .... ———   ———
1786 Cent, Eagle Obverse................... .... ———   ———
1786 Cent Washington Obv.-Eagle Rev. (Unique)....... ———   ———

**1786 Cent
Date Under
Plow Handle**

Good.. ——— Fine.. ———

**1786 Cent
No Coulter**

Good $8.50   Fine $37.50

[33]

NEW JERSEY

	Good	Fine
1786 Cent, Narrow Shield	$4.00	$ 8.50
1786 Cent, Wide Shield	4.50	11.00
1786 Cent, Similar, Bridle Variety	5.50	14.00

Pluribs Variety Large Planchet **Small Planchet** **Outlined Shield**

1787 Cent, Pronounced Outline to Shield	5.50	15.00
1787 Cent, Small Planchet, Plain Shield	4.00	10.00
1787 Cent, Large Planchet, Plain Shield	4.00	10.00
1787 Cent, Similar, PLURIBS Variety	6.00	15.00

Serpent Head **Fox Variety**

1787 Cent, Serpent Head Variety	7.00	17.50
1788 Cent, Horse's Head Facing Right	4.00	10.00
1788 Cent, Similar, Running Fox before Legend	9.00	22.50

1788 Cent, Horse's Head Facing Left	8.50	25.00

TOKENS AND PATTERN COINS
THE CONTINENTAL DOLLAR

The Continental Dollars were probably a pattern issue only and never reached general circulation. It was the first silver dollar size coin ever proposed for the United States. The dies were engraved by someone whose initials were E. G. (possibly Elisha Gallaudet). Some of them have his signature "EG FECIT" on the obverse. The coins were probably struck in Philadelphia.

Varieties are caused by differences in the spelling of the word CURRENCY and the addition of EG FECIT. These coins were struck in silver, pewter and brass, those in silver probably having done service as a dollar.

"CURRENCY"　　　　　　　　　　　　　　　　　　"CURENCY"

★ Dickeson

Copies were struck in various metals for the 1876 Centennial Exposition in Philadelphia.

	Good	Fine	Unc.
1776 CURRENCY — Brass	—	—	—
1776 CURRENCY — Pewter	$67.50	$140.00	$285.00
1776 CURRENCY — Silver	—	—	—
1776 CURRENCY — Pewter	75.00	145.00	320.00
1776 CURRENCY — Pewter, EG FECIT	77.50	155.00	330.00
1776 CURRENCY — Brass, EG FECIT	—	—	—
1776 CURRENCY — Silver, EG FECIT	—	—	—
1776 CURRENCEY — Pewter	—	—	—

NOVA CONSTELLATIO PATTERNS (Silver)

These Nova Constellatio pieces undoubtedly represent the first patterns for a coinage of the United States. They were designed by Benjamin Dudley for Gouveneur Morris to carry out his ideas for a decimal coinage system. The 1000 unit designation he called a "mark," the 500 a "quint." These denominations, together with the smaller 100 unit piece, were designed to standardize the many different coin values among the several states. These pattern pieces represent the first attempt at a decimal ratio, and were the forerunners of our present system of money values. Neither the proposed denominations nor the coins advanced beyond the pattern stage. The pieces are all dated 1783 and are extremely rare. There are two types of the "quint."

NOVA CONSTELLATIO PATTERNS (SILVER)

MARK

QUINT Type 1   Reverse   QUINT Type 2

★ Set of Mickley Electrotypes

Bit 100 Units

1783 MARK (1000), Silver (Unique).....................
1783 QUINT (500), Silver—Type 1 (Unique)...........
1783 QUINT (500), Silver—Type 2 (Unique)...........
1783 Bit (100), Silver (2 known).......................

NOVA CONSTELLATIO COPPERS

The Nova Constellatio pieces were struck supposedly by order of Gouveneur Morris who had been Assistant Financier of the Confederation. The tokens were turned out in fairly large quantities in the years 1783 and 1785. There are a number of varieties of the 1783 and 1785 issues which are similar to the patterns heretofore described. No official records have been found stating where, or by whom the Nova Constellatio coppers were manufactured. Evidence indicates that they were struck in Birmingham from dies made there by Thomas Wyon, and imported for American circulation as a private business venture by Gouveneur Morris.

NOVA CONSTELLATIO COPPERS

1783 Cent
"CONSTELLATIO"
Pointed Rays
Small U.S.

Good..$5.50   Fine..$14.00

1783 Cent, "CONSTELLATIO"
Pointed Rays, Large U.S.

Good..$7.50   Fine..$22.50

1783 Cent
"CONSTELATIO"
Blunt Rays

Good..$5.50   Fine..$16.50

1785 Cent
"CONSTELATIO"
Blunt Rays

Good	Fine	Ex. Fine
$6.50	$17.50	$30.00

	Good	Fine
1785 Cent, CONSTELLATIO Pointed Rays	$ 5.00	$ 10.00
1786 Cent ....(Ex. Rare)		

[37]

IMMUNE COLUMBIA CENTS

These are considered experimental or pattern pieces. No laws describing them are known. There are several types with the seated figure of Justice device. These dies were possibly the work of James F. Atlee.

1785 Cent, Copper..... ———
1785 Cent, Silver...... ———

★ Edwards
1785 Cent, Cop. Ex. Star in Border
Copper, CONSTELLATIO
Gd.—$60 Fine—$150 V.F.—$250
Copper, CONSTELATIO,
Blunt Rays.... (2 known)———
Gold......... (2 known)———
A gold specimen in the National Coin Collection was acquired from Stickney in exchange for an 1804 dollar.

1785
George III Obverse
Good..$75.00 Fine $180.00
1785
Vermon Auctori Obverse
Good..$85.00 Fine $200.00

FRENCH COLONIES

              Good Fine Ex. Fine
1721 French Colonies, Sou,
  Mint Mark B for
  Rouen.....$20.00 $50.00 ———
1721 French Colonies, Sou,
  Mint Mark H for
  Rochelle......5.00 12.50 ———
1722 French Colonies, Sou,
  Mint Mark H 5.00 12.50 ———

1767 French Colonies, Sou
Good................$ 5.00
Fine................ 11.00
Ex. Fine............ 27.50

1767 French Colonies, Sou
Counterstamped RF for
Republic
Good................$ 5.00
Fine................ 12.00
Ex. Fine............ 26.00

CONFEDERATIO CENTS

The Confederatio Cents are usually classed as experimental or pattern pieces. This will explain why the die with the CONFEDERATIO legend was combined with other designs such as bust of George Washington, Libertas et Justitia of 1785, Immunis Columbia of 1786, the "New York Excelsiors," Inimica Tyrannis Americana and others. There were in all thirteen dies struck in fourteen combinations. Some of the dies were believed to have been made by Thomas Wyon of Birmingham, England, whereas others may have been the work of James Atlee, or the New Jersey coiners.

There are two types of the Confederatio reverse. In one instance the stars are contained in a small circle; in the other larger stars are shown in a larger circle.

1785 Cent, Stars in Small Circle

Fine.............$355.00
V. Fine........... 510.00

★ Bolen

Typical Obverse Types

★ Bolen

Reverse

1785 Stars in Large Circle

Fine............$300.00
V. Fine......... 450.00

[39]

BRASHER'S DOUBLOONS

Perhaps the most famous piece brought out before the establishment of the mint at Philadelphia was that produced by a well-known goldsmith and jeweler, Ephraim Brasher, next door neighbor of George Washington, in New York.

Brasher produced a gold piece weighing about 408 grains, approximately equal in value to a Spanish doubloon (about $16.00).

The punch-mark EB appears in either of two positions as illustrated. This mark is found on coins of other countries as well, and probably was so used by Brasher as evidence of his approval of their value.

★ Robinson

V. Fine
1787 Doubloon, Punch on Breast, Gold (Unique).................. ─────
1787 Doubloon, Punch on Wing, Gold............................ ─────
1787 Half Doubloon (Unique).................................... ─────
The half doubloon is struck from the usual doubloon dies, but on a smaller planchet.

AMERICAN TOKENS
Struck in America or England by Order of American Merchants

GLOUCESTER TOKENS

According to S. S. Crosby, in his book "The Early Coins of America" this piece appears to have been intended as a pattern for a shilling, a private coinage by Richard Dawson of Gloucester (county?), Virginia. The only specimens known are struck in brass, none in silver.

The denomination XII indicates that a silver coinage (one shilling) was planned but never issued. Known specimens are imperfect and a full description cannot be given.

The building may represent a warehouse or some public building, possibly a court house. The legend on the reverse may have been designed to read GLOUCESTER COURT HOUSE VIRGINIA.

1714 Shilling (2 known) Brass................................... ─────

[40]

HIGLEY OR GRANBY COPPERS

John Higley owned an unprofitable copper mine near Granby, Conn. The mines were worked until the American revolution, when the General Court of Connecticut took them over. They were used by the state as a public work house, and the prisoners worked the mines.

The Higley coppers were never officially authorized. All the tokens were made of pure copper. There were seven obverse and four reverse dies. The first issue, in 1737, bore the legend THE VALUE OF THREEPENCE. After a time the quantity exceeded the local demand, and a protest arose against the value of the piece. Higley, a resourceful individual, promptly created a new design, still with the Roman III, but with the inscription VALUE ME AS YOU PLEASE. On the reverse appeared the words I AM GOOD COPPER.

(Electrotypes and Casts Exist)

★ Bolen

	Good	V. Good
1737 THE • VALVE • OF • THREE • PENCE.— 3 Hammers CONNECTICVT	$165.00	$285.00
1737 THE • VALVE • OF • THREE • PENCE.— 3 Hammers — I • AM • GOOD • COPPER	165.00	285.00
1737 VALUE • ME • AS • YOU • PLEASE— 3 Hammers—I • AM • GOOD • COPPER	150.00	275.00
1737 VALVE • ME • AS • YOU • PLEASE— 3 Hammers—I • AM • GOOD • COPPER		(Ex. Rare)
(1737) VALUE • ME • AS • YOU • PLEASE— Broad Axe—J • CUT • MY • WAY • THROUGH	165.00	300.00
(1737) Similar, Wheel Design (Unique)		
1739 VALUE • ME • AS • YOU • PLEASE— Broad Axe—J • CUT • MY • WAY • THROUGH	300.00	

J. CHALMERS
Annapolis, Maryland

J. Chalmers, a goldsmith, struck a series of silver tokens at Annapolis in 1783. The shortage of change and the refusal of the people to use underweight cut Spanish coins, or "bits," prompted the issue of these pieces.

The shilling with rings on the reverse is very rare. The common type shilling has two clasped hands on the obverse. The reverse shows two doves pulling what appears to be a worm.

The sixpence has a star within a wreath on the obverse, and a cross with hands clasped on the reverse. The three pence has the clasped hands on the obverse side, and the reverse shows a branch encircled by a wreath.

	Good	Fine
1783 Shilling — Birds, Long or Short Worm	$40.00	$ 80.00
1783 Shilling — Rings (Ex. Rare)		

1783 Sixpence, Small Date	$ 92.50	$190.00
1783 Sixpence, Large Date	90.00	182.50
1783 Threepence	40.00	95.00

STANDISH BARRY, BALTIMORE, MARYLAND

Standish Barry, a Baltimore silversmith, circulated a silver three pence in 1790. He was a watch and clockmaker, engraver and later a silversmith. The tokens were believed to have been an advertising venture at a time when small change was scarce. The precise date, July 4, 90, on this piece may indicate that Barry intended to commemorate Independence Day, but there are no records to substantiate this belief. The head shown on the obverse is probably that of George Washington. The legend BALTIMORE TOWN JULY 4, 90 appears in the border. STANDISH BARRY THREE PENCE is on the reverse.

1790 Threepence . . . . $ 57.50 $140.00

THE BAR CENT

The Bar Cent is undated and of uncertain origin.

It has thirteen parallel and disconnected bars on one side. On the other side is the large Roman USA monogram.

The significance of the design is clearly defined by its extreme simplicity. The separate thirteen states (bars) unite into a single status as symbolized by the interlocking letters (USA).

This coin is believed to have been issued at the same time as the Nova Constellatio coppers by Thomas Wyon at Birmingham, England, for America. It first circulated in New York during November, 1785. The design was supposedly copied from an old Continental button.

★ Bolen (A is under S)

	Good	Fine	Unc.
Undated (about 1785) Bar Cent	$30.00	$55.00	$125.00

THE MOTT TOKEN

This was one of the first tradesman's tokens issued in America. Manufactured in England, they were issued by Messrs. Mott of New York in 1789. The firm was composed of William and John Mott, located at 240 Water Street, a fashionable section of New York at that time.

	Good	Fine	Ex. Fine
1789 Mott Token, Thick Planchet	$5.50	$12.50	$30.00
1789 Mott Token, Thin Planchet	6.50	15.00	35.00

TALBOT ALLUM & LEE CENTS

Talbot, Allum & Lee, engaged in the India trade and located at 241 Pearl Street, New York, placed a large quantity of English-made coppers in circulation during 1794 and 1795. ONE CENT appears on the 1794 issue, and the legend PAYABLE AT THE STORE OF―― on the edge. The denomination is not found on the 1795 reverse but the edge legend was changed to read: WE PROMISE TO PAY THE BEARER ONE CENT.

TALBOT ALLUM & LEE CENTS

1794 Cent NEW YORK
V. Good............$ 5.50
V. Fine............. 12.50
Unc................. 26.00

1794 Cent without NEW YORK
V. Good............$ 27.50
V. Fine............. 62.50
Unc................. ———

1795 Cent
V. Good............$ 5.00
V. Fine............. 9.00
Unc................. 25.00

ANGLO-AMERICAN TOKENS
Supposedly of English Origin
Speculative Ventures

CAROLINA and NEW ENGLAND ELEPHANT TOKENS

Although no law is known authorizing coinage for Carolina, two very interesting pieces known as Elephant Tokens were current with the date 1694. These copper coins were of half-penny denomination. The reverse reads GOD PRESERVE CAROLINA AND THE LORDS PROPRIETORS. 1694.

The second and more common variety has the last word spelled PROPRIETORS. The correction was made on the original die, for the E shows plainly beneath the O. The elephant's tusks nearly touch the milling on the second variety.

The Elephant Pieces were probably struck in England and perhaps intended only as tokens, or, as we might say today, as an advertising stunt to enliven interest in the Carolina Plantation.

Like the Carolina Tokens, the New England Elephant Tokens were believed to have been struck in England as a promotional piece to increase interest in the American Colonies. Some of these tokens were said to have been struck in brass.

NEW ENGLAND

★ Robinson

1694 NEW ENGLAND .... (Ex. Rare)

CAROLINA ELEPHANT TOKENS

                                                              Good   Fine
1694 PROPRIETERS (3 known)......................

★ Bolen

1694 PROPRIETORS $80.00 $150.00

The London Token, an early historian states, was produced during the great plague raging in London. The legend on this piece relates directly to that crisis. It has also been stated that the London Token was to have been current in Tangier, Africa, but was never used in that locality. No date appears on this coin.

(1694) Halfpenny GOD PRESERVE LONDON
    (Both thick and thin)......................... $11.00 $25.00
(1694) Halfpenny GOD PRESERVE LONDON
    (Diagonals in center of shield).................. 35.00   75.00
(1694) Halfpenny, similar. Variety with sword in
    second quarter of shield instead of first...........
(1694) Halfpenny LON DON........................ 45.00   85.00

[45]

VIRGINIA HALFPENNY

In 1773, George III issued this half-penny. There are also known to have been a few specimens struck on a larger planchet with a wide milled border, known as pennies.

The Virginia piece of 1774 known as a shilling may have been a pattern piece for a half-penny.

Halfpenny   Penny

	Good	Fine	Unc.
1773 Halfpenny Period after Georgius.........	$4.50	$ 7.50	$18.50
1773 Halfpenny No period after Georgius......	5.50	10.00	30.00
1773 Penny..Proof 150.00			

Virginia Shilling 1774

1774 Shilling.................................

GEORGIUS TRIUMPHO TOKEN

Although the head shown on this token bears a strong resemblance to that upon some coins of George III, many collectors consider the Georgius Triumpho (Triumphant George) a token intended to commemorate the successful termination of the Revolutionary War—a triumph justly claimed for Washington.

The reverse side shows the Goddess of Liberty behind a framework of thirteen bars and fleur de lis. She holds an olive branch in her right hand and staff of liberty in her left. VOCE POPOLI (By the Voice of the People) 1783.

	Good	Fine
1783 GEORGIUS TRIUMPHO	$5.00	$12.00

AUCTORI PLEBIS TOKEN

This token is sometimes included with the coins of Connecticut as it greatly resembles issues of that state. The coin was struck in England, maker unknown, for use in America.

1787 AUCTORI PLEBIS

Good	Fine
$8.00	$17.50

KENTUCKY TOKEN

These tokens were struck in England about 1792-94. Each star in the triangle represents a state, identified by its initial letter. These pieces are usually called Kentucky Cents because the letter K (for Kentucky) happens to be at the top. Some of the edges are plain; others are engrailed with an oblique reeding, and some have the edge lettered: "PAYABLE IN LANCASTER LONDON OR BRISTOL," or "PAYABLE AT BEDWORTH NUNETON OR UNKIET."

	V. Good	V. Fine	Unc.
Cent, (1792) Plain Edge	$ 8.50	$17.50	$40.00
Cent, Engrailed Edge	14.00	37.50	85.00
Cent, Lettered Edge, PAYABLE AT BEDWORTH, Etc	—	—	—
Cent, Lettered Edge, PAYABLE IN LANCASTER, Etc	9.00	22.00	42.50
Cent, Lettered Edge, Thin Planchet	—	—	—

MYDDELTON TOKENS

These copper tokens were from the establishment of Boulton and Watt near Birmingham, England. They are unsurpassed in beauty and design by any piece issued for American circulation.

1796 Myddelton Token (Copper), Proof .. $120.00

1796 Myddelton Token (Silver), Proof 145.00

COPPER COMPANY OF UPPER CANADA

The reverse of this piece, according to S. S. Crosby, properly belongs upon another token and was apparently intended for Canadian circulation, or it was used to give the coin creditability.

                                Proof
1796 Bronze......$100.00

NORTH WEST COMPANY TOKEN

Used among fur traders throughout western Canada, Oregon and Washington. The token was good for one beaver.

1820 North West Token,
    Brass...............$100.00

All but one known specimen is holed.

MISCELLANEOUS TOKENS
THE NEW YORKE TOKEN

Although only three or four specimens of this piece were known to S. S. Crosby, the authority on early American coins, a number have since been discovered. From an account in the Historical Magazine for 1861, he infers that this token is of Dutch origin. The following is quoted from the magazine article mentioned.

"The style in which it is executed is more Dutch than English; and as the only existing specimen has been preserved in Holland, it is probable that the dies were originally cut there.... There is no date upon the token; but it evidently belongs to the period between 1664, when the name New Yorke was first adopted, and 1710, after which it was rarely spelled with an e. It should probably be referred to the latter part of this period, for the currency of the colonies was then in a very unsettled state, and the amount in circulation was not adequate to the wants of trade....

"Without venturing to claim that this coin contains the earliest display of the American eagle, we think it unquestionably deserves to be considered the earliest New York token."

	Good	Fine
UNDATED Brass....	$95.00	$180.00
Pewter...	—	—

[48]

NEW ENGLAND STIVER

This token was believed to have originated in Holland and used by Dutch merchants in New Amsterdam for small change. The obverse shows two lions; the upper facing left and the lower inverted facing right.

There has been considerable conjecture concerning the significance of the letters on the obverse side. One interpretation is that they stand for "I Stiver Von Connecticut." Another suggestion has it that they were the initials of a Dutch Trader, as I. S. Van C.

There is no clue to the date of the issue. Crosby judges the time as "that of the seventeenth century."

UNDATED (1650) (Unique)..................................—

FLORIDA TOKEN

★ 19th Century Restrikes Exist

	Good	Fine	Unc.
(1688) Florida, James II Plantation Token, 1/24 part real — Pewter	$10.50	$20.00	$37.50
(1688) Florida, James II Plantation Token, 1/24 part real — Pewter. Sidewise 4 in 24	—	—	—

NORTH AMERICAN TOKEN

This piece was struck in Dublin, Ireland. The obverse shows the seated figure of Hibernia facing left. The date of issue is believed to have been much later than shown on the coins.

Like many Irish tokens, this issue found its way to America in large quantities and was readily accepted owing to a scarcity of small change.

	Good	Fine
1781	$4.00	$8.50

[49]

FRANKLIN PRESS CENT

This piece is an English token but has often been associated with Benjamin Franklin, and has accordingly been placed in American collections.

1794 Franklin Press Cent.
Good	Fine	Unc.
$8.00	$17.50	$32.50

HIBERNIA-VOCE POPULI

These coins, struck in the year 1760, were prepared by one Roche, of King Street Dublin, who was at that period engaged in the manufacture of buttons for the army, for which he held a contract with home government. Like other Irish tokens, many of these pieces found their way to Colonial America.

The origin of the piece dated 1700 is rather obscure. It no doubt circulated in Colonies with numerous other counterfeit halfpence and "Bungtown Tokens."

Halfpenny 1700   Halfpenny 1760

VOOE POPULI   1760 Farthing

	Good	Fine
1700 Halfpenny		
1760 Halfpenny	$ 4.50	$ 9.00
1760 Halfpenny VOOE POPULI	9.50	20.00
1760 Farthing	18.50	37.50

PITT TOKENS

William Pitt, who endeared himself to America, is the subject of these pieces, probably intended as commemorative medalets. The halfpenny served as currency during a shortage of regular coinage. Mr. Smithers of Philadelphia struck the coins which were designed by Colonel Revere of Boston. The reverse legend refers to Pitt's efforts to have the stamp act repealed. The Pitt farthing-size token, found in brass or copper, is rare.

	Good	Fine	Unc.
1766 Halfpenny	$9.00	$20.00	$45.00
1766 Farthing			

RHODE ISLAND SHIP TOKEN

Although this medal has a Dutch inscription, the spelling and design indicate an English or Anglo-American origin. Specimens are known in brass, copper tin and pewter.

1778-1779 Rhode Island Ship Token
Wreath below ship......
V.F. $35.00   E.F. $55.00
No Wreath below ship...
V.F. $30.00   E.F. $50.00
VLUGTENDE below
ship. V.F. ——   E.F. ——

★Grant

THE CASTORLAND MEDAL

This piece is dated 1796 and relates to a settlement of Frenchmen known as Castorland in Carthage, New York, at the time of the French Revolution.

Matte Proof

1796 Silver Original (Reeded edge)............................... ——
1796 Copper Restrike (thin)..................................$ 7.50
1796 Silver Restrike (thin)...................................... 12.50
1796 Gold Restrike (thin)..110.00

WASHINGTON PIECES

An interesting series of coins and tokens were struck during the period from 1783 to 1795, bearing the portrait of George Washington. The likenesses in most instances were faithfully reproduced and were designed to please Washington. Some of these pieces were of English origin.

The legends generally signify a strong unity among the states and a marked display of patriotism such as pervaded the new nation during that period. We find among these tokens an employment of what were soon to become our official coin devices, namely, the American eagle, the United States shield and stars. The one cent value is used in several instances, while on some of the English pieces the halfpenny value will be found. Several pieces were intended to be patterns for half dollars.

Small Military Bust

	Good	Fine	V. Fine
Plain edge.....	$8.00	$14.50	$28.00
Engrailed edge...	10.00	17.50	40.00

Large Military Bust
$6.00 $12.00 $19.00

WASHINGTON PIECES

1783 Draped Bust No Button Plain Edge

Good.................$ 6.00
Fine.................. 10.00
V. Fine............... 17.50

1783 Draped Bust with Button Plain Edge

Good.................$12.50
Fine.................. 22.50
V. Fine............... 40.00

1783 Draped Bust, Copper Restrike, engrailed edge............Proof $25.00
1783 Draped Bust, Silver Restrike, engrailed edge.............Proof 50.00

Unity States

Good..............$ 6.00
Fine............... 11.00
V. Fine............ 20.00

Undated (1783) Double Head Cent

Good...............$ 7.00
Fine................ 14.00
V. Fine............. 21.00

Ugly Head

1784 Ugly Head.....(Ex. Rare)

Presumably of American origin

1791 Cent Small Eagle

Lettered edge—United States of America

Good..........$ 9.50
Fine.......... 23.00
Unc........... 55.00

[52]

WASHINGTON PIECES

1791 Cent
Large Eagle

Lettered edge—United States of America

Good.........$ 9.25
Fine.......... 23.00
Unc........... 50.00

1791 Liverpool
Halfpenny

Lettered edge

Good...........$ 36.50
Fine............ 82.00
Unc............. 175.00

1792 Eagle Half Dollar
Copper....... ———

1792 Eagle Half Dollar
Silver......... ———

1792 Eagle Half Dollar
Gold.......... ———

1792 Cent
"WASHINGTON—
PRESIDENT"

                Fine
Plain edge.......$150.00
Lettered edge..... ———

Undated
(1792) Cent

"WASHINGTON
BORN VIRGINIA"

Restrikes from Obverse Die exist.

            Fine
Copper.......$125.00
Silver......... ———

[53]

WASHINGTON PIECES

1792 Half Dollar, Silver
Good............$200.00
Fine............$500.00
1792 Half Dollar, Copper
Good............$90.00
Fine............$175.00
1792 Half Dollar, Silver or Copper, Ornamented edge—(Circles and Squares)
Extra Rare......

★ Idler

1792 Half Dollar, Large Eagle (Unique).. ———

1792 Cent Roman Head

Lettered edge—United States of America

Proof.........$450.00

1793 Ship Halfpenny

Lettered edge

Good............$ 7.25
Fine............. 15.00
V. Fine.......... 25.00

1795 Grate Cent
Oblique Reeding
Good...............$ 7.50
Fine............... 15.00
Unc............... 32.50
Lettered Edge
Good...............$22.00
Fine............... 45.00
Unc...............

[54]

WASHINGTON PIECES

	Good	Fine	Ex. Fine
1795 Halfpenny, Plain edge	$10.00	$25.00	$42.50
1795 Halfpenny, Lettered edge	5.50	12.50	22.50
1795 Halfpenny, Edge: AN ASYLUM FOR THE OPPRESSED OF ALL NATIONS	——	50.00	70.00
1795 Penny, Similar to Halfpenny (Ex. Rare)	——	——	——

Undated (1795) Penny

Lettered Edge

Good	Fine	Unc.
$9.00	$17.00	$47.50

SUCCESS TOKENS

	Good	Fine
SUCCESS Token, Large Plain, or Reeded Edge	$8.50	$20.00
SUCCESS Token, Small Plain, or Reeded Edge	$8.00	$19.00

NORTH WALES HALFPENNY

	Good	Fine
1795 North Wales Halfpenny, brass	$6.00	$15.00
Copper, lettered edge	——	——
Copper, two stars either side of harp	——	——

[55]

THE FUGIO CENTS

The first coins issued by authority of the United States were the "Fugio" cents. Entries in the Journal of Congress supply interesting information about proceedings relating to this coinage.

"Saturday, April 21, 1787 . . . .

"That the board of treasury be authorized to contract for three hundred tons of copper coin of the federal standard, agreeable to the proposition of Mr. James Jarvis, ... That it be coined at the expense of the contractor, etc."

On Friday, July 6, 1786, there was "Resolved, that the board of treasury direct the contractor for the copper coinage to stamp on one side of each piece the following device, viz: thirteen circles linked together, a small circle in the middle, with the words 'United States,' round it; and in the centre, the words 'We are one'; on the other side of the same piece the following device, viz: a dial with the hours expressed on the face of it; a meridian sun above on one side of which is the word 'Fugio,' (The meaning is, 'time flies' and on the other the year in figures '1787' below the dial, the words 'Mind Your Business.'"

The legends have been credited to Benjamin Franklin by many, and the coin, as a consequence, has been referred to as the Franklin Cent.

These cents were coined in New Haven, Conn., and it has been suggested, also in New York City, Rupert, Vt. and elsewhere. Most of the copper used in this coinage came from military stores. It is believed to have been the copper bands which held together the powder kegs sent to us by the French. The dies were made by Abel Buel of New Haven.

We list below major varieties, some of considerable rarity:

WITH CLUB RAYS

	Good	Fine	Unc.
Club Rays, concave ends to rays: FUCIO (C instead of G)	—	—	—
Club Rays, concave ends, FUGIO (Ex. Rare)	—	—	—
Club Rays, rounded ends	$12.50	$27.50	—

WITH POINTED RAYS

	Good	Fine	Unc.
UNITED above, STATES below (Rare)	—	—	$125.00
UNITED STATES at sides of circle	$8.00	$18.50	55.00

[56]

THE FUGIO CENTS

	Good	Fine	Unc.
STATES UNITED at sides of circle. Cinquefoils (small, five bladed clover design) on label....	$ 7.50	$16.50	$47.50
STATES UNITED. Eight-pointed stars on label	13.00	30.00	
STATES UNITED. Label with raised rims (simply two concentric circles). Large letters in WE ARE ONE.............................	27.50	57.50	

Note: The preceding types with pointed rays have regular obverses punctuated with four cinquefoils.
Obv. no cinquefoils. Cross after date.
   Rev. UNITED STATES. (Very Rare).......
Same Obv. Rev. STATES UNITED. (Very Rare)
Same Obv. Rev. label with raised rims. (Ex. Rare)

American Congress   **New Haven Restrike**

Copper Pattern. Same obv.; reverse with rays and
   AMERICAN CONGRESS. (Ex. Rare).......
New Haven Restrikes. Narrow rings on reverse.
   Gold (2 known)...........................
   Silver.................................... $75.00
   Copper...................................   25.00
   Brass....................................   35.00

New Haven Restrikes were struck from dies discovered by the fourteen-year-old C. Wyllys Betts in 1858 on the site of the Broom & Platt Store in New Haven, Conn., where the originals were made. Three pairs of dies were found and are still extant.

BIBLIOGRAPHY—Early American Coins

Crosby, S. S., Early Coins of America.................1875 (Reprint 1945)
Dickeson, Dr. M. W., American Numismatic Manual..................1859
Miller-Ryder, The State Coinage of New England.....................1920
Maris, Dr. Edward, New Jersey Cents......................(Reprint 1925)
Nelson, Philip, The Coinage of William Wood (1722-1733).............1903
Noe, Sydney P., The New England and Willow Tree Coinages
   of Massachusetts...1943
Wurtzbach, Carl, Massachusetts Colonial Silver Money...............1937
Newman, Eric, Secret of Good Samaritan Shilling 1959

FIRST UNITED STATES MINT ISSUES

Many members of the House favored a representation of the president's head on the obverse of each coin. Others considered the idea a monarchial practice. Washington is believed to have expressed disapproval of the use of his portrait on our coins.

The majority considered a figure emblematic of Liberty more appropriate and the Senate finally concurred in this opinion. Robert Birch was an engraver employed at designing proposed devices for our coins. He engraved the dies for the disme and half-disme. He has also been associated with a large copper cent of unusual design, which is known as the Birch Cent.

DISME

	Good	Fine	Unc.
1792 Silver (3 Known)	—	—	—
1792 Copper ————	$525	$750	$850

HALF DISME

	Good	Fine	V. Fine
1792 Silver	$170	$300	$450
1792 Copper (Unique)			

1792 SILVER CENTER CENT

	Fine	Ex. Fine
1792 Silver Center Cent	$800	———
1792 Cent, No Silver Center		

1792 BIRCH CENT (Very Rare)
Copper.....................$1250

G.W. Pt. Below Wreath
White Metal (Unique)

1792 PATTERN HALF EAGLE

Copper.......(2 Known)
White Metal....(Unique)

UNITED STATES REGULAR ISSUES
HALF CENTS
1793-1857

From the standpoint of face value the half cent is the smallest coin struck by the United States. All half cents are scarce, but the series has never enjoyed the popularity of some of the other series, hence the more common dates are reasonably priced.

There were various intermissions in coinage, and during the period 1831 to 1849 the coinage was very small causing a very noticeable lapse in the series for the average collector.

While 1796 is the rarest date the originals and restrikes of 1831, 1836, 1840, 1841, 1842, 1843, 1844, 1845, 1846, 1847, 1848, and 1849 are difficult to obtain.

The half cent was authorized to be coined April 2, 1792. Originally the weight was to have been 132 grains, but this was changed to 104 grains by the Act of January 14, 1793, before coinage commenced. The weight was again changed January 26, 1796 by presidential proclamation in conformity with the Act of March 3, 1795 to 84 grains. Coinage was discontinued by the Act of February 21, 1857.

This series is divided into five types:
1. Liberty Cap, head left, 1793.
2. Liberty Cap, head right, 1794 to 1797.
3. Draped Bust, 1800 to 1808.
4. Turban Head, 1809 to 1836.
5. Braided Hair, 1840 to 1857

LIBERTY CAP TYPE

	Good	Fine
1793	$82.50	$155.00
1794	35.00	52.50
1795 Let. Edge, Pole	27.00	50.00

No Pole to Cap   Pole to Cap

	Good	Fine
1795 Plain Edge, no Pole	$24.00	$46.00
1,795 Let. Edge, Punct. Date	26.00	50.00
1,795 Plain Edge, Punct. Date	24.00	47.00
1796 Plain Edge, Pole	255.00	535.00

★ Edwards Copy

HALF CENTS

	Good	Fine
1796 Plain Edge, no Pole	$395.00	$800.00
1797 Plain Edge	23.00	50.00
1797 Let. Edge	100.00	217.50
1797 1 above 1, Plain Edge	21.50	46.50

DRAPED BUST TYPE

	Good	Fine
1800	5.50	13.50
1802 over 1800 (as all are)	43.00	97.50
1802 (Rev. of 1800)	90.00	200.00
1803	4.00	11.00

Plain 4   Crosslet 4

Stemless Wreath   Stems to Wreath

	Good	Fine
1804 Plain 4, stemless	$3.50	$7.00
1804 Plain 4, stems	12.50	28.50
1804 Crosslet 4, stemless	5.00	10.50
1804 Crosslet 4, stems	3.75	7.25
1804 Spiked Chin Var.	4.25	8.00
1805 Small 5, stemless	5.00	10.00
1805 Small 5, stems	29.00	87.50
1805 Large 5, stems	4.50	8.75
1806 Small 6, stems	19.00	46.00
1806 Small 6, stemless	4.50	8.00
1806 Large 6, stems	4.00	7.50
1807	4.50	9.00

[60]

HALF CENTS

	Good	Fine
1808 over 7	$19.50	$43.50
1808 Normal date	5.00	10.00

TURBAN HEAD TYPE

	Good	Fine
1809 Circle inside 0	5.25	10 75
1809 Over 6	5.00	10.00

	Good	Fine	Unc.
1809	3.75	6.00	27.50
1810	6.00	13.50	92.50
1811	22.00	43.00	242.50
1811 Restrike Rev. of 1802, V. Rare			
1825	3.75	6.50	23.50
1826	3.50	6.00	22.50

13 Stars   12 Stars

	Good	Fine	Unc.
1828 13 Stars	3.25	5.50	18.50
1828 12 Stars	4.75	10.50	49.50
1829	3.00	6.00	18.50

Original   Restrike
Large Berries   Small Berries

	Fine	Unc.	Proof
1831 Original Beware of Altered Date			$227.50
1831 Restrike. Large Berries (Rev. of 1836)			205.00
1831 Restrike. Small Berries (Rev. of 1852)			210.00
1832	$5.00	$22.50	
1833	4.50	17.50	75.00
1834	4.50	15.50	80.00
1835	4.50	15.00	80.00
1836 Original			207.50
1836 Restrike (Rev. of 1852)			197.50
1837 Token, not a coin	17.00	42.50	

BRAIDED HAIR TYPE

	Proof
1840 Original	$205.00
1840 Restrike	147.50
1841 Original	175.00
1841 Restrike	147.50
1842 Original	187.50
1842 Restrike	145.00
1843 Original	190.00
1843 Restrike	145.00
1844 Original	145.00
1844 Restrike	122.50
1845 Original	190.00
1845 Restrike	160.00
1846 Original	162.50
1846 Restrike	130.00
1847 Original	165.00
1847 Restrike	145.00
1848 Original	175.00
1848 Restrike	145.00

HALF CENTS

Brilliant or Red Uncirculated Half Cents Are Worth More Than Prices Shown.

Small Date   Large Date

	Fine	Unc.	Proof
1849 Sm. Date, Original..		$190.00	
1849 Sm. Date, Restrike..		150.00	
1849 Lg. Date..	$14.00	$45.00	
1850		8.25	21.00

	Fine	Unc.	Proof
1851	$5.75	$16.25	
1852 Original...			—
1852 Restrike...			$190.00
1853		5.75	17.00
1854		6.00	17.00	—
1855		5.75	16.25	105.00
1856		6.75	18.50	100.00
1857	13.25	35.00	125.00

BIBLIOGRAPHY

Crosby, S. S., United States Coinage of 1793 (Cents and Half Cents). 1897. Reprint 1933.
Frossard, Ed., U. S. Cents and Half Cents 1793-1857. 1879.
Gilbert, Ebenezer, The United States Half Cents. 1916.

LARGE CENTS
1793-1857

Laws affecting the coinage of large cents were the same as those covering the half cents. In each instance the weights of cents are twice that of the half cents. Proofs are known to exist of some dates and all are rare.

THE 1793 CHAIN OR LINK CENT

The dies for the first type cent were believed to have been cut by Jean Pierre Droz, a Swiss.

The Boston Argus of March 26, 1793, contains the following note: "The American Cents (says a letter from Newark) do not answer our expectations. The chain on the reverse is but a bad omen for Liberty, and Liberty herself appears to be in a fright . . . ."

Comments similar to the above were believed responsible for the change of type to the wreath device on the reverse.

THE WREATH CENTS OF 1793

These cents might be more easily identified if they were called single-bow Wreath Cents. The Liberty Cap Cents also have wreaths but the stems are tied with a double bow knot. There are other differences to be seen on the Wreath type cents such as a bolder relief to the head of Liberty, more loosely flowing hair and a three-leaf sprig above the date. Some types have the vine and bars, and one variety has ONE HUNDRED FOR A DOLLAR on the edge.

LARGE CENTS

	Good	Fine
1793 Chain type, AMERI	$112.50	$285.00
1793 Chain type, AMERICA	95.00	250.00

Wreath Type

1793 Chain type, Period after date and Liberty	97.50	265.00
1793 Wreath type, Edge has Vine and Bars	75.00	155.00
1793 Wreath type, Lettered edge one Leaf on Edge	75.00	145.00
1793 Wreath type, Lettered edge, Double Leaf Edge	80.00	165.00

1793 Strawberry Leaf Var.   1793 Liberty Cap Type

1793 Wreath type; strawberry leaf var	Ex. Rare	—
1793 Liberty Cap type	200.00	550.00

Jefferson Head

1794 (Many Varieties)	14.00	32.50
1794 Head of 1793	25.00	62.50
1794 Head of 1795	17.50	35.00
1794 No fraction Bar	22.50	55.00
1795 Jefferson Head (Not Regular Mint Issue)	92.50	210.00

[63]

LARGE CENTS

                One Cent in Center of Wreath   High in Wreath
                                                          Good   Fine
1795 Lettered Edge ONE CENT in Center of Wreath.....$27.50 $62.50
1795 Lettered Edge ONE CENT High in Wreath......... 50.00   105.00
1795 Plain Edge, ONE CENT, Center of Wreath......... 15.00   27.50
1795 Plain Edge, ONE CENT, High in Wreath.......... 14.00   26.00
1795 Reeded Edge.................................... V. Rare

1796 Liberty Cap.................................... 23.00   57.50

DRAPED BUST TYPE

              Draped Bust Type   LIHERTY Variety
1796 Draped Bust.................................... 18.50   45.00
1796 LIHERTY Variety (error)........................ 32.50   87.50

                       Gripped or
                       Milled Edge
                             Stems   Stemless
1797 Stems on Wreath............................... 7.50   20.00

LARGE CENTS

	Good	Fine
1797 Stemless Wreath	$35.00	$90.00
1797 Crudely Gripped or Milled Edge. Rev. of 1796	14.00	45.00
1797 Plain Edge. Rev. of 1796	16.00	47.50

1798 Over 97 **Small Date** **Large Date**

1798 over 97	17.50	53.50
1798 Small Date	6.50	14.00
1798 Large Date	7.50	16.50

Reverse of 1796

1798 Reverse of 1796, Wide date . 18.50 50.00
1798 Reverse of 1796, Close date . . V. Rare

1799 Over 98 **(Normal Date)** **Chip Reverse**

1799 over 98 .... 165.00 385.00
1799 Normal Date 147.50 330.00

Genuine coins can usually be identified by the chip in the reverse die between E and T of ONE and CENT.

1800 Over 1798 **Normal Date**

[65]

LARGE CENTS

	Good	Fine
1800 over 1798	$8.25	$21.50
1800 over 179	6.75	16.00
1800 Normal Date	6.25	14.50

Normal Dies   1801 Reverse 3 Errors

	Good	Fine
1801 Normal Dies—Blunt 1's	6.50	17.50
1801 First 1 Perfect	8.00	24.00
1801 3 errors—1/000, one stem and IINITED	16.00	55.00

1801 Error 1/000   1/100 Over 1/000

	Good	Fine
1801 Fraction 1/000	11.00	24.00
1801 Fraction 1/100 over 1/000	12.50	35.00

Normal Dies   Double Fraction Bar   Stemless Wreath

	Good	Fine
1802 Normal Dies	5.00	11.00
1802 Stemless Wreath—Single Fraction Bar	6.00	18.50
1802 Stemless Wreath—Double Fraction Bar	7.00	20.00
1802 Fraction 1/000	7.00	21.50

1803 Small Date   Small Fraction   Large Fraction

LARGE CENTS

	Good	Fine
1803 Small Date—Small Fraction (Blunt 1)	$ 4.25	$ 9.00
1803 Small Date—Large Fraction (Blunt 1)	4.25	9.00
1803 Large Date—Small Fraction (Pointed 1)	67.50	207.50
1803 Large Date—Large Fraction (Pointed 1)	36.50	105.00
1803 Stemless Wreath	8.25	24.00
1803 1/100 over 1/000	11.25	32.00

1804 Normal Dies................................... 95.00   210.00
On all genuine 1804 Cents the O of the date is in line with the O in OF on the reverse of the coin.

1804 Broken Obv. Die............................... 92.50   205.00
1804 Broken Obv. and Rev. Dies..................... 90.00   200.00

RESTRIKE OF THE 1804 CENT

A fake 1804 was manufactured in the U. S. Mint by some employees of that institution about the year 1860 to satisfy the demand for this rare date. This piece is known as the "restrike" but fortunately for collectors it was a patchwork job and easily distinguished from a genuine 1804 cent. An old rusty die was used for the obverse which makes the field of the coin pitted and a die of about the year 1818, which is much different from an 1804, was used for the reverse. To aid collectors, an illustration of the 1804 restrike is shown here.

1804 Restrike of 1860.....................................Unc. $50.00

LARGE CENTS

	Blunt 1 in Date			Pointed 1	
				Good	Fine
1805 Blunt 1 in date				$6.00	$12.50
1805 Pointed 1 in date				6.75	19.00

1806	13.00	35.00

1807 Over 6

1807 over 6, Large 7	5.50	16.50
1807 over 6, Small 7	38.00	96.00

Small Fraction — Large Fraction — 1807 Comet Variety

1807 Small Fraction	5.75	15.00
1807 Large Fraction	5.50	13.50
1807 Comet Var. Die Break Behind Head	8.50	25.00

[68]

LARGE CENTS—Turban Head Type

1808 to 1814: THE TURBAN HEAD SERIES: This group does not compare in sharpness and quality to those struck before, (1793-1807), nor to those struck after (1816 on). The copper used was "softer," having less alloy. This impaired the wearing quality of the series. For this reason collectors find greater difficulty in obtaining these dates in choice condition.

13 Stars   **12 Stars Caused by Die Break.**

	Good	Fine
1808 13 Stars	$7.50	$22.50
1808 12 Stars	8.50	27.50
1809	32.50	80.00

1810 Over 9   **Normal Date**

1810 over 9	7.25	16.50
1810 Normal Date	6.25	14.00

1811 Over 10   **Normal Date**

LARGE CENTS

	Good	Fine
1811 over 10	$15.00	$48.00
1811 Normal Date	14.00	42.50

1812 Large Date **1813**

1812 Small Date	5.00	12.50
1812 Large Date	6.00	13.50
1813	11.00	25.00

1814 Plain 4 **1814 Crosslet 4**

1814 Plain 4	4.75	10.50
1814 Crosslet 4	4.75	10.50

Coronet Type

Red to bright red uncirculated large cents (not cleaned) command higher prices.

	Good	Fine	Unc.
1816	$2.50	$6.50	$33.00

1817 Wide Date **1817 Close Date** **1817 15 Stars**

1817 Wide Date	$2.25	$ 6.50	$31.50
1817 Close Date	2.25	5.50	25.00
1817 15 Stars	4.50	11.00	52.50
1818	2.25	5.00	21.00

LARGE CENTS

1819 Over 18   1819 Small Date   1819 Large Date

	Good	Fine	Unc.
1819 over 18	$3.00	$6.75	$44.00
1819 Small Date	2.00	4.50	27.50
1819 Large Date	2.50	5.50	30.00

1820 Over 19   1820 Small Date   1820 Large Date

1820 over 19	2.00	5.75	38.00
1820 Small Date	2.00	6.00	32.50
1820 Large Date	2.00	4.75	22.50

1821 Wide Date   1821 Close Date

1821 Wide Date	8.00	24.00	125.00
1821 Close Date	9.00	27.50	145.00

LARGE CENTS

1822 Wide Date

1822 Close Date

	Good	Fine	Unc.
1822 Wide Date	$ 3.00	$ 6.50	$47.50
1822 Close Date	3.00	6.50	50.00

1823 Over 22

1823 Normal Date

1823 over 22	14.00	32.50	590.00
1823 Normal Date	17.00	40.00	785.00
1823 Restrike, from broken obverse die			35.00

1824 Over 22   1824 Wide Date   1824 Close Date

1824 over 22	8.00	19.00	170.00
1824 Wide Date	3.25	8.50	110.00
1824 Close Date	3.25	8.50	100.00

1825 Small A's   1825 Large A's

[72]

LARGE CENTS

	Good	Fine	Unc.
1825 Small A's in Legend	$3.00	$7.25	$70.00
1825 Large A's in Legend	3.00	7.25	75.00

1826 Over 25   1826 Wide Date   1826 Close Date

1826 over 25 (Trace of 5 inside of 6)	7.50	18.50	90.00
1826 Wide Date	2.75	7.50	65.00
1826 Close Date	2.25	6.50	55.00

1827	2.00	5.00	40.00

1828 Small Date   1828 Large Date

1828 Small Date	4.25	12.50	85.00
1828 Large Date	2.75	6.00	42.50

1829 Small Letters   1829 Large Letters

LARGE CENTS

	Good	Fine	Unc.
1829 Small Letters	$ 4.00	$ 9.50	$70.00
1829 Large Letters	2.25	5.25	38.50
1830 Small Letters	8.50	22.50	———
1830 Large Letters	2.25	5.50	45.00
1831 Small Letters	1.90	4.50	33.00
1831 Large Letters	1.90	4.50	33.00
1832 Small Letters	2.00	5.75	43.50
1832 Large Letters	2.00	5.75	40.00
1833	2.00	5.00	30.00

Large Date, Large Stars.   Small Date, Large Stars.   Large Date, Small Stars

1834 Lg. Date Lg. Stars, Lg. Let. on Rev.	3.25	9.50	45.00
1834 Small Date, Lg. Stars, Sm. Let. on Rev.	3.00	7.50	36.00
1834 Lg. Date, Sm. Stars, Sm. Let. on Rev.	3.75	10.00	46.00

Large Date, Large Stars   Small Date, Small Stars   Type of 1836

1835 Lg. Date, Lg. Stars	3.25	7.25	36.00
1835 Sm. Date, Sm. Stars	3.25	8.25	42.50
1835 Type of 1836	2.25	6.50	30.00

1836	2.25	5.50	36.00

LARGE CENTS

1837 Plain Hair Cord

1837 Beaded Hair Cord

	Good	Fine	Unc.
1837 Plain Hair Cord, Sm. Let	$3.25	$8.25	$48.00
1837 Plain Hair Cord, Lg. Let	2.00	4.25	25.00
1837 Beaded Hair Cord, Sm. Let	2.25	5.25	27.50
1838	1.75	3.75	17.50

1839 over 36 (Actually a Die-Break)

Line Under CENT No Center Dot

1839 over 36 Line under CENT; No center dot. 60.00   125.00   ———

Type of 1838

Silly Head Variety

1839 Type of 1838, Line under CENT 4.00   9.50   52.50
1839 Silly Head, Line under CENT; No center dot 5.25   12.00   65.00

Booby Head Variety, No Line Under CENT   1839 Type of 1840
1839 Booby Head, No line under CENT 3.75   8.50   50.00
1839 Type of 1840, No line under CENT 4.00   10.00   56.00

[75]

LARGE CENTS
BRAIDED HAIR TYPE

1840 Small Date

1840 Large Date

	Good	Fine	Unc.
1840 Small Date	$3.00	$5.75	$35.00
1840 Large Date	2.75	5.50	32.50
1841	2.75	5.25	28.50

1842 Small Date

1842 Large Date

1842 Small Date	2.50	6.00	32.50
1842 Large Date	2.25	5.50	30.00

1843 Obverse of 1842

1843 Reverse of 1842

1843 Obv. and Rev. of 1842	2.25	5.00	25.00
1843 Obv. of 1842, Rev. of 1844	11.00	30.00	150.00

1843 Obverse of 1844

1843 Reverse of 1844

1843 Obv. and Rev. of 1844	3.25	8.00	48.50

[76]

LARGE CENTS

1844

1844 Over 81

	Good	Fine	V. Fine	Unc.
1844	$2.00	$3.50	$6.00	$24.00
1844 over 81 (die defect)	4.00	8.00	12.00	37.50
1845	1.75	3.50	5.00	16.00

1846 Small Date

1846 Tall Date

1846 Small Date	1.25	2.75	4.50	16.00
1846 Medium Date	1.40	3.25	5.25	18.50
1846 Tall Date	1.85	4.50	8.00	25.00
1847	1.25	3.00	4.50	14.50

	Good	Fine	V. Fine	Unc.
1848	$1.25	$2.75	$4.25	$14.00
1849	1.35	2.75	4.75	15.50
1850	1.25	2.75	4.25	14.50
1851	1.25	2.60	3.75	13.50

	Good	Fine	V. Fine	Unc.
1851 over 81 (die defect)	4.00	7.25	12.00	45.00
1852	1.25	2.75	3.75	13.50
1853	1.25	2.75	3.75	13.50
1854	1.25	2.75	3.75	14.50

BIBLIOGRAPHY
Crosby, S. S., The Cents and Half Cents of 1793.
Hays, W. W., The Cents of 1794.
Gilbert-Elder, The Cents of 1796.
Doughty, Francis W., United States Cents.
Clapp, Geo. H., Cents of 1798 and 1799.
Newcomb, H. R., United States Copper Cents 1816-1857.
Sheldon, Wm. H., Penny Whimsy (1793-1814).

LARGE CENTS

1855 Upright 5's

1855 Slanting 5's

Original sketches of Engraver James B. Longacre's work reveal that slanting 5's were a peculiarity of his work. The upright 5's were probably the work of an apprentice.

	Good	Fine	V.Fine	Unc.
1855 Upright 5's	$1.50	$3.25	$4.75	$14.50
1855 Slanting 5's	1.60	3.75	5.75	15.50
1855 Slanting 5's Knob on Ear	2.00	4.75	7.25	22.50

1856 Upright 5

1856 Slanting 5

| 1856 Upright 5 | 1.60 | 3.25 | 4.75 | 15.00 |
| 1856 Slanting 5 | 1.50 | 3.00 | 4.25 | 15.00 |

1857 Small Date

1857 Large Date

| 1857 Small Date | 10.00 | 16.00 | 22.00 | 46.00 |
| 1857 Large Date | 10.00 | 16.00 | 22.00 | 46.00 |

Passing of the Large Cent and Half Cent

By 1857 the cost of making and distributing copper coins had risen. Mint Director Snowden reported that they "barely paid expenses." Both cents and half cents had become unpopular; in fact, they hardly circulated outside of the larger cities. The practice of issuing subsidiary silver coins which began in 1853, brought about a reform of the copper coinage. The half cent was abandoned and a smaller cent was introduced late in 1857.

The law of 1857 brought important benefits to the citizens. By its terms Spanish coins were redeemed and melted at the Mint in exchange for new small cents. The decimal system became popular and official thereafter, and the old method of reckoning in reals, medios, shillings, etc., was gradually given up, although the terms, "two bits" and "penny" are still commonly used. The new, convenient small cent won popular favor and soon became a useful instrument of retail trade and a boon to society generally.

FLYING EAGLE CENTS
1856-1858

The Act of February 21, 1857 provided for the coinage of the small cent, and made uncurrent the coins of other countries, particularly the Spanish and Mexican dollars. The new cents weighed 72 grains composed of 88 per cent copper and 12 per cent nickel. Because the large proportion of nickel imparts a light color to the coins, they are often called "white cents."

The 1858 cent is found in two major varieties. The differences in them are clearly demonstrated in the accompanying illustrations. The A and M in the word AMERICA are joined in the large letter variety, and separated in the small letter variety. The reverse design of the eagle cents is dominated by a wreath of corn, wheat, cotton and tobacco.

THE 1856 FLYING EAGLE CENT

The 1856 Eagle Cent was not an authorized mint issue, as the law governing the new size coin was enacted after the date of issue. It is believed that about 1000 of these pieces were struck. They are usually referred to as patterns.

1858 Cent

Large Letters

Small Letters

	Good	Fine	Ex. Fine	Unc.	Proof
1856	$350.00	500.00	650.00	850.00	1100.00
1857	2.50	6.00	12.00	33.50	240.00
1858 Large Letters	3.75	8.50	22.50	60.00	300.00
1858 Small Letters	3.50	8.00	20.00	60.00	300.00

[79]

INDIAN HEAD CENTS

1859-1864

Copper Nickel

The small cent was redesigned in 1859, and a representation of an Indian girl was adopted as the obverse device. The 1859 reverse was also changed to represent a laurel wreath. In 1860 the reverse only was modified to display an oak wreath with a small shield at the top. The weight and composition of the coin was not changed.

Without shield at top of wreath on reverse

Date	Good	Fine	Ex. Fine	Unc.	Proof
1859	$2.00	5.50	12.00	40.00	100.00

With shield on reverse

1860	1.75	4.50	9.00	21.00	62.50
1861	5.00	10.00	16.00	35.00	100.00
1862	1.25	3.00	5.00	9.00	60.00
1863	1.10	2.50	4.00	8.00	55.00
1864	3.00	7.50	10.00	16.00	60.00

1864-1909

Bronze

During the year 1864 the alloy of the cent was changed to 95 per cent copper and five per cent tin and zinc. The weight was reduced to 48 grains, resulting in a thinner coin than the "White Cents." The design remained unchanged. The first 1864 bronze cents did not have the designer's initial L on the bonnet ribbon. Later in the year the letter appeared on only a small quantity. The initial appeared on all dates of Indian Cents thereafter. Consult the illustration details.

1864 (No L on ribbon)	1.50	6.00	9.50	18.50	110.00

SMALL CENTS

1864 Bronze Indian Head Cent With "L"

If the coin is turned slightly (so Indian faces observer) the highlighted details of the "L" will appear to better advantage. The point of the bust is pointed on the variety with "L"; rounded without "L." The "L" is the initial of the engraver, Longacre.

closed 3   open 3

Select brilliant Unc. and Proof small cents command higher prices.

	Good	Fine	Ex. Fine	Unc.	Proof		Good	Fine	Ex. Fine	Unc.	Proof
1864 (L on ribbon must show)						1886(Var.1)	1.50	4.75	8.25	16.00	20.00
	$11.00	40.00	70.00	115.00	—	1886 (*Var. 2)					
1865...	1.25	3.50	6.00	13.50	50.00		1.50	4.75	8.25	16.00	20.00
1866...	6.50	15.00	35.00	55.00	77.50	1887....	.35	1.75	4.00	9.00	16.50
1867...	6.00	14.00	30.00	50.00	75.00	1888....	.40	2.25	4.50	8.00	16.00
1868...	6.00	14.00	27.50	40.00	70.00	1889....	.35	1.75	3.25	7.25	16.00
‡1869 over 8						1890....	.35	1.75	3.25	7.50	16.00
	35.00	55.00	80.00	150.00	—	1891....	.35	1.75	3.25	7.50	15.00
1869...	8.00	23.00	37.50	65.00	90.00	1892....	.50	2.00	4.50	10.00	16.00
1870...	8.00	22.50	35.00	55.00	85.00	1893....	.35	1.75	3.25	7.00	16.00
1871...	13.00	28.50	45.00	75.00	115.00	1894....	.80	5.50	8.50	15.00	21.00
1872...	16.00	40.00	60.00	95.00	125.00	1895....	.35	2.00	3.25	8.00	16.50
1873 Closed 3						1896....	.40	2.25	4.50	11.00	21.00
	4.50	11.00	19.00	40.00	42.50	1897....	.35	1.85	3.75	10.00	19.00
1873 Open 3						1898....	.35	1.60	3.00	8.50	21.00
	3.50	7.50	16.00	35.00	—	1899....	.35	1.60	2.75	8.00	18.50
1874...	2.50	8.00	15.00	28.50	42.50	1900....	.20	1.25	2.00	5.75	13.50
1875...	3.00	8.00	15.00	30.00	42.50	1901....	.20	.75	2.00	4.50	13.50
1876...	4.50	11.00	17.50	32.50	40.00	1902....	.20	.75	2.00	4.50	13.50
1877...	47.50	80.00	155.00	275.00	325.00	1903....	.20	.75	2.00	4.50	13.50
1878...	5.00	13.00	19.00	35.00	42.50	1904....	.20	.75	2.00	4.50	13.50
1879...	1.25	3.25	6.50	14.00	20.00	1905....	.20	.75	2.00	4.50	13.50
1880...	1.00	2.75	5.75	13.00	18.00	1906....	.20	.75	2.00	4.50	13.50
1881...	1.00	2.75	5.75	13.00	18.00	1907....	.20	.75	2.00	4.50	18.50
1882...	.90	2.25	5.50	11.00	17.50	1908....	.25	.75	2.00	4.75	17.00
1883...	.90	2.10	4.25	8.50	14.00	1908S...	9.50	15.00	27.50	50.00	
1884...	1.25	4.00	8.50	17.00	22.50	1909....	.35	1.25	2.40	5.25	20.00
1885...	2.25	8.00	12.00	22.50	27.50	1909S...	45.00	57.50	80.00	117.50	

‡Do not confuse with recut variety.
*1886 VAR. 1 Last feather points between I and C.
*1886 VAR. 2 Last feather points between C and A.

SMALL CENTS
Lincoln Head Type 1909 to Date

Victor D. Brenner designed this cent which was issued to commemorate the hundredth anniversary of Lincoln's birth. The designer's initials VDB appear on a limited quantity of cents of 1909. The San Francisco mint produced the smallest issue before the initials were removed, creating the scarcest though not the highest priced Lincoln Head Cent. The initials were restored, in 1918, to the obverse side as illustrated below. This type cent was the first to have the motto "In God We Trust."

Frank Gasparro designed the Lincoln Memorial reverse which was introduced on the 150th anniversary of Lincoln's birth in 1959.

Select brilliant uncirculated cents command higher prices.

Cents with well-struck mint marks are also worth more.

	Good	Fine	Ex. Fine	Unc.	Proof
1909 V D B	$ .25	.50	1.00	2.50	105.00
1909S, V D B	50.00	65.00	82.50	115.00	

Same as the preceding type, but VDB omitted from the reverse.

	Good	Fine	Ex. Fine	Unc.	Matte Proof
1909	$ .20	.35	.75	4.00	18.00
1909S	11.00	13.50	25.00	42.50	
1910	.10	.35	.85	4.00	17.50
1910S	1.25	3.25	7.50	21.50	
1911	.10	.40	.85	4.50	19.00
1911D	.75	2.25	6.00	16.00	
1911S	3.50	6.50	10.50	27.50	
1912	.10	.40	1.00	5.50	17.00
1912D	1.00	3.50	10.00	35.00	
1912S	2.00	4.50	12.00	27.50	
1913	.10	.40	.85	4.50	15.00
1913D	.40	2.50	7.50	27.50	
1913S	1.50	3.50	9.00	25.00	
1914	.35	2.00	4.00	13.00	28.50
*1914D	25.00	47.50	100.00	310.00	
1914S	2.25	4.50	15.00	67.50	
1915	.30	2.25	4.50	15.00	41.00
1915D	.50	2.00	4.25	11.50	
1915S	1.50	3.00	7.00	24.00	
1916	.10	.40	.85	5.00	50.00
1916D	.30	2.00	4.00	12.50	
1916S	.50	2.75	5.75	20.00	
1917	.10	.40	.90	4.00	
1917D	.30	1.50	6.00	17.50	
1917S	.30	1.50	6.00	17.50	

Designer's Initials Restored

	Good	Fine	Ex. Fine	Unc.
1918	$ .10	.40	1.00	5.25
1918D	.25	1.50	5.75	22.00
1918S	.25	1.50	5.75	22.00
1919	.10	.35	.75	4.00
1919D	.20	.90	3.50	11.00
1919S	.20	.90	3.50	11.00
1920	.10	.40	.90	4.00
1920D	.20	1.35	5.00	27.50
1920S	.20	1.35	6.00	27.50
1921	.25	1.35	4.00	11.00
1921S	.50	3.00	20.00	125.00
1922D	1.75	4.50	7.50	24.00
1922 Plain (No D)	7.00	13.50	38.00	185.00
1923	.10	.30	.85	4.00
1923S	.75	4.00	30.00	150.00

*Beware of Altered Date. No VDB on Genuine 1914 D Coin.

SMALL CENTS

	Good	Fine	Ex. Fine	Unc.	Proof
1924....	$ .10	.30	1.00	12.50	
1924D..	3.00	6.00	17.50	70.00	
1924S...	.80	2.50	12.50	50.00	
1925....	.10	.30	.90	4.00	
1925D..	.20	1.10	2.75	12.50	
1925S...	.35	1.75	4.50	22.50	
1926....	.10	.30	.75	2.75	
1926D..	.20	.85	2.50	11.50	
1926S...	.75	3.50	15.00	65.00	
1927....	.10	.25	.50	3.00	
1927D..	.20	.75	3.00	12.00	
1927S...	.25	1.75	6.00	26.00	
1928....	.10	.25	.50	2.50	
1928D..	.20	.75	2.50	11.00	
1928S...	.20	.85	3.50	16.00	
1929....		.15	.35	2.25	
1929D..		.25	.85	5.50	
1929S...		.25	.75	2.50	
1930....		.15	.30	1.30	
1930D..	.15	.25	1.00	4.25	
1930S...	.15	.25	.75	2.50	
1931....	.15	.65	1.25	7.50	
1931D..	.75	2.00	7.00	35.00	
1931S...	9.00	13.00	17.00	25.00	
1932....	.30	.60	1.50	6.50	
1932D..	.30	.65	1.75	7.50	
1933....	.40	.85	2.25	9.00	
1933D..	.50	1.00	2.25	7.50	
1934....				1.50	
1934D....				3.75	
1935....				.90	
1935D....				2.00	
1935S....				2.25	
1936....				.90	40.00
1936D....				1.10	
1936S....				1.40	
1937....				.65	15.00
1937D....				.90	
1937S....				1.10	
1938....				1.60	5.00
1938D....				1.25	
1938S....				1.65	
1939....				.75	3.00
1939D..	.35	.55	1.10	3.75	
1939S....				1.40	
1940....				.55	2.50
1940D....				.55	
1940S....				.60	
1941....				.50	2.00
1941D....				.55	
1941S....				.75	
1942....				.45	2.00
1942D....				.45	
1942S....				1.35	

WARTIME STEEL CENTS

Owing to a shortage of copper during the critical war year 1943 the Treasury Department resorted to the use of zinc coated steel for our cents. No bronze cents were officially issued in 1943. A few specimens struck on bronze planchets by error are known to exist. Through a similar error, a few of the 1944 cents were struck on steel planchets.

	Unc.
1943....	$ .50
1943D....	.60
1943S....	1.35

"SHELL CASE" COPPER

Shell cases were salvaged for coinage in 1944. Although the color is a little different, the coin has proved satisfactory in every respect.

	Unc.	Proof
1944....	$ .35	
1944D....	.35	
1944S....	.45	
1945....	.50	
1945D....	.40	
1945S....	.45	

Pre-War Composition — Bronze

	Unc.	Proof
1946....	.35	
1946D....	.35	
1946S....	.35	
1947....	.70	
1947D....	.40	
1947S....	.50	
1948....	.55	
1948D....	.40	
1948S....	.55	
1949....	.65	
1949D....	.55	
1949S....	1.15	
1950....	.50	9.00
1950D....	.35	
1950S....	.65	
1951....	.45	5.00
1951D....	.35	
1951S....	.75	
1952....	.45	3.50
1952D....	.35	
1952S....	.65	
1953....	.25	3.00
1953D....	.25	
1953S....	.45	
1954....	.45	1.50
1954D....	.25	
1954S....	.35	
1955....	.20	1.50

[83]

SMALL CENTS

	Unc.	Proof
1959	$ .05	.75
1959D	.05	

Small Date   **Large Date**

	Unc.	Proof
1955 Doubled Die Obv.—		
Ex. Fine $55.00	$95.00	
1955D	.20	
1955S	.40	
1956	.15	1.00
1956D	.10	
1957	.10	.75
1957D	.10	
1958	.10	1.50
1958D	.05	
1960 Large date	.05	.50
1960 Small date	2.50★	15.00★
1960D Large date	.05	
1960D Small date	.15★	
1961	.05	.50
1961D	.05	
★Speculative		

TWO-CENT PIECES—1864-1873 Bronze

The Act of April 22, 1864 which changed the weight and composition of the cent included a provision for the bronze two-cent piece. The weight was specified as 90 grains, the alloy being the same as for the cent.

The two-cent piece is one of the short-lived issues of United States coinage. The motto "In God We Trust" appeared for the first time. Its presence on the new coin was due largely to the increased religious sentiment during the Civil War crisis.

There are two varieties for the first year of issue, 1864: the small motto and the large motto. The differences are explained in the illustrations below. The small motto variety of 1864 is scarce.

It will be noted that the shield device is very similar to the nickel five-cent piece introduced in 1866.

Small Motto   **TWO CENTS OF 1864**   **Large Motto**

Details explain the differences in these two well-known varieties. Observe the D in God, it is narrow on the large motto. The stem to the leaf shows plainly on the small motto variety. There is no stem on the large motto coin.

Letter T in TRUST touches ribbon crease at left on small motto variety; there is a $\frac{1}{32}''$ gap on the large motto variety.

TWO-CENT PIECES
Select uncirculated and proof coins command higher prices.

	Good	Fine	Ex. Fine	Unc.	Proof
1865	$ 1.00	3.00	5.75	9.50	50.00
1866	1.50	4.00	7.00	17.50	40.00
1867	1.50	4.00	7.00	15.00	40.00
1868	1.50	4.00	7.00	15.00	40.00
1869	1.75	5.00	9.00	18.00	40.00
1870	2.50	7.00	11.00	20.00	45.00
1871	3.50	8.00	15.00	27.00	48.50
1872	22.00	30.00	40.00	60.00	100.00
1873 Proofs only (Closed 3)....					220.00
1873 Proofs only (Open 3).....					220.00
(See page 81)					

	Good	Fine	Ex. Fine	Unc.	Proof
1864 Small Motto	$27.50	45.00	70.00	145.00	1,375.00
1864 Large Motto	.85	2.35	4.50	8.50	70.00

Adoption of the motto IN GOD WE TRUST can be credited to Rev. M. R. Watkinson who suggested a similar wording to Secretary of the Treasury Salmon P. Chase in 1861. He offered the legend GOD, LIBERTY, LAW which he explained "would relieve us from the ignominy of heathenism." Secretary Chase requested Mint Director Pollock to submit designs for a coin to include a motto "expressing in the fewest and tersest words" the "trust of our people in God." Ideas submitted included OUR COUNTRY: OUR GOD and GOD, OUR TRUST. Secretary Chase made the final change of wording which gave us the famous motto in its present familiar form.

The motto was first employed on the two-cent piece of 1864. Its use was extended to include other denominations by the Law of March 3, 1865.

THREE-CENT PIECES (NICKEL) 1865-1889

Dr. Lewis Feuchtwanger produced a metal which was really a variety of German silver consisting of nickel, copper and some zinc. He suggested to Congress that his metal be substituted for copper as early as 1837. He made some one-cent and three-cent trial pieces in this metal at that time.

The regular series which was issued uninterruptedly from 1865 until 1889 offers no type variations. The edge is plain.

	Good	Fine	Ex. Fine	Unc.	Proof
1874	$ 2.00	4.00	9.00	15.00	28.50
1875	4.00	7.50	11.00	21.50	40.00
1876	3.50	6.50	11.00	21.00	30.00
1877 Proof only................					225.00
1878 Proof only................					95.00
1879	2.75	4.50	7.50	12.50	17.00
1880	2.75	4.50	7.50	12.50	16.00
1881	1.00	1.50	3.00	6.25	14.00
1882	2.50	4.00	6.00	12.00	14.00
1883	2.25	3.50	5.50	11.00	14.00
1884	2.75	5.00	7.00	12.00	15.00
1885	2.75	5.00	7.50	14.00	17.00
1886					19.50
1887 87 over 86					90.00
1887	10.00	15.00	22.50	45.00	75.00
1888	2.75	4.50	7.50	12.00	15.00
1889	3.00	5.00	8.00	13.00	16.00

	Good	Fine	Ex. Fine	Unc.	Proof
1865	$ .80	1.25	2.75	6.50	200.00
1866	.90	1.50	3.00	7.00	50.00
1867	.80	1.50	2.75	6.00	25.00
1868	.80	1.50	2.75	6.00	30.00
1869	1.15	1.85	3.50	7.50	27.50
1870	1.10	1.85	3.50	8.00	25.00
1871	2.00	4.00	6.00	12.00	30.00
1872	2.00	4.00	6.00	12.00	30.00
1873 (Closed 3)	2.25	4.00	6.00	11.00	22.50
1873 (Open 3)	1.00	2.00	3.00	7.00	

NICKEL FIVE-CENT PIECES
1866 to Date

The shield type nickel was made possible by the act of May 16, 1866. Its weight was set at 77-16/100 grains with the same composition as the nickel three-cent piece which was authorized in 1865. In 1866 the coin was designed with rays between the stars on the reverse. Some of the pieces minted in 1867 have the same details, but later the rays were eliminated creating two varieties for that year. There was no further change in the type until it was replaced by the Liberty head device in 1883.

Proofs only were struck in 1877 and 1878.

With Rays   **Without Rays**

	Good	Fine	Ex. Fine	Unc.	Proof		Good	Fine	Ex. Fine	Unc.	Proof
1866	$3.75	8.00	17.50	35.00	290.00	1874	$5.00	9.00	12.50	21.00	50.00
1867 Rays	5.00	16.00	35.00	87.50	—	1875	10.00	15.00	35.00	63.00	95.00
						1876	5.00	7.50	12.50	19.00	32.00
1867 Without Rays	1.20	2.25	4.50	10.00	36.00	1877					400.00
						1878					100.00
1868	1.25	2.50	4.75	10.50	36.00	1879	9.00	12.00	17.50	25.00	35.00
1869	2.00	3.50	6.00	14.50	40.00	1880	11.50	16.50	22.00	34.00	42.50
1870	2.50	5.00	8.00	16.00	40.00	1881	9.00	12.00	17.50	25.00	35.00
1871	25.00	40.00	65.00	115.00	170.00	1882	1.50	3.00	5.50	10.00	17.00
1872	3.00	5.50	9.00	19.00	32.00	1882 over 1				110.00	
1873 (Closed 3) See page 81.						1883	1.40	2.75	4.75	9.50	16.00
	3.00	7.00	10.00	21.00	27.50	1883 over 2				110.00	
1873 (Open 3) See page 81.											
	2.50	5.00	8.00	16.00							

LIBERTY HEAD TYPE

In 1883 the type was changed to the familiar "Liberty head." This type first appeared without the word CENTS on the coin, merely a large letter "V." These "centless" coins were goldplated and passed for five dollars. Later in that year the word CENTS was added.

It has been reported that five 1913 Liberty head nickels were originally owned by Col. Green (the deceased son of the famous Hetty Green). These have since been dispersed and are now held in the collections of several individuals. These were not a regular mint issue and were never placed in circulation.

Liberty Head Type Without CENTS

	Good	Fine	Ex. Fine	Unc.	Proof
1883 No CENTS	$ .35	.90	1.90	4.00	13.50

[86]

LIBERTY HEAD NICKELS

With CENTS

	Good	Fine	Ex. Fine	Unc.	Proof
1883 with CENTS	$3.00	6.50	9.50	16.00	22.00
1884	3.25	7.50	12.00	20.00	27.50
1885	37.50	60.00	85.00	115.00	125.00
1886	19.00	30.00	40.00	55.00	65.00
1887	1.75	4.00	7.00	15.00	21.00
1888	3.50	7.50	12.50	18.00	24.00
1889	1.75	3.50	6.50	15.00	20.00
1890	2.50	5.00	10.00	15.00	20.00
1891	1.50	3.50	6.50	15.00	20.00
1892	1.50	4.50	7.50	15.00	19.00
1893	1.50	3.50	6.50	15.00	20.00
1894	3.00	6.50	11.00	19.00	25.00
1895	1.00	3.00	6.00	15.00	24.00
1896	1.25	6.50	13.50	33.00	55.00
1897	.85	2.50	5.00	15.00	26.00
1898	.85	2.50	5.00	15.00	26.00
1899	$ .85	2.50	4.50	15.00	26.00
1900	.40	2.00	4.50	12.50	23.00
1901	.35	1.75	3.50	12.00	22.50
1902	.35	1.75	3.50	10.00	21.00
1903	.35	1.75	3.50	10.00	20.00
1904	.35	1.75	3.50	10.00	18.00
1905	.35	1.75	3.50	10.00	18.00
1906	.35	1.75	3.50	10.00	19.00
1907	.35	1.75	3.50	10.00	22.50
1908	.35	1.75	3.50	9.50	18.00
1909	.35	1.75	3.50	9.50	17.50
1910	.35	1.75	3.50	9.50	18.00
1911	.35	1.75	3.00	9.50	20.00
1912	.35	1.75	3.00	9.50	34.00
1912D	1.00	8.00	30.00	100.00	
1912S	13.00	25.00	45.00	120.00	
1913 Liberty Hd. (5 Known)					

INDIAN HEAD OR BUFFALO TYPE

These pieces are known as Buffalo, Bison or Indian head nickels. In the first year of issue, 1913, there were two distinct varieties; the first showing the bison on a mound, and the second has the base redesigned to a thinner straight line.

James E. Fraser designed this nickel employing three different Indians as models. His initial (**F**) is beneath the date. The bison was modeled after "Black Diamond" in the New York Zoological gardens.

Variety 1 **Variety 2**

Well-struck uncirculated pieces have substantially higher values.

	Good	Fine	Ex. Fine	Unc.	Matte Proof
1913 Var. 1	$ .65	1.10	1.75	4.00	22.50
1913D Var. 1	1.75	3.00	6.00	12.00	
1913S Var. 1	3.00	6.00	11.00	21.00	
1913 Var. 2	.60	1.00	2.00	4.50	25.00
1913D Var. 2	$10.00	17.50	27.50	45.00	
1913S Var. 2	16.00	35.00	55.00	80.00	
1914	.85	2.25	3.75	8.00	27.00
1914D	8.50	17.00	25.00	46.00	
1914S	2.25	7.00	18.50	40.00	
1915	.75	1.75	4.00	9.00	28.50

INDIAN HEAD OR BUFFALO NICKELS

	Good	Fine	Ex. Fine	Unc.	Matte Proof
1915D..	$2.00	6.00	15.00	30.00	
1915S...	4.50	10.00	22.00	45.00	
1916....	.30	1.00	3.00	7.00	37.50
1916D..	1.50	4.00	10.00	32.50	
1916S...	1.50	4.50	11.00	37.50	
1917....	.30	.75	2.00	7.50	
1917D..	2.00	6.50	21.00	50.00	
1917S...	2.00	6.00	27.00	65.00	
1918....	.35	1.50	3.50	18.50	
1918D over 7..	$65.00	200.00	750.00	—	
1918D Normal Date...	2.50	6.00	27.50	70.00	
1918S...	2.50	6.50	30.00	75.00	
1919....	.30	.75	2.25	10.00	
1919D..	2.50	8.50	45.00	92.50	
1919S...	2.50	9.00	51.50	105.00	
1920....	.25	.75	2.25	9.00	
1920D..	1.85	5.50	37.50	90.00	
1920S...	1.85	5.50	37.50	87.50	
1921....	.50	1.50	3.75	16.00	
1921S...	7.50	12.50	50.00	110.00	
1923....	.30	.75	2.00	8.00	
1923S...	1.50	5.50	32.50	70.00	
1924....	.30	.75	2.25	10.00	
1924D..	1.50	4.75	28.00	75.00	

	Good	Fine	Ex. Fine	Unc.	Proof
1924S...	$4.00	11.00	57.50	135.00	
1925...	.25	.70	2.25	10.00	
1925D..	4.00	11.00	22.50	50.00	
1925S...	3.50	9.00	32.50	120.00	
1926....	.25	.60	1.25	8.00	
1926D..	1.50	3.00	6.00	22.50	
1926S...	2.75	15.00	75.00	210.00	
1927....	.25	.60	1.35	7.00	
1927D..	.80	1.85	5.00	17.50	
1927S...	1.75	11.00	42.50	150.00	
1928....	.15	.30	1.00	5.75	
1928D..	.20	.60	1.50	6.00	
1928S...	.35	1.25	5.00	27.50	
1929....	.10	.20	.85	4.50	
1929D..	.20	.50	1.85	6.75	
1929S...	.20	.50	1.75	6.50	
1930....	.10	.25	1.00	5.50	
1930S...	.50	1.50	3.00	17.50	
1931S...	1.50	3.00	7.00	17.50	
1934....		.25	.85	5.00	
1934D..		.50	1.50	6.00	
1935....		.15	.45	1.65	
1935D..		.25	.85	4.75	
1935S...		.30	1.10	4.25	
1936....			.35	1.50	100.00
1936D..			.35	1.75	
1936S...			.50	2.25	
1937....			.30	1.10	45.00
1937D..			.40	1.50	
*1937D 3-Legged variety		12.00	22.50	35.00	60.00
1937S...			.40	1.75	
1938D..			.30	1.00	

*Beware of removed leg.

JEFFERSON TYPE

The most recent type of five-cent coin was designed by Felix Schlag. His representation of Thomas Jefferson and Monticello won an award of $1000 in a competition with some 390 artists. It was the first United States Minor coin design to be selected in an open competition, and established the definite public approval of portrait and pictorial rather than symbolic devices on our coinage.

	Fine	Ex. Fine	Unc.	Proof
1938........	$ .10	.20	1.25	8.00
1938D.......	.40	.75	2.50	
1938S.......	.45	.90	4.00	
1939........	$ .10	.50	2.50	6.50
1939D.......	2.25	8.00	40.00	
1939S.......	1.00	3.50	17.50	
1940........			.85	6.50
1940D.......			1.60	
1940S.......			1.90	
1941........			.80	5.50
1941D.......			.90	
1941S.......			1.60	
1942........			1.00	3.50
1942D.......		.50	2.50	13.50

[88]

JEFFERSON NICKELS

On October 8, 1942, the wartime five-cent piece composed of copper, (56%) silver (35%) and manganese (9%) made its first appearance. The mint mark was made larger and placed above the dome of Monticello. The letter P for the Philadelphia Mint was used for the first time on this piece to indicate the change of alloy. Nickel, a critical war material, was entirely eliminated.

(Mint Mark Above Dome On Reverse Side)

Jefferson 5c Silver, 1942 and later. Mint mark above dome on reverse side.

	Unc.	Proof		Unc.	Proof
1942P.	$3.00	4.00	1944D	$1.40	
1942S..	1.75		1944S	1.40	
1943P.	1.40		1945P	1.10	
1943D	1.60		1945D	1.00	
1943S..	1.40		1945S	1.00	
*1944P	1.40				

*1944P Nickels without mint mark are counterfeits.

REGULAR COPPER-NICKEL COMPOSITION

Small Mint Mark at Right of Building

	Ex. Fine	Unc.	Proof		Ex. Fine	Unc.	Proof
1946	$	.50		1952S		$ .90★	
1946D		.50		1953		.50★	2.50
1946S		.80		1953D		.40★	
1947		.50		1953S		.60★	
1947D		.50		1954		.40★	2.00
1947S		.75		1954D		.40★	
1948		.60		1954S		.50★	
1948D		.60		1955		1.10★	2.00
1948S		1.50		1955D		.35	
1949		1.00		1956		.25	1.25
1949D		1.00		1956D		.25	
1949S		2.25		1957		.25	.75
1950		2.25★	10.00	1957D		.20	
1950D	2.00	5.00★		1958		.40★	1.75
1951		.50★	6.00	1958D		.20	
1951D		1.50★		1959		.30★	.50
1951S	.75	3.00★		1959D		.15	
1952		.60★	4.00	1960		.15	.60
1952D		3.00★		1960D		.15	
				1961		.15	.60
★Speculative.				1961D		.15	

SILVER THREE-CENT PIECES
1851-1873

This smallest of United States coins was authorized by Congress March 3, 1851. The first three-cent silver pieces had no lines bordering the six-pointed star. From 1854 through 1858 there were three lines, while issues of the last fifteen years show only two lines. Issues from 1854 through 1873 have an olive sprig over the III and a bundle of three arrows beneath.

The original weight of this piece was $12\frac{3}{8}$ grains, .750 fine, which was changed by the law of March 3, 1853, to 11.52 grains, .900 fine.

mint mark
o

	Good	Fine	Unc.	Proof
1851	$ 3.00	5.00	16.00	
1851O	7.50	20.00	55.00	
1852	1.75	4.50	12.00	
1853	1.75	4.50	12.00	

1854 Three outlines to star

	Good	Fine	Unc.	Proof
1854	5.00	9.50	20.00	
1855	9.00	20.00	75.00	350.00
1856	5.50	10.00	31.50	165.00
1857	4.50	9.50	25.00	185.00
1858	4.50	9.00	17.50	160.00

	Good	Fine	Unc.	Proof
1859 Two outlines to star		5.50	8.50	17.00	51.00
1860	5.00	8.00	15.00	51.00
1861	4.50	8.00	12.00	33.00
1862	4.50	8.00	13.00	30.00
1863				100.00
1864				120.00
1865				90.00
1866				47.50
1867				47.50
1868				52.50
1869				52.50
1870				35.00
1871				40.00
1872				47.50
1873 (Closed 3 only)				75.00

HALF DIMES
1794-1873

The half-dime types present the same general characteristics as larger United States silver coins. Authorized by the Act of April 2, 1792, they were not coined until 1794. At first the weight was 20.8 grains, and fineness 892.4. By the Act of January 18, 1837 the weight was slightly reduced to $20\frac{5}{8}$ grains and the fineness changed to 900. Finally the weight was reduced to 19.2 grains by the Act of February 21, 1853. Both half dimes and dimes offer many varieties in the early dates. Until 1829 there was no indication of value on the half dimes.

Proofs prior to 1855 are known to exist of some dates and all are rare.

Note: Some early half dimes, while strictly uncirculated, bear file or adjustment marks.

	Good	Fine	Unc.
1794	$70.00	140.00	500.00
1795	45.00	80.00	260.00
1796 6 over 5	175.00	315.00	700.00

	Good	Fine	Unc.
1796 Normal Date	$65.00	130.00	350.00
1796 LIBERTY	—	—	—

HALF DIMES

	Good	Fine	Unc.
1797 15 Stars	$37.50	80.00	275.00
1797 16 Stars	42.50	90.00	275.00
1797 13 Stars	55.00	100.00	325.00

1800 .... 37.50 82.50 260.00

1800 LIBEKTY ... 42.50 85.00 290.00

	Good	Fine	Unc.
1801	$ 50.00	165.00	550.00
1802	375.00	750.00	——
1803	30.00	80.00	375.00
1805	60.00	140.00	——

1829	3.00	5.00	13.50
1830	2.00	4.00	12.00
1831	2.00	4.00	12.00
1832	2.00	4.00	12.00
1833	2.00	4.00	12.00
1834	2.00	4.00	12.00
1835 Large Date, Large 5c	2.00	4.00	11.50
1835 Large Date, Small 5c	2.00	4.00	11.50
1835 Small Date, Large 5c	2.00	4.00	11.50
1835 Small Date, Small 5c	2.00	4.00	11.50
1836 Small 5c	2.00	4.00	11.50
1836 Large 5c	2.00	4.00	11.50
1837 Small 5c	6.50	17.50	52.50
1837 Large 5c	3.00	5.00	16.50

LIBERTY SEATED TYPE

1838 No Drapery	$2.00	4.00	16.00
1839 No Drapery	1.75	3.75	15.00
1839O No Drapery	4.00	8.00	30.00
1840 No Drapery	1.50	3.25	12.50
1840O No Drapery	4.00	11.00	50.00

1837 No Stars, Sm. Date	$15.00	31.00	75.00
1837 No Stars, Large Date	14.50	30.00	72.50
1838O No Stars	24.00	47.50	175.00

No Drapery from Elbow (Enlarged)

Drapery from Elbow (Enlarged)

1840 Drapery	1.75	4.00	25.00
1840O Drapery	5.00	11.00	55.00
1841	1.50	3.75	12.00
1841O	2.50	6.50	42.50
1842	1.50	3.50	12.00

[91]

HALF DIMES

	Good	Fine	Unc.	Proof
1842O	$ 3.75	12.50	75.00	
1843	1.50	3.00	10.00	
1844	2.00	7.00	17.50	
1844O	4.50	15.00	72.50	
1845	1.50	3.00	10.00	
1846	27.50	50.00	125.00	
1847	1.50	3.00	10.00	
1848 Small Date	1.50	3.25	12.00	
1848 Medium Date	1.50	3.25	11.00	
1848 Large Date	1.50	4.00	15.00	
1848O	4.00	11.00	50.00	
1849 Over 48	2.00	4.50	17.50	
1849 Over 46	2.00	4.00	16.00	
1849	1.50	3.00	10.50	
1849O	20.00	47.50	120.00	
1850	1.50	3.00	10.00	
1850O	2.50	7.00	40.00	
1851	1.50	3.00	10.00	
1851O	2.00	6.50	35.00	
1852	1.50	3.00	10.00	
1852O	4.50	12.00	57.50	
1853 No Arrows	7.00	16.00	45.00	
1853O No Arrows	52.50	90.00	225.00	

Like the dimes, quarters and halves' arrows were placed at the sides of the date for a short period starting in 1853. They were placed there to denote the reduction of weight under the terms of the Act of February 21, 1853.

1853 with Arrows

	Good	Fine	Unc.	Proof
1853	$1.50	2.50	12.00	
1853O	1.50	3.00	13.00	
1854	1.00	2.00	10.50	
1854O	1.50	3.00	14.00	
1855	1.00	2.00	11.00	150.00
1855O	2.50	6.00	30.00	

Arrows at Date Removed

1856	.75	1.50	8.50	125.00
1856O	1.50	3.50	12.00	
1857	.75	1.50	7.50	90.00
1857O	1.25	3.00	12.00	
1858	.75	1.50	7.50	70.00
1858O	1.25	3.00	12.50	

New die 1859 Phil. only. Stars hollow in center. Arms slimmer.

	Good	Fine	Unc.	Proof
1859	$1.75	4.00	12.00	45.00
1859O	1.75	4.00	13.00	

In the years 1859 and 1860 a half-dime type was struck which does not bear our nation's identity. These coins are known as transitional patterns, and were struck at the time the inscription UNITED STATES OF AMERICA was being transferred from the reverse to the obverse side of the coin.

1859 Obv. of 59, Rev. of 60 .... Unc. Proof $750.00
1860 Obv. of 59, Rev. of 60 (with stars) .. $450.00

Legend on Obverse

	Good	Fine	Unc.	Proof
1860 Legend	$1.25	2.50	7.00	30.00
1860O Legend	2.25	4.00	13.50	
1861	1.25	2.25	7.50	30.00
1862	1.25	2.25	7.50	30.00
1863	7.00	12.00	35.00	70.00
1863S	8.00	16.00	52.50	
1864 Proof Only				100.00
1864S	9.00	23.00	80.00	
1865	6.00	11.00	45.00	60.00
1865S	6.00	12.50	50.00	
1866	4.00	8.00	35.00	40.00
1866S	5.00	8.50	45.00	
1867	4.00	8.00	36.00	41.00
1867S	4.00	8.00	40.00	
1868	2.00	4.00	14.00	37.50
1868S	2.00	4.00	16.00	
1869	1.50	3.00	11.00	40.00
1869S	1.50	3.50	16.00	
1870	1.00	2.00	10.00	21.00
1871	1.00	2.00	10.00	21.00
1871S	8.00	19.00	60.00	
1872	1.00	2.25	11.00	24.00

HALF DIMES

Mint Mark Within Wreath, Reverse Side.

Mint Mark Below Wreath, Reverse Side.

Date	Good	Fine	Unc.	Proof
1872S Mint Mark within Wreath	$1.25	3.00	10.50	
1872S Mint Mark below Wreath	1.50	3.50	12.00	
1873 (Closed 3 only)	1.00	2.25	10.50	37.50
1873S (Closed 3 only)	1.50	4.50	15.00	

BIBLIOGRAPHY

Newlin, H. P., Early Half Dimes. 1883.
Valentine, D. W., U. S. Half Dimes. 1931.
Breen, W., U. S. Half Dimes; A Supplement. 1958.

DIMES
1796 To Date

The designs of the dimes, first coined in 1796, follow closely those of the half dimes up through the liberty seated type. The dimes in each instance weigh twice as much as the half dimes.

Note: File or adjustment marks as on half dimes.

Proofs prior to 1855 are known to exist of some dates, and all are rare.

	Good	Fine	Unc.
1796	$120.00	210.00	525.00
1797 16 Stars	95.00	220.00	600.00
1797 13 Stars	77.50	175.00	525.00

	Good	Fine	Unc.
1798 over 97, 13 Stars on Reverse (Very Rare)	—	—	—
1798 over 97, 16 Stars on Reverse	$40.00	75.00	250.00
1798	35.00	65.00	225.00
1798 Small 8	—	—	—
1800	35.00	65.00	250.00
1801	50.00	100.00	350.00
1802	40.00	65.00	275.00
1803	40.00	65.00	270.00
1804 13 Stars on Reverse	65.00	130.00	525.00
1804 14 Stars on Reverse	65.00	125.00	500.00
1805 4 Berries	25.00	50.00	125.00
1805 5 Berries	25.00	52.50	140.00
1807	21.00	45.00	110.00

DIMES

	Good	Fine	Unc.
1809	$22.50	50.00	175.00
1811 over 9	13.00	27.50	100.00
1814 Small Date	6.00	12.50	50.00
1814 Large Date	6.00	12.50	42.50
1820 Large O	3.25	8.00	35.00
1820 Small O	2.75	7.50	33.00
1821 Small Date	3.25	7.50	40.00
1821 Large Date	2.50	6.50	35.00

	Good	Fine	Unc.
1822	$22.00	55.00	300.00

Small E's   **Large E's**

	Good	Fine	Unc.
1823 over 22, Small E's	4.00	12.00	50.00
1823 over 22, Large E's	4.00	11.50	47.50
1824 over 22	6.50	17.00	70.00
1825	4.00	9.00	35.00
1827	4.00	8.00	32.50

Small Date   **Large Date**

	Good	Fine	Unc.
1828 Small Date	6.00	13.00	60.00
1828 Large Date	11.00	30.00	80.00

1829 Sm. 10c   Lg. 10c

[94]

DIMES

	Good	Fine	Unc.
1829 Sm. 10¢	$1.50	3.50	16.00
1829 Med. 10¢	3.75	8.00	27.50
1829 Lg. 10¢	6.00	14.50	45.00
1830 Sm. 10¢	1.50	3.00	15.00
1830 Lg. 10¢	1.25	2.50	14.00
1831	1.25	2.50	14.00
1832	1.25	2.50	14.00

	Good	Fine	Unc.
1833	$1.50	3.00	13.50
1833 Last 3 high	1.50	3.00	14.00
1834 Small 4	2.00	4.00	20.00
1834 Large 4	1.50	3.00	15.00
1835	1.50	3.00	12.50
1836	1.50	3.00	13.50
1837	2.00	4.00	21.00

LIBERTY SEATED TYPE

No Drapery From Elbow
No Stars On Obverse

	Good	Fine	Unc.
1837 Sm. Date	16.00	40.00	100.00
1837 Lg. Date	16.00	40.00	95.00
1838O	22.50	60.00	250.00

No Drapery From Elbow
With Stars On Obverse

	Good	Fine	Unc.
1838 Sm. Stars	7.00	18.50	55.00
1838 Lg. Stars	2.50	4.50	19.00
1838 with Partial Drapery	10.00	25.00	65.00
1839	2.00	4.00	17.50
1839O	3.00	7.00	22.50
1840	2.00	4.50	15.00
1840O	3.00	6.00	20.00
1841			

With Drapery From Elbow

	Good	Fine	Unc.
1840	4.00	9.00	30.00
1841	1.50	3.00	15.00
1841O	1.50	4.50	22.00
1842	1.50	3.00	14.00
1842O	2.50	6.50	35.00
1843	1.50	2.50	14.00
1843O	10.00	25.00	90.00

Drapery From Elbow (Enlarged)

	Good	Fine	Unc.
1844	15.00	45.00	145.00
1845	1.50	3.00	14.00
1845O	5.00	10.50	47.50
1846	9.00	19.00	60.00
1847	3.25	6.25	30.00
1848	2.00	4.00	20.00
1849	1.50	3.00	14.00
1849O	4.00	9.00	40.00
1850	1.25	2.50	12.00
1850O	3.75	9.50	42.50
1851	1.25	2.50	12.00
1851O	3.00	6.00	32.00
1852	1.25	2.50	12.00
1852O	3.00	7.50	40.00
1853 (No Arrows)	10.00	18.00	70.00

Arrows At Date

	Good	Fine	Unc.
1853 (w/Arrows)	1.50	3.00	12.50
1853O	2.75	5.50	16.00
1854	1.25	2.50	11.00
1854O	1.60	3.25	12.50

	Good	Fine	Unc.	Proof
1855	$.90	2.00	10.00	175.00

Small Date, Arrows Removed

	Good	Fine	Unc.	Proof
1856 Small Date	1.00	2.50	10.00	175.00
1856O	1.65	3.50	13.00	
1856S	22.00	45.00	210.00	
1856 Large Date	1.50	3.00	22.50	
1857	1.00	2.50	9.00	150.00
1857O	1.50	3.00	15.00	

[95]

DIMES

	Good	Fine	Unc.	Proof
1858	$1.00	2.50	9.00	150.00
1858O	3.25	6.50	25.00	
1858S	13.50	27.50	150.00	
1859	1.10	2.35	12.50	60.00
1859O	1.15	2.75	15.00	
1859S	12.00	20.00	90.00	

1860 With Stars, S Mint

	Good	Fine	Unc.
1860S	6.00	15.00	65.00

Transitional Pattern
Same as Half Dimes of 1859 and 1860

Obverse of 1859   Reverse of 1860

1859.........................

Legend Replaces Stars

	Good	Fine	Unc.	Proof
1860	1.35	2.75	10.00	50.00
1860O	57.50	125.00	425.00	
1861	.85	1.75	8.00	42.50
1861S	10.00	25.00	90.00	
1862	1.50	3.00	9.00	37.50
1862S	6.50	17.50	75.00	
1863	6.50	12.00	26.00	52.50
1863S	6.50	17.50	85.00	
1864	6.25	12.00	26.00	50.00
1864S	6.50	17.50	65.00	
1865	6.50	11.00	29.00	47.50
1865S	7.50	17.50	67.50	
1866	5.75	11.50	30.00	42.50
1866S	6.00	15.00	65.00	
1867	6.25	12.00	29.00	45.00
1867S	6.00	14.00	45.00	

	Good	Fine	Unc.	Proof
1868	$1.25	2.60	9.00	37.00
1868S	4.75	10.50	35.00	
1869	1.50	3.25	13.00	35.00
1869S	4.75	10.50	35.00	
1870	1.35	3.00	10.00	27.00
1870S	35.00	65.00	165.00	
1871	1.25	2.75	9.50	27.00
1871S	7.50	15.00	55.00	
1871CC	110.00	200.00		
1872	1.10	2.50	9.00	27.00
1872S	7.50	15.00	45.00	
1872CC	75.00	150.00		
1873 Closed 3	1.25	3.00	10.00	35.00
1873 Open 3	3.50	10.00	19.00	
1873CC (Probably Unique)				

Arrows At Date

In 1873 the dime was slightly increased in weight to 38.58 grains. Arrows at the date in 1873 and 1874 indicate this change.

	Good	Fine	Unc.	Proof
1873	5.00	11.00	47.50	85.00
1873S	10.00	21.00	60.00	
1873CC	285.00	500.00	900.00	
1874	5.00	11.00	45.00	85.00
1874S	10.00	20.00	80.00	
1874CC	67.50	150.00	550.00	

Arrows At Date Removed

	Good	Fine	Unc.	Proof
1875	.75	1.75	6.00	30.00
1875S under Wreath				
	1.00	2.00	8.50	
1875S in Wreath				
	1.00	2.00	8.50	
1875CC under Wreath				
	2.50	5.00	17.50	
1875CC in Wreath				
	1.00	2.50	11.00	
1876	.60	1.15	6.00	22.50
1876S	1.00	2.00	8.00	
1876CC	1.25	2.50	8.50	
1877	.75	1.50	6.00	55.00
1877S	1.00	2.00	8.00	
1877CC	1.00	2.00	8.00	
1878	1.50	3.00	8.00	22.50
1878CC	9.00	20.00	50.00	

DIMES

	Good	Fine	Unc.	Proof
1879	$4.00	6.50	15.00	30.00
1880	4.50	8.00	15.00	32.00
1881	6.00	10.00	18.00	35.00
1882	.75	1.50	6.00	20.00
1883	.75	1.50	6.00	20.00
1884	.75	1.50	7.00	22.00
1884S	6.00	11.00	45.00	
1885	.75	1.50	6.00	22.00
1885S	45.00	90.00	300.00	
1886	.75	1.50	6.50	22.00
1886S	6.00	12.00	37.50	
1887	$ .75	1.50	6.00	23.50
1887S	1.50	3.00	11.00	
1888	.75	1.50	7.00	21.00
1888S	2.00	4.00	11.00	
1889	.75	1.50	6.00	22.00
1889S	6.00	13.00	90.00	
1890	.75	1.50	7.00	27.00
1890S	1.25	2.75	13.00	
1891	.75	1.50	7.00	28.00
1891O	1.50	3.25	27.50	
1891S	1.25	2.00	14.00	

BARBER OR LIBERTY HEAD TYPE

This type dime was designed by Charles E. Barber who was Chief Engraver of the Mint. He also designed the 25 and 50-cent pieces. His initial (B) is at the truncation of the neck.

	Good	Fine	Ex. Fine	Unc.	Proof
1892	$ .60	2.00	4.00	9.00	30.00
1892O	1.50	5.00	10.00	25.00	
1892S	14.00	27.50	60.00	90.00	
1893	1.50	3.50	6.00	12.50	42.50
1893O	4.25	9.00	15.00	42.50	
1893S	4.25	9.00	15.00	42.50	
1894	2.40	6.00	9.00	17.50	42.50
1894O	25.00	65.00	100.00	220.00	
1894S Hydeman Sale 1961					13,500.00
1895	20.00	40.00	60.00	100.00	175.00
1895O	40.00	115.00	250.00	500.00	
1895S	7.00	17.50	45.00	90.00	
1896	2.50	6.00	10.00	20.00	60.00
1896O	16.00	40.00	85.00	165.00	
1896S	25.00	50.00	110.00	190.00	
1897	.75	2.25	4.00	10.00	47.50
1897O	17.50	42.50	85.00	165.00	
1897S	6.00	17.50	40.00	90.00	
1898	.50	1.75	3.50	10.00	42.50
1898O	3.25	9.50	40.50	100.00	
1898S	3.00	7.50	30.00	65.00	
1899	.50	1.60	3.50	9.00	37.50
1899O	3.00	9.00	40.00	80.00	
1899S	2.75	8.00	25.00	55.00	
1900	.40	1.60	3.50	9.00	35.00
1900O	2.75	9.50	30.00	80.00	
1900S	2.00	6.50	16.50	45.00	
1901	.40	1.60	3.50	9.00	35.00
1901O	$ 1.00	7.50	30.00	75.00	
1901S	17.50	85.00	200.00	450.00	
1902	.40	1.50	2.50	8.00	45.00
1902O	1.00	5.50	25.00	55.00	
1902S	3.00	9.00	30.00	70.00	
1903	.35	1.00	2.50	8.50	42.50
1903O	.75	5.50	15.00	45.00	
1903S	8.00	17.50	40.00	100.00	
1904	.30	1.00	2.50	8.50	45.00
1904S	7.00	16.50	40.00	85.00	
1905	.35	1.00	2.50	8.50	43.50
1905O	1.25	5.50	15.00	50.00	
1905S	.90	4.00	9.00	20.00	
1906	.25	1.00	2.50	9.00	43.50
1906D	.75	2.00	4.00	12.00	
1906O	.75	3.75	7.50	22.50	
1906S	.35	3.25	6.50	17.50	
1907	.75	1.00	2.50	8.50	45.00
1907D	.60	4.00	10.00	27.50	
1907O	.65	2.00	5.00	20.00	
1907S	.30	2.25	6.00	20.00	
1908	.30	1.00	2.50	8.00	50.00
1908D	.40	1.50	3.50	10.00	
1908O	.75	3.75	9.50	25.00	
1908S	1.00	2.75	9.00	25.00	
1909	.30	1.00	2.50	8.50	45.00
1909D	1.75	8.00	20.00	40.00	
1909O	1.75	9.50	20.00	40.00	
1909S	1.75	8.00	17.50	37.50	
1910	.25	1.00	2.50	9.00	55.00
1910D	.50	1.75	5.00	12.50	
1910S	1.25	4.00	10.00	30.00	
1911	.25	1.00	2.50	8.50	60.00
1911D	.50	1.75	5.00	15.00	
1911S	.80	2.75	9.00	22.50	
1912	.25	1.00	2.50	8.50	55.00
1912D	.40	1.50	5.00	15.00	
1912S	.75	5.00	10.00	32.50	
1913	.25	1.00	2.50	10.00	80.00

[97]

DIMES

	Good	Fine	Ex. Fine	Unc.	Proof
1913S	$5.00	25.00	70.00	150.00	
1914	.25	1.00	3.00	8.50	165.00
1914D	.35	1.35	3.50	9.00	
1914S	.75	3.75	10.00	32.50	
1915	$ .25	1.25	3.00	10.50	175.00
1915S	1.50	4.00	10.00	25.00	
1916	.25	.75	2.00	8.00	
1916S	.30	1.75	4.00	10.00	

WINGED HEAD LIBERTY OR "MERCURY" TYPE

This dime was designed by A. A. Weinman. Although it is commonly called the "Mercury Dime" the main device is in fact a representation of Liberty. The wings crowning her cap are intended to symbolize liberty of thought. The designer's initials AW are found back of the neck.

	Good	Fine	Ex. Fine	Unc.	Proof
1916	$ .25	.50	1.00	3.50	
1916D	47.50	100.00	220.00	400.00	
1916S	.35	1.00	3.00	7.00	
1917	.25	.75	1.25	4.50	
1917D	.75	2.50	10.00	35.00	
1917S	.50	1.00	3.00	14.00	
1918	.35	1.00	3.00	20.00	
1918D	.65	1.50	6.00	27.50	
1918S	.65	1.50	6.00	20.00	
1919	.35	1.00	7.00	21.00	
1919D	1.25	4.00	35.00	100.00	
1919S	1.25	3.00	30.00	80.00	
1920	.35	1.00	1.50	7.50	
1920D	.50	1.25	7.00	22.50	
1920S	.50	1.25	7.00	22.50	
1921	4.00	20.00	50.00	190.00	
1921D	5.00	25.00	50.00	130.00	
1923	.35	.75	1.50	8.00	
1923S	1.00	2.50	12.50	60.00	
1924	.35	.75	2.00	10.00	
1924D	.50	1.25	6.00	20.00	
1924S	.50	1.50	10.00	50.00	
1925	.35	.75	2.00	8.50	
1925D	1.00	3.00	7.00	30.00	
1925S	.50	2.00	10.00	42.50	
1926	.35	.75	1.50	6.50	
1926D	.50	1.00	5.00	20.00	
1926S	2.00	6.00	30.00	72.50	
1927	.35	.60	1.00	6.00	
1927D	.50	3.00	30.00	160.00	
1927S	.40	1.75	15.00	57.50	
1928	.25	.50	1.00	6.00	
1928D	.50	1.50	12.50	65.00	
1928S	.60	1.25	10.00	40.00	
1929	.25	.50	1.00	3.50	
1929D	.40	.75	2.00	6.50	
1929S	.50	.75	4.00	10.00	
1930	.35	.75	1.00	5.75	
1930S	1.00	2.50	6.00	25.00	
1931	.75	1.00	1.50	9.50	
1931D	1.25	3.00	6.50	27.50	
1931S	1.00	2.00	6.00	22.50	
1934	.20	.35	.65	3.50	
1934D	.25	.45	.85	5.00	
1935	.15	.30	.60	2.00	
1935D	.25	.50	2.50	9.50	
1935S	.20	.40	1.00	5.00	
1936				1.10	45.00
1936D			2.00	7.50	
1936S			2.00	6.00	
1937				1.00	29.00
1937D			1.00	3.50	
1937S			1.00	4.00	
1938				1.10	7.00
1938D				2.25	
1938S			1.00	3.50	
1939				.85	7.00
1939D				1.25	
1939S			1.00	3.25	
1940				.85	7.00
1940D				1.00	
1940S				1.25	
1941				.75	6.00
1941D				1.00	
1941S				1.35	

1942 over 41 —
37.50 55.00 90.00 150.00

1942				.50	6.00
1942D				.65	
1942S				1.25	

[98]

DIMES

	Unc. Proof
1943	$ .50
1943D	.60
1943S	.85
1944	.45
1944D	.50
1944S	.75

	Fine	Ex. Fine	Unc.	Proof
1945			$ .45	
1945D			.50	
1945S			.60	
1945S Microscopic S	5.00	9.00	15.00	

ROOSEVELT TYPE

John R. Sinnock (whose initials JS are at the truncation of the neck) designed this dime showing a portrait of the late President Franklin D. Roosevelt. The design has heavier lettering and a more modernistic character than preceding types. The reverse displays the torch of liberty between sprays of laurel and oak.

	Fine	Ex. Fine	Unc.	Proof
1946	$		.60	
1946D			.65	
1946S			.85	
1947			1.75	
1947D			1.25	
1947S			1.50	
1948			2.50	
1948D			1.25	
1948S			1.75	
1949			6.50★	
1949D			1.00	
1949S	.25	1.00	7.50★	
1950			2.50	11.00
1950D			.85	
1950S	.25	1.00	6.50★	
1951			.60	8.00
1951D	$		.60	
1951S	.25	.75	5.00★	
1952			.50	5.00
1952D			.50	
1952S			1.75	
1953			.50	3.50
1953D			.50	
1953S			.55	
1954			.40	2.50
1954D			.40	
1954S			.45	
1955			.75★	2.50
1955D			.65★	
1955S			.65★	
1956			.35	1.50
1956D			.35	
1957			.35	1.00
1957D			.35	
1958			.40	2.25
1958D			.30	
1959			.25	1.25
1959D			.25	
1960			.20	.60
1960D			.20	
1961			.20	.60
1961D			.20	

★Speculative

Bibliography, U.S. Dimes—A. Kosoff.

TWENTY-CENT PIECES 1875 - 1878

This short-lived coin was authorized by the Act of March 3, 1875. Soon after the appearance of the first twenty-cent pieces, the people complained about the similarity in design and size with the quarter-dollar. The eagle is very similar to that used on the Trade Dollar. The edge of the coin is plain. Most of the 1876CC coins were melted at the mint and never released.

	Good	Fine	Ex. Fine	Unc.	Proof
1875	$10.00	17.50	25.00	47.50	70.00
1875S	8.00	14.00	21.00	36.00	
1875CC	9.00	19.00	40.00	67.50	
1876	11.00	19.00	30.00	50.00	80.00
1876CC (14 Known) Hydeman Sale 1961				6900.00	
1877					290.00
1878					200.00

[99]

QUARTER DOLLARS
1796 To Date

The first date, 1796, follows the pattern of the early half-dimes and dimes by the absence of a mark of value. In 1804 25C was added to the reverse. Figures were used until 1838 when QUAR DOL. appeared. It was not until 1892 that the value was spelled out entirely.

Authorized in 1792 it was not issued until four years later followed by a lapse of about eight years. The first type weighed 104 grains which remained standard until modified by the Act of January 18, 1837 to 103½ grains. Like the dime and half-dime the weight was reduced and arrows placed at the date in 1853, and rays were placed in the field of the reverse during that year only.

The law of 1873 also affected the quarter, for the weight was slightly increased and arrows again placed at the date.

Many dates of quarters are difficult to obtain among them being 1823, 1827, 1901S and several early dates of Liberty standing type.

Proofs prior to 1855 are known to exist of some dates, and all are rare.

Date	Good	Fine	Unc.
1796	$350.00	800.00	1800.00
1804	80.00	200.00	
1805	25.00	65.00	300.00

[100]

QUARTER DOLLARS

1806 Over 5   Reverse   1806 Normal Date

Date	Good	Fine	Unc.
1806 over 5	$22.50	60.00	300.00
1806	20.00	45.00	225.00
1807	20.00	45.00	250.00

LIBERTY HEAD FACING LEFT

1818 Over 15

1815	10.00	27.50	175.00
1818 over 15	10.00	27.50	190.00
1818	9.00	20.00	80.00
1819 Small 9	9.00	22.00	90.00
1819 Large 9	9.00	22.00	90.00

1820 Small O   1820 Large O   1822, 25 Over 50c

1820 Small O	8.00	17.50	70.00
1820 Large O	7.50	17.50	65.00
1821	7.50	17.50	65.00
1822	9.00	25.00	100.00
1822 25 over 50c	100.00	200.00	600.00

[101]

QUARTER DOLLARS

	Good	Fine	Unc.	Proof
1823 over 22	$450.00	800.00		
1824	13.00	30.00	125.00	

1825 Over 22   1825 Over 23

1825 over 22	10.00	20.00	70.00
1825 over 23	10.00	20.00	70.00
1825 over 24	10.00	20.00	70.00
1827 Original (Curled base 2 in 25c)	(6 or 7 Known)		
1827 Restrike (Square base 2 in 25c)			
1828	8.00	16.50	70.00
1828 25 over 50c	27.50	50.00	170.00

Reduced Size—No Motto On Reverse

The motto was omitted because it was said that it would have crowded the design on the new reduced size coin.

Nevertheless the new motto "IN GOD WE TRUST" was added to the reverse in 1866.

	Small Letters	Large Letters
1831 Small Letters	7.50	35.00
1831 Large Letters	8.00	35.00
1832	6.50	30.00
1833	6.50	30.00
1834	6.50	30.00
1835	6.00	30.00
1836	6.00	30.00
1837	6.50	30.00
1838	7.00	32.50

QUARTER DOLLARS
Liberty Seated Type

No Drapery From Elbow

	Fine	Unc.	Proof
1838	$10.00	35.00	
1839	7.00	25.00	
1840O	7.50	30.00	

Drapery From Elbow

1840	11.00	35.00	
1840O	8.00	32.50	
1841	20.00	60.00	
1841O	6.50	25.00	

Small Date   Large Date

	Fine	Unc.	Proof
1842 Small date. Proofs only			
1842 Large date	7.00	25.00	
1842O Small date	20.00	65.00	
1842O Large date	8.50	35.00	
1843	6.00	22.50	
1843O	6.00	25.00	
1844	6.00	25.00	
1844O	7.00	27.50	
1845	5.00	19.00	
1846	6.00	22.50	
1847	6.00	17.50	
1847O	7.00	26.00	
1848	7.00	25.00	
1849	5.00	21.00	
1849O	100.00	275.00	

QUARTER DOLLARS

	Fine	Unc.		Fine	Unc.
1850	$7.00	27.50	1851O	$7.00	45.00
1850O	6.00	25.00	1852	7.00	35.00
1851	6.00	27.50	1852O	11.00	55.00

	Fine	Unc.
1853 over 52. No Arrows or Rays	$82.50	235.00

The reduction in weight is indicated by the arrows at the date. Rays were added on the reverse side in the field above the eagle. The arrows were retained until 1855, but the rays were omitted after 1853.

Arrows At Date

Rays Around Eagle

	Fine	Unc.
1853	5.50	27.50
1853O	11.00	37.50

Arrows At Date—Rays Removed From Reverse

	Fine	Unc.	Proof		Fine	Unc.	Proof
1854	$4.00	22.50		1855O	$60.00	250.00	
1854O	4.50	24.00		1855S	60.00	250.00	
1855	4.00	17.50	230.00				

Arrows At Date Removed

	Fine	Unc.	Proof		Fine	Unc.	Proof
1856	3.00	11.00	200.00	1857S	30.00	175.00	
1856O	4.00	14.00		1858	4.00	10.00	150.00
1856S	30.00	150.00		1858O	5.00	16.00	
1857	2.50	10.00	185.00	1858S	32.50	150.00	
1857O	3.50	15.00					

QUARTER DOLLARS

	Fine	Unc.	Proof
1859	$ 3.50	11.00	45.00
1859O	4.00	12.50	
1859S	32.00	175.00	
1860	3.00	12.00	42.50
1860O	3.50	12.00	
1860S	20.00	145.00	
1861	3.00	11.00	42.50
1861S	17.50	125.00	
1862	3.00	10.00	42.50
1862S	14.00	120.00	
1863	4.00	15.00	50.00
1864	4.00	15.00	52.50
1864S	16.00	115.00	
1865	5.00	15.00	50.00
1865S	12.00	95.00	
1866 One Known (proof) Hydeman Sale 1961			24,500.00

Motto Over Eagle

The motto IN GOD WE TRUST was added to the reverse side in 1866. Like the half-dollar and silver dollar the motto has been retained since that time.

	Fine	Unc.	Proof
1866	$ 5.00	17.50	47.50
1866S	15.00	100.00	
1867	4.50	14.00	42.50
1867S	14.00	90.00	
1868	5.00	15.00	42.50
1868S	12.00	75.00	
1869	5.50	15.00	40.00
1869S	12.00	80.00	
1870	3.50	12.00	32.50
1870CC	160.00	550.00	
1871	3.00	9.50	30.00
1871S	11.00	70.00	
1871CC	145.00	550.00	
1872	3.00	10.00	27.50
1872S	20.00	80.00	
1872CC	195.00	725.00	
1873 Closed 3	2.50	10.00	35.00
1873 Open 3	10.00	27.50	
1873CC	525.00	—	

QUARTER DOLLARS

Arrows were placed at the date in the years 1873 and 1874 to denote the change of weight from 96 to 96.45 grains.

Arrows At Date

	Fine	Unc.	Proof
1873	$ 20.00	70.00	150.00
1873S	27.50	90.00	
1873CC	425.00	1250.00	
1874	20.00	67.50	130.00
1874S	30.00	100.00	

Arrows At Date Removed

	Fine	Unc.	Proof
1875	$ 2.50	9.00	40.00
1875S	10.00	60.00	
1875CC	6.00	20.00	
1876	2.50	8.00	28.00
1876S	2.50	9.00	
1876CC	3.00	15.00	
1877	2.50	8.00	40.00
1877S	2.50	9.00	
1877S (Over Horizontal S)	80.00	170.00	
1877CC	3.50	15.00	
1878	3.00	9.00	32.00
1878S	175.00	465.00	
1878CC	6.00	22.50	
1879		30.00	60.00

	Fine	Unc.	Proof
1880	$14.00	22.50	30.00
1881	15.00	25.00	35.00
1882	14.00	22.50	35.00
1883	14.00	22.50	35.00
1884	20.00	35.00	50.00
1885	15.00	25.00	40.00
1886	30.00	60.00	90.00
1887	15.00	25.00	40.00
1888	15.00	25.00	36.00
1888S	3.00	13.00	
1889	15.00	25.00	40.00
1890	4.00	13.50	55.00
1891	3.00	10.00	40.00
1891O	95.00	300.00	
1891S	3.00	14.00	

QUARTER DOLLARS
BARBER OR LIBERTY HEAD TYPE

Like other silver coins of this type the quarter dollars minted from 1892 to 1916 were designed by Charles E. Barber. His initial B is found at the base of the neck of Liberty.

	Good	Fine	Ex. Fine	Unc.	Proof		Good	Fine	Ex. Fine	Unc.	Proof
1892....	$ .90	2.25	5.00	11.00	37.50	1904O...	$ 5.50	15.00	65.00	240.00	
1892O...	3.00	7.50	15.00	35.00		1905....	.50	1.75	3.50	10.50	45.00
1892S...	9.00	25.00	65.00	120.00		1905O...	4.50	13.50	40.00	135.00	
1893....	.90	2.00	4.00	10.00	40.00	1905S...	2.50	7.00	25.00	55.00	
1893O...	1.75	5.50	15.00	35.00		1906....	.50	1.75	3.50	10.50	42.50
1893S...	2.75	7.50	16.00	37.50		1906D..	1.25	3.25	6.00	15.00	
1894....	.90	2.35	5.00	11.50	40.00	1906O...	1.25	4.00	8.50	30.00	
1894O...	1.75	7.00	15.00	42.50		1907....	.50	1.75	3.50	10.50	50.00
1894S...	2.00	6.00	14.00	36.00		1907D..	1.25	3.00	6.00	15.00	
1895....	.85	2 00	5.00	11.50	47.50	1907O..	1.25	3.00	6.00	15.00	
1895O...	2.00	6.50	30.00	82.50		1907S..	1.75	5.00	20.00	45.00	
1895S...	2.50	7.00	15.00	47.50		1908....	.50	1.75	3.50	10.50	52.50
1896....	1.00	2.50	5.50	14.00	42.50	1908D..	.60	2.00	6.00	12.50	
1896O...	3.50	15.00	55.00	165.00		1908O...	.60	2.00	6.00	12.50	
1896S...	47.50	140.00	300.00	800.00		1908S...	4.00	8.50	25.00	60.00	
1897....	.85	2.00	4.00	12.00	45.00	1909....	.50	1.75	3.50	10.00	50.00
1897O...	6.50	16.00	45.00	100.00		1909D..	.50	2.75	5.00	12.00	
1897S...	7.50	17.50	50.00	125.00		1909O...	10.00	32.50	90.00	275.00	
1898....	.75	1.75	4.00	12.00	45.00	1909S...	1.00	5.00	15.00	40.00	
1898O...	1.90	7.00	30.00	75.00		1910....	.75	3.25	6.00	15.00	52.50
1898S...	2.00	7.00	30.00	77.50		1910D..	1.50	3.50	6.50	15.00	
1899....	.75	1.75	4.00	10.50	42.50	1911....	.50	1.75	3.00	10.50	62.50
1899O...	1.90	6.50	20.00	60.00		1911D..	1.50	5.50	15.00	40.00	
1899S...	5.50	10.00	25.00	70.00		1911S...	1.60	5.50	15.00	40.00	
1900....	.65	1.75	4.00	10.50	40.00	1912....	.50	1.75	3.00	10.50	57.50
1900O...	2.50	8.00	20.00	60.00		1912S...	2.00	9.00	35.00	90.00	
1900S...	1.35	6.50	35.00	75.00		1913....	2.50	6.00	10.00	45.00	110.00
1901....	.60	1.75	4.00	10.50	37.50	1913D..	1.25	3.50	8.50	20.00	
1901O...	8.00	32.50	100.00	250.00		1913S...	55.00	135.00	300.00	850.00	
1901S...	130.00	340.00	650.00	1300.00		1914....	.50	1.75	6.00	15.00	200.00
1902....	.50	1.75	3.50	10.50	40.00	1914D..	.50	2.50	5.00	13.00	
1902O...	2.00	8.50	25.00	55.00		1914S...	3.50	16.00	80.00	225.00	
1902S...	2.50	9.50	37.50	85.00		1915....	.50	2.75	6.00	15.00	200.00
1903....	.50	1.75	3.50	10.50	45.00	1915D..	.50	2.00	3.50	10.00	
1903O...	2.25	10.50	60.00	140.00		1915S...	1.50	5.00	15.00	35.00	
1903S...	3.00	11.50	60.00	130.00		1916....	.50	3.50	8.00	20.00	
1904....	.50	1.75	3.50	10.50	42.50	1916D..	.50	2.50	4.25	10.00	

[107]

QUARTER DOLLARS
STANDING LIBERTY TYPE

This type quarter was designed by Herman A. MacNeil. The left arm of Liberty is upraised bearing a shield in the attitude of protection, from which the cover is being drawn. The right hand bears the olive branch of peace. The designer's initial M is located above and to the right of the date.

There was a modification in 1917. The reverse has a new arrangement of the stars and the eagle is higher.

In 1925 a depression was made in the pedestal on which Liberty stands, and which bears the date. On the first issues the dates wore off easily because they were too high and were not protected by other features of the coin. The new "recessed" dates proved more durable as a result of this change.

Uncirculated Standing Liberty Quarters with full head are worth more than prices listed below.

Variety 1

	Good	Fine	Ex. Fine	Unc.
1916	$100.00	175.00	240.00	400.00
1917 Variety 1	2.00	4.00	7.50	12.50
1917D Variety 1	2.50	6.50	16.00	30.00
1917S Variety 1	3.00	8.50	16.00	35.00

Variety 2   1918S Over 7

	Good	Fine	Ex. Fine	Unc.		Good	Fine	Ex. Fine	Unc.
1917 Var. 2	$1.75	5.00	10.00	16.00	1924D	$3.50	5.50	9.00	15.00
1917D Var. 2	4.00	11.00	22.50	45.00	1924S	4.00	9.00	20.00	50.00
1917S Var. 2	4.00	11.00	22.50	45.00	1925		2.50	5.00	11.00
1918	2.25	7.00	22.50	42.50	1926		2.50	5.00	11.00
1918D	3.50	8.00	25.00	52.50	1926D		2.00	3.50	8.50
1918S	2.25	7.00	17.50	39.00	1926S	3.00	10.00	50.00	100.00
1918S over 7	75.00	185.00	350.00	900.00	1927		2.00	4.00	13.00
1919	3.00	7.00	22.00	37.50	1927D		2.00	5.00	15.00
1919D	12.00	30.00	70.00	120.00	1927S	5.00	13.50	95.00	390.00
1919S	18.00	45.00	90.00	190.00	1928		1.50	4.50	12.50
1920	1.50	3.50	6.50	13.00	1928D		1.50	4.50	10.00
1920D	7.00	16.00	40.00	72.50	1928S		1.50	4.50	11.00
1920S	3.50	7.50	17.50	45.00	1929		1.50	4.50	9.50
1921	11.00	24.00	55.00	110.00	1929D		1.50	4.50	11.00
1923	1.50	3.50	6.00	11.50	1929S		1.50	4.50	11.00
*1923S	20.00	42.50	85.00	150.00	1930		1.50	4.50	8.50
1924	1.50	3.50	6.00	11.50	1930S		1.50	4.50	11.00

*Beware altered date.

QUARTER DOLLARS
WASHINGTON HEAD TYPE

This type was intended to be a commemorative issue marking the two-hundredth anniversary of Washington's birth. John Flanagan, a New York sculptor, was the designer. The initials JF are found at the base of the neck.

	Good	Fine	Ex. Fine	Unc.	Proof		Unc.	Proof
1932....	$	.85	1.75	6.50		1946D.............	$1.00	
1932D..	5.00	16.00	40.00	100.00		1946S.............	1.25	
1932S...	3.50	11.00	19.00	42.50		1947.............	1.00	
1934....		1.00	2.50	8.50		1947D.............	1.00	
1934D..		2.00	6.00	22.50		1947S.............	1.25	
1935....			2.00	6.50		1948.............	1.10	
1935D..		1.25	4.50	19.00		1948D.............	1.10	
1935S...		1.50	5.00	20.00		1948S.............	1.25	
1936....			1.00	5.00	90.00	1949.............	4.00	
1936D..		3.50	35.00	95.00		1949D.............	1.25	
1936S...			4.00	18.00		1950.............	1.50	13.00
1937....			1.10	5.50	38.50	1950D.............	1.00	
1937D..			1.10	6.00		1950S.............	2.25	
1937S...		2.25	4.50	40.00		1951.............	1.00	9.00
1938....			7.00	32.50	32.50	1951D.............	1.00	
1938S...			2.25	10.00		1951S.............	2.75	
1939....			1.00	6.00	16.50	1952.............	1.00	7.50
1939D..			1.00	6.00		1952D.............	1.00	
1939S...			2.50	14.00		1952S.............	1.75	
1940....			2.00	7.50	13.00	1953.............	.75	4.50
1940D..			3.00	15.00		1953D.............	.75	
1940S...				4.50		1953S.............	1.00	
1941....			2.50	11.50		1954.............	.65	3.50
1941D..				3.00		1954D.............	.65	
1941S...				4.00		1954S.............	.75	
1942....			2.50	10.00		1955.............	.75	3.50
1942D..				3.00		1955D.............	1.25	
1942S...		2.00	6.00			1956.............	.60	2.00
1943....				1.50		1956D.............	.60	
1943D..				1.75		1957.............	.50	1.50
1943S...				3.50		1957D.............	.50	
1944....				1.25		1958.............	.60	3.25
1944D..				1.25		1958D.............	.50	
1944S...				2.00		1959.............	.50	1.50
1945....				1.00		1959D.............	.50	
1945D..				1.10		1960.............	.50	.60
1945S...				1.25		1960D.............	.50	
1946....				1.00		1961.............	.50	.60
						1961D.............	.50	

BIBLIOGRAPHY
Browning, A. W., Early Quarter Dollars of the U. S. (1796-1838). 1925.
Haseltine, J. W., Type Table of U. S. Dollars, Half and Quarter Dollars. 1881. Reprint 1933.

HALF DOLLARS
1794 To Date

The half-dollar, authorized by the Act of April 2, 1792 was not minted until 1794. This is a series that has been extensively collected by varieties and many dates contain both rare and common varieties.

The weight of the half-dollar was 208 grains and its fineness 892.4 when first issued. This standard was not changed until 1837 when the law of January 18, 1837 specified 206¼ grains, .900 fine.

Arrows at the date in 1853 indicate the reduction of weight to 192 grains in conformity with the Act of February 21, 1853. During that year only, rays were added to the field on the reverse side. Arrows remained on issues of 1854 and 1855.

In 1873 the weight was raised by law to 192.9 grains and arrows were again placed at the date, to be removed in 1875.

The half-dollars had FIFTY CENTS OR HALF A DOLLAR lettered on the edge until 1836 after which the edge of the coins were reeded.

From 1806 until 1840 large quantities of half-dollars were coined to take the place of the silver dollars which were not made during that period. For that reason half-dollars of most dates during that span of years are fairly common.

Proofs prior to 1855 are known to exist of some dates and all are rare.

	Good	Fine
1794	$100.00	200.00
1795	45.00	85.00

	Good	Fine
1795 Three leaves under each wing	$200.00	450.00

	Good	Fine
1796 Fifteen stars (Donlon Sale Unc. $1,525.00)	$500.00	1000.00

HALF DOLLARS

	Good	Fine
1796 16 stars	$600.00	1250.00

	Good	Fine
1797	$400.00	900.00

	Good	Fine	Unc.
1801—	$45.00	100.00	500.00
1802—	40.00	80.00	325.00

Large 3

	Good	Fine	Unc.
1803 Small 3	$25.00	45.00	250.00
1803 Large 3	19.00	35.00	200.00

HALF DOLLARS

1805 Over 4

1806 Over 5

	Good	Fine	Unc.
1805 over 4	$27.50	55.00	200.00
1805	12.50	22.00	100.00
1806 over 5	20.00	35.00	160.00
1806 over inverted 6	40.00	95.00	375.00

Round Top 6 Large Stars

Branch Stem Through Claw

Pointed Top 6

Branch Stem Not Through Claw

1806 Round top 6. Large stars	12.00	22.00	100.00
1806 Round top 6. Small stars	12.00	22.00	100.00
1806 Pointed top 6. Stem through claw	12.00	22.00	100.00
1806 Pointed top 6. Stem not through claw	12.00	22.00	100.00
1807	12.00	22.00	100.00

John Reich designed the first Turban Head concept of Liberty. The head of Liberty facing left was used on all U.S. coin denominations for the next thirty years. Reich was the first artist to consistently include the denomination on our gold and silver coins. He was from Germany and a bondman freed from servitude by a mint official.

HALF DOLLARS

Small Stars   Large Stars   50 Over 20c

	Good	Fine	Unc.
1807 Small stars	$10.00	19.00	175.00
1807 Large stars	7.50	17.00	100.00
1807 50 over 20	9.00	25.00	125.00

1808 Over 7

1808 over 7	$6.50	13.50	57.50
1808	3.75	7.00	55.00
1809	3.50	6.75	50.00
1810	3.50	6.75	45.00

1811 Small 8

(18.11) Punctuated Date

1811 Small 8	3.00	6.50	37.50
1811 Large 8	3.75	9.00	65.00
1811 Date 18.11	5.25	10.00	65.00
1812 over 11	7.00	13.50	85.00
1812	3.50	6.50	27.50
1813	3.25	6.50	32.50

HALF DOLLARS

	Good	Fine	Unc.
1814 over 13	$9.00	17.00	80.00
1814	3.50	7.50	30.00

1814 Over 13

Good Fine Unc.
1815 $50.00 95.00 290.00
All have 1815 over 12.

1817 Over 13

1819 Over 18 Small 9

	Good	Fine	Unc.
1817 over 13	$9.00	20.00	70.00
1817 over 14 (Ex. Rare)	—	—	
1817 Dated 181.7	9.00	20.00	70.00
1817	4.00	8.00	35.00
1818 over 17	4.00	8.00	35.00
1818	3.00	6.00	25.00
1819 over 18. Small 9	3.25	6.00	35.00
1819 over 18. Large 9	3.25	6.00	35.00
1819	3.00	6.00	22.50
1820 over 19	5.00	9.00	40.00
1820 Small Date	5.00	9.00	45.00
1820 Lg. Date	5.00	9.00	45.00

	Good	Fine	Unc.
1821	$ 2.75	4.50	22.50
1822	2.75	4.50	20.00
1822 over 1	30.00	65.00	200.00
1823 over 22 Broken 3	26.00	55.00	125.00
1823 over 22 Patched 3	11.00	27.00	60.00
1823 over 22 Ugly 3	6.00	14.00	40.00
1823	3.25	5.50	20.00
1824 over 21	4.00	7.50	32.50
1824 over various dates	4.50	8.00	35.00
1824	3.50	5.50	20.00
1825	3.50	5.50	20.00
1826	3.25	5.00	17.50

HALF DOLLARS

1827 Over 6

1828 Small 8's Square-base 2

	Good	Fine	Unc.
1827 over 6.......	$9.50	18.50	75.00
1827 Square-base...	2.50	4.50	19.00
1827 Curled 2.....	4.00	8.00	45.00
1828 Curled-base without knobbed 2......	5.00	7.00	35.00
1828 Curled-base knobbed 2......	27.50	47.50	115.00
1828 Large 8's Square-base 2...	5.00	9.00	35.00
1828 Small 8's Square-base 2 Large letters....	3.50	5.00	19.00

	Good	Fine	Unc.
1829 over 21.......	$4.00	9.00	35.00
1829.............	3.00	4.50	16.50
1830 Small O in Date	3.00	4.50	16.50
1830 Large O in Date	3.50	5.50	18.00
1831.............	2.50	4.50	16.50
1832 Sm. letters....	2.50	4.50	16.50
1832 Lg. letters....	3.50	10.00	40.00
1833.............	3.00	4.50	16.50

1828 Large 8 Curled-base Knobbed 2

1834 Small Date Small Stars

	Good	Fine	Unc.
1834 Small date. Small stars. Small letters.........	$2.50	4.50	15.00
1834 Large date. Small letters.................	2.50	4.50	15.00
1834 Large date. Large letters.................	3.50	6.50	30.00
1835...........................	2.50	4.50	15.00
1836 (Lettered edge).........................	2.50	4.50	15.00
1836 (Lettered edge) 50 over 00.................	25.00	45.00	140.00

Reeded Edge—
50 CENTS On Reverse

	Good	Fine	Unc.
1836...	$37.50	70.00	185.00
1837...	7.00	15.00	50.00

HALF DOLLARS

1838-O

HALF DOL.

	Good	Fine	Unc.
1838	$7.00	15.00	50.00
1838O			5,000.00

1838O Not mentioned in Director's report. (Rufus Tyler, coiner of New Orleans Mint, stated that only 20 were coined.)
    First branch mint half-dollar. This and following year mint-mark appears on Obv. All other years (except 1916-17) mint-mark is on Rev.

1839		7.00	14.00	60.00
1839O		45.00	100.00	300.00

LIBERTY SEATED TYPE

1839 No Drapery From Elbow

	Good	Fine	Unc.
1839 No drapery from elbow	17.50	42.50	125.00

Drapery From Elbow

Small Letters in Legend

	Good	Fine	Unc.		Good	Fine	Unc.
1839	$7.00	12.00	50.00	1841	$5.00	10.00	35.00
1840	4.00	8.00	35.00	1841O	4.00	6.00	30.00
1840O	3.50	6.00	25.00	1842O Sm. Date	50.00	100.00	195.00

HALF DOLLARS

Letters on Reverse Larger Than Previous Type

	Good	Fine	Unc.
1840 Similar reverse to 1838. Large letters	$20.00	45.00	140.00

Small Date   Large Date   Larger Letters Than on 1840 Reverse

	Good	Fine	Unc.		Good	Fine	Unc.
1842 Sm. Date	$ 3.25	5.50	27.50	1846O Tall Date	$ 21.00	40.00	135.00
1842 Lg. Date	3.25	5.50	24.00	1847 over 46	125.00	240.00	600.00
1842O Lg. Date	3.25	5.50	24.00	1847	3.00	6.00	27.50
1843	3.25	5.50	24.00	1847O	3.00	6.00	24.00
1843O	3.25	5.50	22.00	1848	3.00	6.00	27.50
1844	3.25	5.50	22.00	1848O	2.50	5.50	24.00
1844O	3.25	5.50	22.00	1849	3.00	6.00	26.00
1845	3.25	5.50	22.00	1849O	3.00	5.00	21.00
1845O	3.25	5.50	22.00	1850	22.50	40.00	85.00
1845O No Drapery	18.00	40.00	97.50	1850O	4.00	8.00	27.50
1846 Sm. Date	3.00	5.50	22.00	1851	7.50	16.00	75.00
1846 Tall Date	4.00	6.50	24.00	1851O	3.25	6.00	24.00
1846 over horizontal 6 (error)	32.50	72.50	155.00	1852	22.50	45.00	150.00
1846O Sm. Date	3.00	5.00	22.00	1852O	16.00	30.00	90.00
				1853O (Ex. Rare)	—	—	—

Arrows at Date   Rays Above Eagle

[117]

HALF DOLLARS

Arrows At Date—Rays Above Eagle

	Good	Fine	Unc.	Proof
1853	$4.50	11.00	47.50	
1853O	5.50	12.00	52.50	

Arrows at Date—No Rays on Reverse

	Good	Fine	Unc.	Proof
1854	3.00	6.50	21.00	
1854O	3.00	6.50	21.00	
1855	4.00	7.50	32.50	450.00
1855O	2.50	7.00	24.00	
1855S	32.50	85.00	300.00	

No Arrows at Date

	Good	Fine	Unc.	Proof
1856	$1.75	4.50	15.00	360.00
1856O	1.75	4.50	15.00	
1856S	10.00	22.00	100.00	
1857	1.75	4.50	14.00	300.00
1857O	3.00	5.50	17.50	
1857S	12.50	27.50	120.00	
1858	1.60	4.00	14.00	185.00
1858O	1.60	4.00	14.00	
1858S	6.00	17.50	70.00	
1859	1.60	4.00	14.00	115.00
1859O	1.60	4.00	14.00	
1859S	5.50	15.00	60.00	
1860	1.60	4.00	14.00	75.00
1860O	1.60	4.00	15.00	
1860S	2.75	8.00	37.50	
1861	$1.60	4.00	15.00	75.00
*1861O	2.00	5.00	25.00	
1861S	3.00	8.00	37.50	
1862	2.50	6.00	16.00	75.00
1862S	2.75	6.00	40.00	
1863	2.50	6.00	16.00	80.00
1863S	2.25	6.00	27.50	
1864	2.50	6.00	16.00	80.00
1864S	2.25	6.00	27.50	
1865	2.25	6.00	19.00	85.00
1865S	2.25	5.50	24.00	

1866 Unique Proof
   Hydeman Sale 1961......$15,500.00
1866S....... 35.00 90.00 275.00

*1861O Struck by U. S. Government....................Quantity 330,000

After the New Orleans Mint was taken over by the Confederate States.

1861O For Louisiana.................................Quantity 1,240,000

1861O For Confederacy.............................Quantity 962,633

As all these 1861O coins were struck from U.S. dies it is impossible to distinguish one from another. Not to be confused with the Confederate half dollar of 1861 on page 226.

[118]

HALF DOLLARS

Motto
Above
Eagle

	Good	Fine	Unc.	Proof		Good	Fine	Unc.	Proof
1866	$ 3.50	8.00	29.00	75.00	1871	$ 2.25	5.00	18.00	52.50
1866S	3.50	7.00	36.00		1871S	2.75	7.00	32.50	
1867	3.25	6.00	25.00	72.50	1871CC	30.00	72.50	250.00	
1867S	2.25	5.00	35.00		1872	2.25	5.00	18.00	52.50
1868	3.25	6.00	25.00	72.50	1872S	3.25	10.00	35.00	
1868S	2.25	5.00	25.00		1872CC	27.50	60.00	185.00	
1869	2.75	5.00	21.00	72.50	1873 Closed 3	3.00	7.00	24.00	60.00
1869S	2.25	5.00	25.00		1873 Open 3	10.00	20.00	40.00	
1870	2.25	5.00	21.00	55.00	1873CC	26.00	55.00	170.00	
1870S	3.00	7.00	36.00		1873S No arrows (Rare) Unknown in				
1870CC	40.00	75.00	300.00		any collection				—

Arrows
At
Date

1873	11.00	27.50	95.00	225.00	1874	10.00	26.00	90.00	185.00
1873S	15.00	35.00	115.00		1874S	16.00	35.00	115.00	
1873CC	15.00	45.00	135.00		1874CC	20.00	55.00	180.00	

No Arrows At Date

1875	2.25	5.00	14.00	60.00	1880	14.00	25.00	45.00	62.50
1875S	2.50	5.00	15.00		1881	14.00	25.00	40.00	62.50
1875CC	2.75	6.00	30.00		1882	14.00	25.00	45.00	62.50
1876	2.00	4.50	12.00	45.00	1883	14.00	24.00	40.00	62.50
1876S	2.00	4.50	12.00		1884	15.00	26.00	45.00	70.00
1876CC	2.75	6.00	26.00		1885	15.00	26.00	45.00	70.00
1877	2.00	4.50	12.00	90.00	1886	18.00	30.00	50.00	100.00
1877S	2.00	4.50	12.00		1887	15.00	25.00	45.00	90.00
1877CC	3.50	7.00	25.00		1888	14.00	21.00	35.00	70.00
1878	2.00	4.50	12.00	85.00	1889	14.00	21.00	35.00	80.00
1878S	240.00	450.00	1600.00		1890	14.00	21.00	35.00	100.00
1878CC	65.00	110.00	350.00		1891	3.00	6.00	17.50	75.00
1879	11.00	22.00	45.00	60.00					

HALF DOLLARS
BARBER OR LIBERTY HEAD TYPE

Like the dime and quarter dollar, this type was designed by Charles E. Barber whose initial B is at the base of the neck.

	Good	Fine	Ex. Fine	Unc.	Proof
1892....	$1.50	6.00	10.00	20.00	60.00
1892O Medium O					
.....	20.00	40.00	65.00	85.00	
1892O Microscopic O					
.....	50.00	85.00	125.00	225.00	
1892S...	20.00	45.00	80.00	150.00	
1893....	1.50	4.50	10.00	17.50	75.00
1893O...	5.00	17.50	40.00	70.00	
1893S...	19.00	40.00	75.00	100.00	
1894....	2.00	7.50	13.50	22.50	70.00
1894O...	2.50	15.00	50.00	100.00	
1894S...	2.75	15.00	50.00	100.00	
1895....	1.50	6.00	10.00	21.00	80.00
1895O...	2.00	12.00	40.00	90.00	
1895S...	5.00	17.50	50.00	110.00	
1896....	1.50	6.00	11.00	25.00	80.00
1896O...	5.00	20.00	90.00	185.00	
1896S...	20.00	50.00	125.00	290.00	
1897....	1.50	6.00	11.00	25.00	80.00
1897O...	20.00	50.00	110.00	275.00	
1897S...	19.00	50.00	115.00	300.00	
1898....	1.25	4.00	10.00	25.00	80.00
1898O...	2.50	10.00	40.00	100.00	
1898S...	2.50	10.00	40.00	100.00	
1899....	1.25	3.75	9.00	22.50	75.00
1899O...	2.00	8.00	40.00	100.00	
1899S...	1.75	8.00	40.00	100.00	
1900....	1.25	3.75	9.00	22.50	65.00
1900O...	1.25	7.00	40.00	95.00	
1900S...	1.75	6.00	35.00	80.00	
1901....	1.25	3.50	8.00	20.00	70.00
1901O...	2.50	20.00	125.00	300.00	
1901S...	6.00	50.00	200.00	600.00	
1902....	1.00	3.50	8.00	19.00	70.00
1902O...	1.75	8.00	35.00	85.00	
1902S...	1.75	8.50	75.00	200.00	
1903....	1.25	3.50	8.00	18.50	70.00
1903O...	1.25	7.50	55.00	150.00	
1903S...	$2.50	15.00	100.00	375.00	
1904....	1.00	3.50	8.00	17.50	75.00
1904O...	1.75	9.00	35.00	110.00	
1904S...	6.00	35.00	100.00	350.00	
1905....	1.25	7.50	15.00	25.00	70.00
1905O...	2.50	15.00	50.00	150.00	
1905S...	1.75	6.50	25.00	80.00	
1906....	1.00	3.25	8.00	18.00	75.00
1906D..	1.25	4.00	10.00	21.00	
1906O...	1.25	6.50	17.50	43.00	
1906S...	1.50	8.00	25.00	85.00	
1907....	1.00	3.25	8.00	17.50	80.00
1907D...	1.25	3.75	10.00	22.50	
1907O...	1.40	3.75	10.00	23.50	
1907S...	1.40	8.00	30.00	90.00	
1908....	1.00	3.25	8.00	20.00	75.00
1908D..	1.00	3.50	8.50	21.00	
1908O...	1.25	3.50	10.00	22.50	
1908S...	1.40	7.00	25.00	80.00	
1909....	1.00	3.00	8.00	19.00	72.50
1909O...	1.75	8.50	30.00	80.00	
1909S...	1.50	6.50	25.00	70.00	
1910....	2.00	7.50	15.00	32.50	120.00
1910S...	1.25	6.50	25.00	60.00	
1911....	1.00	3.00	7.00	18.00	120.00
1911D..	1.25	6.00	15.00	45.00	
1911S...	1.40	6.00	22.50	55.00	
1912....	1.00	3.00	7.00	18.00	95.00
1912D..	1.00	3.50	10.00	24.00	
1912S...	1.40	5.00	17.50	55.00	
1913....	7.50	27.50	55.00	110.00	275.00
1913D..	1.40	6.00	15.00	37.50	
1913S...	1.75	12.50	50.00	140.00	
1914....	7.50	45.00	75.00	190.00	550.00
1914S...	1.50	8.50	30.00	75.00	
1915....	9.00	47.50	95.00	200.00	550.00
1915D..	1.40	5.00	10.00	25.00	
1915S...	1.40	6.50	25.00	75.00	

[120]

HALF DOLLARS
LIBERTY WALKING TYPE

This type was designed by A. A. Weinman. The eagle appears in life-like form. The director's report covering the new issue describes the coin as follows: "The design of the half dollar bears a full-length figure of Liberty, the folds of the stars and stripes flying to the breeze as a background, progressing in full stride toward the dawn of a new day, carrying branches of laurel and oaks, symbolic of civil and military glory. The hand of the figure is outstretched in bestowal of the spirit of Liberty. The reverse of the half dollar shows an eagle perched high upon a mountain crag, his wings unfolded, fearless in spirit and conscious of his power. Springing from a rift in the rock is a sapling of Mountain Pine symbolical of America." The designer's monogram AW appears under the tip of the wing feathers. On the 1916 coins and some of the 1917 coins the mint mark is located on the obverse below the motto.

Uncirculated, well-struck specimens worth 25% to 50% above prices listed below.

	Good	Fine	Ex. Fine	Unc.		Fine	Ex. Fine	Unc.	Proof
1916	$2.25	6.00	10.00	27.50	1934S	$1.00	10.00	42.50	
1916D	2.50	7.00	12.50	30.00	1935		1.00	5.50	
1916S	7.50	17.50	37.50	95.00	1935D	1.00	5.00	22.50	
1917		1.00	5.00	10.50	1935S	1.00	9.00	40.00	
1917D on Obv.	1.50	8.00	15.00	47.50	1936		1.00	4.50	140.00
1917D on Rev.	1.75	9.00	45.00	95.00	1936D		1.00	6.50	
1917S on Obv.	4.50	35.00	100.00	385.00	1936S	1.00	7.50	22.50	
1917S on Rev.	1.25	6.50	15.00	70.00	1937		1.00	6.00	57.50
1918	1.00	3.50	25.00	65.00	1937D	1.00	6.00	20.00	
1918D	1.00	5.00	30.00	82.50	1937S	1.00	6.00	20.00	
1918S	1.00	5.00	30.00	85.00	1938		1.00	6.50	28.00
1919	1.50	7.50	35.00	90.00	1938D	4.00	13.50	45.00	
1919D	2.00	9.00	100.00	285.00	1939		1.00	7.00	24.50
1919S	2.00	25.00	125.00	465.00	1939D		1.00	4.50	
1920	1.00	2.50	7.50	32.50	1939S	1.00	4.00	12.50	
1920D	1.50	6.50	65.00	210.00	1940		1.00	4.00	21.00
1920S	1.50	6.00	65.00	195.00	1940S		1.00	8.00	
1921	6.50	35.00	95.00	225.00	1941			3.00	*16.50
1921D	6.50	35.00	110.00	235.00	1941D		1.00	3.00	
1921S	2.00	14.00	75.00	275.00	1941S		1.00	5.00	
1923S	1.00	4.50	50.00	175.00	1942			2.50	15.00
1927S	1.00	3.00	10.00	65.00	1942D		1.00	3.50	
1928S	1.00	3.00	10.00	65.00	1942S		1.00	5.00	
1929D	1.00	2.50	7.50	29.00	1943			2.00	
1929S	1.00	2.75	7.50	29.00	1943D			3.50	
1933S	1.00	2.75	10.00	47.50	1943S		1.00	4.50	
1934			1.00	5.50					
1934D			1.50	10.50					

*Proofs Struck with or without Engraver's Initials.

HALF DOLLARS

	Unc.		Unc.
1944	$2.00	1946	$1.75
1944D	2.00	1946D	2.00
1944S	3.75	1946S	3.00
1945	1.75	1947	2.00
1945D	2.00	1947D	2.25
1945S	2.50		

FRANKLIN-LIBERTY BELL TYPE

The designer was John R. Sinnock and his initials appear under the shoulder.

Select and well-struck uncirculated halves command higher prices.

	Ex. Fine	Unc.	Proof
1948	$1.00	4.75	
1948D		4.00	
1949	3.50	17.50	
1949D		4.00	
1949S		5.50	
1950		6.00	16.00
1950D		4.50	
1951		2.75	11.00
1951D		2.75	
1951S		4.75	
1952		2.25	9.00
1952D		2.25	
1952S		2.75	
1953		2.75	6.00
1953D		1.75	
1953S		2.00	
1954		1.50	4.50
1954D		1.50	
1954S		1.75	
1955		1.50	4.50
1956		1.25	3.00
1957		1.25	2.00
1957D		1.25	
1958		1.10	4.00
1958D		1.10	
1959		1.00	1.75
1959D		1.00	
1960		1.00	1.00
1960D		1.00	
1961		1.00	1.00
1961D		1.00	

BIBLIOGRAPHY

Beistle, M.L., Register of U. S. Half Dollar Die Varieties. 1929.
Haseltine, J. W., Type Table of U. S. Dollars, Half and Quarter Dollars. 1881. Reprint 1933.

SILVER DOLLARS
1794-1935

The silver dollar was authorized by Congress April 2, 1792. Weight and fineness were specified at 416 grains and 892.4 fine. The first issues appeared in 1794 and until 1804 all silver dollars had the value stamped on the edge: HUNDRED CENTS, ONE DOLLAR OR UNIT. After a lapse in coinage of the silver dollar covering the period 1804 to 1840 these coins had reeded edges and the value was placed on the reverse side.

There were several interesting pattern dollars produced by Christian Gobrecht from 1836 to 1839. The seated figure of Liberty was the resulting type, becoming a regular coinage issue starting in 1840. Thenceforth the edge was reeded.

The weight was changed by the law of January 18, 1837 to $412\frac{1}{2}$ grains fineness .900. The coinage was discontinued by the act of February 12, 1873 and reauthorized by the Act of February 28, 1878. The dollar was again discontinued after 1935.

Origin of the Dollar

The word Dollar evolves from German Taler, the name given to the first large-sized European silver coin. Designed as a substitute for the gold Florin, the coin originated in the Tirol in 1484. So popular did these large silver coins become during the 16th century that many other countries struck similar pieces, giving them names derived from taler. In the Netherlands the coin was called Rijksdalder, in Denmark Rigsdale, in Italy Tallero, in Poland Talar, in France Jocandale, in Russia Jefimok. All these names are abbreviations of "Joachimsthaler." Until the discovery of the great silver deposits in Mexican and South American mines, the mint with the greatest output of large silver coins was that of Joachimsthal in the Bohemian Erzgebirge.

The Spanish Dollar, or piece-of-eight was widely used and familiar to everyone in the English-American colonies. It was only natural therefore that the word "dollar" was adopted officially as the standard monetary unit of the United States by Congress on July 6, 1785.

Regarding Dollars Reported for 1805

The 321 silver dollars reported for 1805 were not dated 1805. An entry in Bullion Journal dated June 28, 1805, mentions these 321 pieces as "being found amongst Spanish Dollars brought to the Mint." They were of earlier coinage and instead of being melted they were transferred to the Director.

	Good	Fine	V. Fine	Unc.
1794	$900.00	2000.00	4000.00	10,000.00

SILVER DOLLARS

	Good	Fine	V. Fine	Unc.
1795 Two leaves beneath each wing (Eleven varieties)	$40.00	85.00	125.00	500.00

Three Leaves Beneath Each Wing

1795 Three leaves beneath each wing (Four varieties)	40.00	85.00	125.00	500.00

BUST TYPE

1795 (Two varieties)	40.00	90.00	125.00	450.00

SILVER DOLLARS

Small Date

Large Letters

	Good	Fine	V. Fine	Unc.
1796 Small date, Small letters (3 var.)....	$35.00	85.00	120.00	375.00
1796 Small date, Large letters............	30.00	80.00	110.00	325.00

Large Date

Small Letters

1796 Large date, Small letters............	32.50	80.00	125.00	350.00

Stars 9 Left 7 Right

Stars 10 Left 6 Right

1797 Stars 9 left 7 right, Small letters.....	100.00	250.00	600.00	1100.00
1797 Stars 9 left 7 right, Large letters.....	60.00	125.00	200.00	500.00
1797 Stars 10 left 6 right................	60.00	125.00	200.00	500.00

SILVER DOLLARS

13 Stars

15 Stars

	Good	Fine	Very Fine	Unc.
1798 13 Stars, Small Eagle...............	$40.00	80.00	175.00	400.00
1798 15 Stars, Small Eagle...............	45.00	100.00	200.00	500.00

Heraldic Eagle Reverse

1798 Large Heraldic Eagle, Knob 9 (5 Varieties).......................	30.00	45.00	70.00	225.00
1798 Large Eagle, 10 Arrows (5 Varieties).	25.00	37.50	65.00	200.00
1798 Close Date, 4 Berries in Branch.....	25.00	45.00	85.00	225.00
1798 Close Date, 5 Berries, 12 Arrows....	25.00	40.00	70.00	200.00
1798 Close Date, High 8 (6 Varieties).....	25.00	40.00	70.00	185.00
1798 Wide Date, 13 Arrows, (11 Varieties).	25.00	35.00	65.00	190.00

SILVER DOLLARS

1799 Over 98, Stars 7 & 6

Stars 8 & 5

	Good	Fine	Very Fine	Unc.
1799 Over 98 Rev. with 15 Stars	$27.50	60.00	90.00	225.00
1799 Over 98 Rev. with 13 Stars	27.50	55.00	85.00	200.00
1799 Irregular Date, 15-Star Rev	27.50	55.00	92.50	225.00
1799 Irregular Date, 13-Star Rev	23.50	52.50	75.00	200.00
1799 Perfect Date, No Berries in Branch	23.50	50.00	72.50	185.00
1799 Perfect Date, Small Berries	21.00	47.50	77.50	190.00
1799 Perfect Date, Medium Large Berries (15 Varieties)	20.00	32.50	70.00	170.00
1799 Perfect Date, Extra Large Berries	20.00	37.50	62.50	175.00
1799 Stars 8 Left, 5 Right	32.50	75.00	120.00	300.00
1800 LIBERTY with R Double Cut	20.00	37.50	60.00	165.00
1800 First T in STATES Double Cut	21.00	55.00	90.00	200.00
1800 Both R in LIBERTY and First T in STATES Double Cut	20.00	42.50	70.00	180.00
1800 Letter T in UNITED Double Cut	20.00	40.00	70.00	175.00
1800 Very Wide Date, Low 8	20.00	40.00	70.00	175.00
1800 Small Berries in Branch	20.00	45.00	75.00	190.00
1800 "Dotted Date" from Die Breaks	21.00	45.00	90.00	200.00
1800 Only 12 Arrows	22.00	45.00	75.00	185.00
1800 Only 10 Arrows	22.50	50.00	85.00	195.00
1800 AMERICAI (2 Varieties)	25.00	55.00	95.00	200.00
1801 Four Varieties	25.00	55.00	110.00	225.00
1801 Proof Restrike (Reverse Struck from First Die of 1804 Dollar)			(Proof)	

SILVER DOLLARS

1802 Over 1

	Good	Fine	Very Fine	Unc.
1802 Over 1, Close Overdate	$30.00	60.00	85.00	210.00
1802 Over 1, Wide Overdate	25.00	50.00	80.00	190.00
1802 Close, Perfect Date	25.00	40.00	65.00	150.00
1802 Wide, Perfect Date	35.00	60.00	100.00	225.00
1802 Proof Restrike			(Proof)	

Small 3

Large 3

	Good	Fine	Very Fine	Unc.
1803 Large 3 (One variety)	20.00	40.00	65.00	150.00
1803 Small 3 (Five varieties)	25.00	50.00	85.00	190.00
1803 Proof Restrike			(Proof)	

BIBLIOGRAPHY

Bolender, M. H., The UNITED STATES EARLY SILVER DOLLARS from 1794 to 1803. 1950.

SILVER DOLLARS

THE 1804 DOLLAR

This piece is one of the most publicized rarities in the United States series. There are specimens known as originals (type 1) of which seven are known, and restrikes (type 2) of which seven are known.

Opinion is divided regarding the origin, date of issue and authenticity of this coin. Those who adhere to the belief that these coins were struck in 1804 point to such evidence as the letter written by Robert Patterson, Director of the Mint, to President Thomas Jefferson. This letter stated that no dollars had been minted "during the last two years." Inasmuch as the letter was dated April 2, 1807, they infer that dollars were struck during 1804.

Mint records show that 19,570 silver dollars were coined in 1804 and that these coins were struck before March 28, 1804. Years later a die with the date 1804 was found at the mint among discarded dies.

It is a matter of record that Director Boudinot stopped the coinage of silver dollars in 1804 to prevent their exportation because their face value was less than their bullion value. It can be logically supposed that the coins were never released, but thrown back into the melting pot. The record also shows that seven 1804 dollars were reserved for assay. These may well be the 1804 original type silver dollars now held by museums and collectors.

Some numismatists believe that the 1804 dollars were struck at the mint between 1836 and 1842, during the period when Christian Gobrecht was creating his well known patterns in preparation for the new issue of silver dollars. The first known specimen, a proof, was obtained from a mint officer by Mr. Stickney on May 9, 1843, in exchange for an "Immune Columbia" piece in gold. Proponents of the theory that these pieces were struck during the later period, base their contention on the fact that the 1804 dollars differ from issues of 1803 or earlier and conform more closely to those struck in 1836 to 1842 — their edges or borders having beaded segments and raised rim, not elongated, denticles such as are found on the earlier dates.

Although the mint records state that 19,570 dollars were coined in 1804, in no place does it mention that they were dated 1804. It was the practice in those days to use old dies as long as they were serviceable with no regard in the annual reports for the dating of the coins. It is entirely possible that the 1804 total for dollars may actually have covered coins which were dated 1803.

The 1804 dollar has been and probably will continue to be a subject of much discussion. Unless some new evidence is uncovered the mystery of its existence or disappearance will always be a matter of speculation for the numismatic fraternity.

SILVER DOLLARS

TYPE 1

Note Position of Words STATES OF With Relation to Clouds

1804 Type 1, Original (Stickney specimen sold for $10,500.00 in 1946.)
(Dexter specimen sold for $10,000.00 in 1950.)

TYPE 2

Compare With Type 1 Above

1804 Type 2, Restrike (Idler Specimen sold for $29,000.00 in 1961).

(Davis-Hale Specimen sold for $28,000.00 in 1960.)

CHRISTIAN GOBRECHT

Christian Gobrecht was born December 23, 1785. He went to Philadelphia in 1811 and became an engraver of bank notes, seals, calico printers' rolls, bookbinders' dies, etc. He was appointed assistant to Mint Engraver William Kneass in 1836. According to Edgar H. Adams, he prepared a series of dies for pattern dollars, after designs by Sully, exquisite in design and character. The first pattern shows the familiar seated figure of Liberty on the obverse. The name C. Gobrecht F. was placed just under the figure of Liberty and over the date. In the field on the reverse was a large eagle in full flight surrounded by twenty-six stars and the legend UNITED STATES OF AMERICA ONE DOLLAR.

In response to criticism Gobrecht removed his name from the die after eighteen specimens had been struck, some in silver and some in copper.

Director Patterson ordered the name replaced, this time on the base. Patterns were also made in 1836 with the stars omitted from the field of the reverse.

In 1838 the engravers name was omitted altogether from the design and thirteen stars were placed around the seated figure of Liberty on the obverse. Stars were omitted from the reverse on one pattern and retained on another. Similar pieces were struck in 1839.

	Proof
1836 C. Gobrecht F. in field between base and date. Rev. Eagle flying left amid stars. Plain edge (Rare.) (18)	$1150.00
1836 Obv. as above. Rev. Eagle flying in plain field. Plain edge (Very rare.) (5)	1500.00

1836 C. Gobrecht on base. Rev. Eagle flying left in field containing stars.

SILVER DOLLARS

	Very Fine	Proof
Plain edge. Although scarce, this is the most common variety. (1000)	$375.00	750.00
1836. As above, reeded edge. (Very rare.) (3)		1,750.00

	Proof
1838 As above, reeded edge. Generally considered to be very rare. 25 Struck. Also unknown quantity of restrikes	1,600.00
1838 Obv. as above. Rev. Eagle in plain field. Plain edge. (Very rare.) (3)	1,800.00
1838 Seated Liberty. Obv. name of designer is left off and stars added around obverse border. Rev. Eagle flying left surrounded by stars. Plain edge. (Very rare.) (3)	1,800.00
1839 Obv. same as 1838. Rev. Eagle in plain field. Plain edge. (Very rare.) (3)	1,800.00
1839 Obv. as above. Rev. Eagle amid stars. Plain edge. (Very rare.) (3)	1,800.00
1839 Obv. as above. Rev. Eagle in plain field. Reeded edge. Most common 1839 variety. (Rare.) (300)	1,000.00

Quantities shown for the above patterns are probably inaccurate as restrikes of many are known to have been made.

When in 1840 silver dollars were again issued for general circulation the seated figure of Liberty device was adopted for the obverse. For some mysterious reason the flying eagle design was rejected and the more familiar form with olive branch and arrows was used.

SILVER DOLLARS
Liberty Seated Type
Regular Issues

	V. Fine	Unc.	Proof
1840	$ 27.50	70.00	400.00
1841	22.50	60.00	350.00
1842	20.00	50.00	350.00
1843	20.00	50.00	350.00
1844	28.50	65.00	350.00
1845	28.50	65.00	330.00
1846	20.00	50.00	325.00
1846O	30.00	70.00	
1847	20.00	50.00	325.00
1848	30.00	60.00	325.00
1849	25.00	55.00	350.00
1850	55.00	120.00	350.00
1850O	35.00	65.00	
1851 (Orig. High Date)	550.00	1000.00	1300.00
1851 (Restrike Center Date)			1000.00
1852 (Original)		1200.00	
1852 (Restrike)			1000.00

	V. Fine	Unc.	Proof
1853	$40.00	90.00	1000.00
1854	65.00	125.00	300.00
1855	55.00	110.00	500.00
1856	35.00	80.00	225.00
1857	37.50	70.00	175.00
1858			825.00
1859	22.50	60.00	125.00
1859O	20.00	55.00	
1859S	50.00	150.00	
1860	22.50	60.00	110.00
1860O	20.00	45.00	
1861	30.00	70.00	120.00
1862	32.50	75.00	120.00
1863	30.00	65.00	120.00
1864	30.00	60.00	110.00
1865	30.00	60.00	105.00
1866 (No Motto) 2 known —			
Fairbanks Sale 1960 Pf.			$13,000.00

Motto "In God We Trust" Added To Reverse

1866	25.00	52.50	90.00
1867	20.00	45.00	85.00
1868	20.00	45.00	85.00
1869	18.50	36.00	85.00
1870	18.00	36.00	70.00
1870S Fairbanks Sale 1960 V.F.			9,000.00
1870CC	50.00	175.00	
1871	16.00	35.00	70.00
1871CC	650.00	1200.00	
1872	16.00	35.00	70.00
1872S	80.00	210.00	
1872CC	325.00	750.00	
1873	19.00	40.00	85.00
1873CC	800.00	1500.00	
1873S (Unknown in any collection.)			

[133]

SILVER DOLLARS
Liberty Head or Morgan Type

The mint law of 1873 made no provision for the standard silver dollar. During the lapse in coinage of this piece the gold dollar became the unit coin and the trade dollar was used for our commercial transactions with the Orient.

The legal tender character was restored to the silver dollar by the Act of February 28, 1878 known as the Bland-Allison Act. The weight, $412\frac{1}{2}$ grains and fineness 900 were to conform with the act of January 18, 1837.

George T. Morgan, formerly a pupil of Wyon in the Royal Mint in London, designed the new dollar. His initial M is found at the truncation of the neck, at the last tress. It also appears on the reverse on the left-hand loop of the ribbon. It is very difficult to detect.

Coinage of the silver dollar was again suspended after 1904 when the bullion supply became exhausted. Under provisions of the Pittman Act of 1918 coinage of the silver dollar was resumed in 1921. The Morgan design, with some slight refinements, was employed until the new Peace design was adopted later in that year.

Beware of early strike Philadelphia mint uncirculated dollars being offered as proofs.

8 Tail Feathers
1878 Philadelphia Only

7 Tail Feathers
1878 and Later Dates

	Ex. Fine	Unc.	Proof		Ex. Fine	Unc.	Proof
1878 8 Tail Feathers	$	10.00	75.00	1879CC	$15.00	85.00	
1878 7 Tail Feathers over 8 Tail Feathers	5.00	11.00		1880		2.75	60.00
				1880O	1.75	6.00	
1878 7 Tail Feathers		3.00	115.00	1880S		3.00	
1878S		3.00		1880CC	5.00	20.00	
1878CC	2.00	7.50		1881		2.75	65.00
1879		3.00	70.00	1881O		3.50	
1879O	2.00	7.50		1881S		3.75	
1879S		3.75		1881CC	5.00	20.00	

SILVER DOLLARS

	Ex. Fine	Unc.	Proof		Ex. Fine	Unc.	Proof
1882	$	2.75	60.00	1892CC	$ 6.00	25.00	
1882O	1.75	3.50		1893	5.00	12.50	75.00
1882S		3.00		1893O	4.50	40.00	
1882CC	3.50	9.50		1893S	125.00	600.00	
1883		2.75	62.50	1893CC	12.50	50.00	
1883O		3.50		1894	12.50	60.00	70.00
1883S	3.50	10.00		1894O	3.00	10.00	
1883CC	3.00	9.50		1894S	4.00	25.00	
1884		3.50	62.50	*1895			925.00
1884O		3.50		1895O	7.50	60.00	
1884S	3.50	16.00		1895S	20.00	125.00	
1884CC	3.50	12.00		1896	1.50	2.50	75.00
1885		3.00	60.00	1896O	4.50	15.00	
1885O		3.00		1896S	4.50	50.00	
1885S		10.00		1897	1.50	3.00	72.50
1885CC	3.75	20.00		1897O	3.00	10.00	
1886		3.50	67.50	1897S		4.50	
1886O	3.50	12.50		1898	1.50	3.50	75.00
1886S		15.00		1898O	50.00	300.00	
1887		3.00	75.00	1898S		15.00	
1887O	1.75	4.50		1899	2.00	7.50	70.00
1887S		9.50		1899O	2.00	7.50	
1888		4.00	70.00	1899S		15.00	
1888O	1.75	4.50		1900		3.50	70.00
1888S		15.00		1900O		6.00	
1889		2.50	70.00	1900S		15.00	
1889O	3.00	9.00		1901	5.00	25.00	75.00
1889S		15.00		1901O	2.50	6.50	
1889CC	85.00	185.00		1901S		15.00	
1890		3.00	110.00	1902	1.50	3.50	75.00
1890O		6.50		1902O	7.00	30.00	
1890S		4.00		1902S		15.00	
1890CC		10.00		1903		3.00	80.00
1891		3.00	80.00	1903O	150.00	600.00	
1891O	2.50	10.00		1903S	7.50	75.00	
1891S		4.50		1904		8.50	92.50
1891CC		10.00		1904O	15.00	250.00	
1892	2.00	9.50	60.00	1904S	5.00	35.00	
1892O	3.50	12.50		*Beware removed mint letter.			
1892S	15.00	125.00					

270,232,722 silver dollars were melted under the Pittman Act of April, 1918. 259,121,554 for export to India, and 11,111,168 for domestic subsidiary coins, which probably accounts for the scarcity of 1903 O.

1921		2.25	190.00
1921D		2.50	
1921S		2.50	

BIBLIOGRAPHY

Haseltine, J. W., Type Table of U. S. Dollars, Half and Quarter Dollars. 1881. Reprint 1933.

SILVER DOLLARS
PEACE TYPE

During the Chicago Convention of the American Numismatic Association in August, 1920, a resolution agitating the coinage of "a Commemorative peace coin" was passed. Through the efforts of a special A.N.A. committee, a resolution authorizing the coinage of a "Peace Dollar" was introduced in the House of Representatives on May 9, 1921.

A half dollar was under consideration for a time, but the silver dollar, being of larger size, afforded a better opportunity for art effect than a smaller coin. The object was to produce a coin for general circulation to commemorate the declaration of peace between the Allied Nations and the German government.

No special legislation was passed, however, and the coin was struck under the law authorizing the issue of the standard silver dollar—that of February 28, 1878. The metal for the coinage of the old type silver dollars of 1921 and the new peace coins was made available under the Pittman Act. This act referred to the bullion and in no way affected the design.

Eight medalists were in the competition for the design award. The design submitted by Anthony de Francisci was accepted by the commission on December 19, 1921. His monogram is located in the field of the coin under the neck.

The new Peace Dollar was placed in circulation January 3, 1922. 1,006,473 pieces were struck in December, 1921.

The high relief of the 1921 design was found impractical for coinage and was slightly modified in 1922.

	Ex. Fine	Unc.	Matte Proof		Ex. Fine	Unc.
1921	$5.00	12.50	——	1926D	$3.00	16.00
1922 Type of 1921			——	1926S		5.00
1922		2.50		1927	2.00	12.50
1922D		4.50		1927D	3.00	22.50
1922S		4.50		1927S	2.00	14.00
1923		2.50		1928	10.00	30.00
1923D		8.00		1928S	2.00	16.00
1923S		4.00		1934	2.00	7.50
1924		3.00		1934D	2.00	10.00
1924S		8.50		1934S	9.00	75.00
1925		2.50		1935	2.00	8.00
1925S		6.50		1935S	4.00	17.50
1926		4.00				

TRADE DOLLARS
1873 - 1885

This coin was issued for circulation in the Orient to compete with the Mexican peso. It is 420 grains in weight compared to 412½ grains which is the standard weight of the regular silver dollars.

When first coined they were legal tender in the United States to the extent of $5.00 but with the decline in price of silver bullion Congress repealed the legal tender provision in 1876 and authorized the Treasury to limit coinage to export demand. In 1887 a law was passed authorizing the Treasury to redeem all Trade dollars which were not mutilated. U. S. Trade dollars are still circulating in the Orient. Those struck in the last few years of coinage were undoubtedly all specimen proof strikings.

The trade dollars of 1884 and 1885 were unknown to collectors generally until 1908. None is listed in the Director's report. The law authorizing Trade Dollars was repealed in February, 1887.

	Fine	Ex. Fine	Unc.	Proof
1873	$13.50	22.50	50.00	110.00
1873S	15.00	40.00	77.50	
1873CC	25.00	50.00	110.00	
1874	11.00	16.00	27.50	90.00
1874S	11.00	16.00	30.00	
1874CC	20.00	40.00	72.50	
1875	13.50	21.00	45.00	100.00
1875S	10.00	16.00	25.00	
1875CC	17.50	32.50	47.50	
1876	10.00	16.00	27.50	70.00
1876S	10.00	15.00	25.00	
1876CC	17.50	35.00	60.00	
1877	10.00	13.50	20.00	130.00
1877S	9.00	13.50	20.00	
1877CC	32.50	65.00	110.00	
1878				100.00
1878S	9.00	13.50	20.00	
1878CC	90.00	150.00	260.00	
1879				65.00
1880				65.00
1881				80.00
1882				75.00
1883				80.00
1884 Fairbanks Sale 1960				6,000.00
1885				9,000.00

GOLD

Gold, the earliest known and most beautiful of all metallic substances, has been and remains of the greatest commercial consequence. Of the precious metals, gold particularly has for ages been the chief material used for coins.

In ancient times gold in the form of nuggets was found imbedded in fragments of rocks or blended with other metals or minerals. In more recent times this precious metal has been gathered in the form of small grains in deposits called placers, in lodes and in veins. "Gold dust" mingled with sand and earth is found in many places throughout the world.

Gold is the most ductile and malleable of metals. It can be beaten to a thinness of 1/365,000 of an inch or a grain can be drawn into a wire 500 feet long. The entire available world supply of gold, estimated to be worth $35,000,000,000 could be housed in a vault fifty feet square and twenty-six feet high. Because gold in its pure state is rather soft, similar in consistency to lead, it is usually alloyed with copper or other metals to improve its wearing qualities.

Gold fired the avaricious imagination of all Europe when America was discovered. The adventurers who followed Columbus were principally controlled by private greed and ambition. Gold and silver was their only object. The slow and unsatisfactory progress of the Spanish-American colonies can be attributed to this spirit.

The presence of gold in California was known to Sir Francis Drake who sailed from England in 1577. The gold fields were to be thoroughly exploited almost three centuries later, by the Forty-niners.

In the United States proper the first important gold mining operations were conducted in the hills along the eastern slope of the Appalachian Mountains, particularly in North Carolina. During the years following the 1849 gold rush, the principal source of gold and silver has been the Western Mountain areas and, more recently, Alaska.

Gold is common to most nations as a standard for measurement of all other values. In our own country paper currency and token coins now serve exclusively as money. Gold continues to serve as the yardstick of money values, although it is no longer used for actual coinage. The gold possessed by the United States treasury is held as a reserve to back up our token or representative money.

The amount of money in circulation in the United States is tied to the amount of gold reserves. Our money will remain stable so long as we adhere to the gold standard with a fixed weight of gold as the dollar (now 13.71 grains of pure gold).

Since gold has not circulated as money since 1933 it has been stored in bullion form thus saving the expense of coinage. Being a standard of value its worth is the same whether in the shape of coins or in bars.

As a result of the gold surrender order, United States gold coins have become scarce, and the small remaining supply of these beautiful and respected representatives of our monetary past are being legally and carefully preserved by the Numismatic fraternity.

GOLD DOLLARS

1849 - 1889

Coinage of the gold dollar was authorized by the Act of March 3, 1849. The weight was 25.8 grains fineness .900. The first type, struck until 1854, is known as the Liberty Head or small-sized type. In 1854 the piece was made larger in diameter and thinner. The design was changed to a feather headdress on a female generally referred to as the Indian Head or Large-sized type. In 1856 the type was changed slightly by enlarging the size of the head.

GOLD DOLLARS

Type 1

Type 3

	V. Fine	Unc.
1849 Open Wreath	$ 32.50	55.00
1849 Closed wreath (wreath ends closer to Figure 1)	30.00	50.00
1849C Closed wreath	92.50	250.00
1849C Open wreath (2 known) (1956 A.N.A. Sale $6,000.00)		
1849D Open wreath	82.50	200.00
1849O Open wreath	30.00	45.00
1850	28.50	40.00
1850C	150.00	500.00
1850D	110.00	225.00
1850O	30.00	55.00
1851	27.50	40.00
1851C	85.00	130.00
1851D	85.00	200.00
1851O	28.00	42.50
1852	27.50	40.00
1852C	105.00	155.00
1852D	90.00	175.00
1852O	28.50	40.00
1853	28.50	37.50
1853C	85.00	175.00
1853D	125.00	225.00
1853O	28.50	40.00
1854	28.50	40.00
1854D	160.00	325.00
1854S	75.00	150.00

Type 2

	V. Fine	Unc.	Proof
1854	50.00	85.00	
1854C (Unknown)			
1855	50.00	85.00	500.00
1855C	110.00	200.00	
1855D	500.00	1,000.00	
1855O	50.00	110.00	
1856S	60.00	125.00	

Type 3

1856 Slant 5	30.00	40.00	400.00
1856 Upright 5	32.50	47.50	
1856D	$600.00	1,000.00	
1857	30.00	40.00	300.00
1857C	85.00	165.00	
1857D	250.00	400.00	
1857S	55.00	125.00	
1858	30.00	40.00	300.00
1858D	175.00	325.00	
1858S	75.00	130.00	
1859	32.00	42.50	200.00
1859C	115.00	250.00	
1859D	125.00	275.00	
1859S	70.00	120.00	
1860	32.00	45.00	200.00
1860D	800.00	1,450.00	
1860S	70.00	90.00	
1861	30.00	42.50	
1861D	950.00	1,600.00	
1862	30.00	40.00	150.00
1863	110.00	225.00	300.00
1864	60.00	140.00	340.00
1865	110.00	225.00	275.00
1866	60.00	125.00	260.00
1867	45.00	95.00	235.00
1868	45.00	75.00	300.00
1869	60.00	105.00	250.00
1870	50.00	85.00	200.00
1870S	225.00	600.00	
1871	50.00	110.00	225.00
1872	45.00	85.00	225.00
1873 (Closed 3)	30.00	40.00	190.00
1873 (Open 3)	30.00	40.00	
1874	32.00	42.50	200.00
1875	250.00	550.00	600.00
1876	45.00	75.00	175.00
1877	45.00	82.50	225.00
1878	45.00	82.50	225.00
1879	45.00	80.00	180.00
1880	57.50	95.00	185.00
1881	45.00	70.00	125.00
1882	45.00	70.00	125.00
1883	45.00	70.00	125.00
1884	35.00	52.50	75.00
1885	35.00	52.50	75.00
1886	37.50	55.00	75.00
1887	35.00	52.50	75.00
1888	35.00	52.50	80.00
1889	35.00	52.50	75.00

QUARTER EAGLES
($2.50 GOLD PIECES)

Authorized by the Act of April 2, 1792 they weighed 67.5 grains, 916⅔ fine until the weight was changed to 64.5 grains fineness 899.225 by the Act of June 28, 1834. The Act of January 18, 1837 established fineness at .900. Most dates before 1834 are rare. The first issue was struck in 1796 most of which had no stars on the obverse.

Proofs prior to 1855 are known to exist of some dates, and all are rare.

	Fine	V. Fine	Unc.
1804	$ 225.00	450.00	750.00
1805	225.00	500.00	775.00

	Fine	V. Fine	Unc.
1796 No Stars	$1,200.00	1,950.00	3,750.00

1806 over 4   **1806 over 5**

1806 over 4	275.00	650.00	900.00
1806 over 5	375.00	535.00	800.00

1796 Stars	1,050.00	1,950.00	3,750.00

1807	200.00	375.00	650.00

1797	575.00	875.00	1,300.00

New Type Bust Facing Left— Round Cap

1808 New Type, Bust Facing Left — Round Cap	1,000.00	1,450.00	2,450.00

1798	750.00	1,100.00	2,950.00

Small Size—No Change in Weight

1802 over 1	300.00	450.00	775.00

1821 Reduced Size	200.00	300.00	700.00

QUARTER EAGLES

	Fine	Very Fine	Unc.
1824 over 21	$150.00	225.00	350.00
1825	140.00	235.00	300.00
1826 over 25	300.00	600.00	950.00
1827	200.00	400.00	625.00
1829	160.00	260.00	400.00
1830	150.00	250.00	425.00
1831	150.00	250.00	425.00
1832	150.00	250.00	425.00
1833	160.00	260.00	425.00
1834 Motto above eagle	350.00	500.00	775.00

New Type

In 1834 the quarter eagle was redesigned. A ribbon binding the hair, bearing the word LIBERTY, replaces the liberty cap. The motto was omitted from the reverse. In 1840 a coronet and smaller head were designed to conform in appearance with the larger gold coins.

	Fine	Very Fine	Unc.
1834 No Motto	25.00	35.00	45.00
1835	25.00	35.00	45.00
1836	24.00	33.00	42.50
1837	27.50	40.00	50.00
1838	27.50	40.00	50.00
1838C	75.00	100.00	150.00
1839	27.50	33.00	50.00
1839C	65.00	80.00	110.00
1839D	80.00	110.00	150.00
1839O	50.00	65.00	80.00

New Small Head

	Fine	Very Fine	Unc.
1840	$27.50	35.00	50.00
1840C	35.00	50.00	75.00
1840D	60.00	85.00	110.00
1840O	27.50	33.00	52.50
1841 Proofs only			Ex. Rare
1841C	75.00	125.00	175.00
1841D	80.00	135.00	180.00
1841O (Unknown)			
1842	45.00	75.00	100.00
1842C	60.00	85.00	110.00
1842D	60.00	75.00	110.00
1842O	27.50	40.00	55.00
1843	24.00	35.00	47.50
1843C Sm. Date	40.00	50.00	60.00
1843C Lg. Date	40.00	50.00	60.00
1843D Sm. Date	40.00	50.00	70.00
1843O Sm. Date	27.50	35.00	50.00
1843O Lg. Date	35.00	45.00	75.00
1844	27.50	50.00	75.00
1844C	35.00	65.00	90.00
1844D	35.00	65.00	90.00
1845	30.00	42.50	50.00
1845D	37.50	50.00	100.00
1845O	65.00	85.00	140.00
1846	27.50	37.50	55.00
1846C	50.00	85.00	110.00
1846D	35.00	60.00	80.00
1846O	27.50	37.50	50.00
1847	27.50	37.50	50.00
1847C	35.00	60.00	125.00
1847D	40.00	85.00	130.00
1847O	24.00	35.00	50.00
1848	60.00	100.00	300.00

California Gold Quarter Eagle

In 1848 about two hundred and thirty ounces of gold were sent to Secretary of War Marcy by Col. R. B. Mason, Military governor of California. The gold was turned over to the mint and made into quarter eagles. The distinguishing mark "CAL" was punched above the eagle on the reverse side, while the coins were in the die.

QUARTER EAGLES

CAL above eagle on Reverse

	V. Fine	Unc.	Proof
1848 CAL above eagle (2 Proofs known)	$750.00	1,375.00	
1848C	55.00	80.00	
1848D	65.00	100.00	
1849	30.00	70.00	
1849C	70.00	80.00	
1849D	70.00	80.00	
1850	30.00	45.00	
1850C	65.00	85.00	
1850D	65.00	85.00	
1850O	27.50	40.00	
1851	25.00	37.50	
1851C	65.00	80.00	
1851D	65.00	90.00	
1851O	25.00	39.00	
1852	25.00	37.50	
1852C	65.00	90.00	
1852D	85.00	155.00	
1852O	25.00	39.00	
1853	25.00	37.50	
1853D	175.00	300.00	
1854	25.00	37.50	
1854C	70.00	90.00	
1854D	325.00	510.00	
1854O	25.00	39.00	
1854S	1,100.00	2,500.00	
1855	25.00	37.50	700.00
1855C	90.00	125.00	
1855D	350.00	700.00	
1856	25.00	37.50	675.00
1856C	70.00	90.00	
1856D	450.00	800.00	
1856O	30.00	45.00	
1856S	30.00	70.00	
1857	25.00	39.00	510.00
1857D	100.00	175.00	
1857O	30.00	45.00	
1857S	30.00	55.00	
1858	26.00	40.00	375.00
1858C	65.00	85.00	
1858S (Unknown)			
1859	25.00	37.50	325.00
1859D	$100.00	200.00	
1859S	30.00	85.00	
1860	25.00	50.00	250.00
1860C	60.00	105.00	
1860S	32.00	52.50	
1861	25.00	37.50	225.00
1861S	30.00	50.00	
1862	30.00	45.00	225.00
1862S	35.00	80.00	
1863 Proofs only			1,550.00
1863S	35.00	60.00	
1864	100.00	225.00	400.00
1865	110.00	235.00	400.00
1865S	30.00	55.00	
1866	90.00	150.00	275.00
1866S	30.00	55.00	
1867	75.00	100.00	240.00
1867S	35.00	60.00	
1868	50.00	100.00	275.00
1868S	35.00	55.00	
1869	45.00	65.00	275.00
1869S	32.00	55.00	
1870	45.00	80.00	230.00
1870S	30.00	65.00	
1871	45.00	75.00	250.00
1871S	40.00	50.00	
1872	35.00	65.00	250.00
1872S	38.00	60.00	
1873 (Closed 3)	30.00	40.00	260.00
1873 (Open 3)	30.00	40.00	
1873S	32.00	50.00	
1874	40.00	80.00	400.00
1875	250.00	500.00	675.00
1875S	40.00	85.00	
1876	45.00	65.00	195.00
1876S	30.00	60.00	
1877	75.00	150.00	395.00
1877S	30.00	45.00	
1878	28.00	35.00	395.00
1878S	28.00	35.00	
1879	28.00	35.00	260.00
1879S	35.00	50.00	
1880	50.00	90.00	275.00
1881	160.00	300.00	400.00
1882	65.00	100.00	225.00
1883	75.00	90.00	225.00
1884	65.00	115.00	310.00
1885	145.00	275.00	375.00
1886	35.00	65.00	200.00
1887	35.00	60.00	150.00
1888	35.00	45.00	150.00
1889	35.00	45.00	175.00
1890	40.00	55.00	150.00
1891	35.00	55.00	160.00

QUARTER EAGLES

	V. Fine	Unc.	Proof		V. Fine	Unc.	Proof
1892	$55.00	90.00	225.00	1900	$28.00	40.00	125.00
1893	32.50	47.50	185.00	1901	27.00	39.00	125.00
1894	40.00	55.00	275.00	1902	27.00	37.50	125.00
1895	35.00	47.50	200.00	1903	27.00	37.50	125.00
1896	35.00	47.50	150.00	1904	27.00	37.50	125.00
1897	32.50	42.50	150.00	1905	27.00	37.50	125.00
1898	32.50	42.50	150.00	1906	27.00	37.50	125.00
1899	32.50	42.50	150.00	1907	27.00	37.50	150.00

Indian Head Type

The new type represents a departure from all preceding coin types in the United States series. Bela Lyon Pratt was the designer of this and the half eagle piece. The coin has no raised milling and the main devices and legends are incuse.

	Very Fine	Matte Unc.	Proof		Very Fine	Matte Unc.	Proof
1908	$18.50	25.00	175.00	1914	$21.00	37.50	200.00
1909	18.50	25.00	195.00	1914D	19.00	30.00	
1910	17.50	24.00	195.00	1915	17.50	24.00	210.00
1911	17.50	24.00	195.00	1925D	17.50	24.00	
1911D	185.00	275.00		1926	17.50	24.00	
1912	17.50	24.00	195.00	1927	17.50	24.00	
1913	17.50	24.00	195.00	1928	17.50	24.00	
				1929	17.50	24.00	

THREE-DOLLAR GOLD PIECES

1854-1889

The three-dollar gold piece was authorized by Act of February 21, 1853. The coin was first struck in 1854. It was never popular and saw very little circulation.

The coin weighs 77.4 grains, .900 fine. The head on the obverse represents an Indian princess with hair tightly curling over the neck, head crowned with a circle of feathers, the band of which is inscribed LIBERTY. A wreath of tobacco, wheat, corn and cotton occupies the field of the reverse, with the denomination and date within it. No change of type was made during the life of this denomination.

THREE-DOLLAR GOLD PIECES

In the year 1854 only, the word DOLLARS is in much smaller letters than in years 1855 through 1889.

	V. Fine	Unc.	Proof
1854	$135.00	185.00	875.00
1854D	400.00	750.00	
1854O	135.00	195.00	
1855	135.00	175.00	850.00
1855S	140.00	185.00	
1856	135.00	175.00	850.00
1856 Small S	140.00	185.00	
1856 Large S	135.00	175.00	
1857	137.50	185.00	800.00
1857S	135.00	175.00	
1858	190.00	450.00	875.00
1859	140.00	185.00	425.00
1860	140.00	190.00	425.00
1860S	140.00	190.00	
1861	140.00	190.00	350.00
1862	140.00	190.00	350.00
1863	140.00	190.00	350.00
1864	160.00	225.00	375.00
1865	190.00	375.00	675.00
1866	140.00	190.00	475.00
1867	160.00	225.00	375.00
1868	150.00	200.00	600.00
1869	145.00	195.00	600.00

	V. Fine	Unc.	Proof
1870	$145.00	195.00	550.00
1870S (Unique)			
1871	185.00	250.00	550.00
1872	185.00	225.00	550.00
1873 (Open 3)			975.00
1873 (Closed 3)*		450.00	900.00
1874	135.00	175.00	700.00
1875 (Proofs Only)			6,250.00
1876 (Proofs Only)			3,000.00
1877	200.00	350.00	950.00
1878	135.00	175.00	650.00
1879	150.00	200.00	450.00
1880	190.00	300.00	450.00
1881	300.00	450.00	950.00
1882	180.00	250.00	450.00
1883	200.00	300.00	450.00
1884	185.00	300.00	400.00
1885	200.00	300.00	450.00
1886	185.00	275.00	375.00
1887	160.00	200.00	325.00
1888	160.00	200.00	325.00
1889	165.00	225.00	450.00

*All closed 3's are restrikes.

$4.00 GOLD OR "STELLA"

These pattern coins were first suggested by Hon. John A. Kasson, then U. S. Minister to Austria; and it was through the efforts of Dr. W. W. Hubbell who patented the goloid metal, used in making the goloid metric dollars, that we have these beautiful and interesting pieces.

There are two distinct types in both years of issue. Barber designed the flowing hair type, and Morgan the coiled hair. They were struck in gold, aluminum, copper and white metal. Only those struck in gold are listed.

	Proof		Proof
1879 Flowing hair (415)	$4,500.00	1880 Flowing hair (15)	$9,000.00
1879 Coiled hair (10)	10,500.00	1880 Coiled hair (10)	11,000.00

Set sold for $38,000 at Kreisberg-Schulman Sale, 1961.

HALF EAGLES ($5.00 Gold Pieces)
1795-1929

The half-eagle was the first gold coin actually struck for the United States. The $5.00 piece was authorized to be coined by the Act of April 2, 1792 and the first type weighed 135 grains, 916⅔ fine. The weight was changed by Act of June 28, 1834 to 129 grains, 899.225 fine. Fineness became 900 by Act of January 18, 1837.

There are many varieties among the early dates caused by changes in the number of stars, style of eagle, over-dates, and differences in the size of figures in the dates. Those dated prior to 1807 do not bear any mark of value. The 1822 half-eagle is considered the rarest regular issue coin of the entire United States series. Proofs prior to 1855 are known to exist of some dates, and all are rare.

Small Eagle   Large Eagle

	Fine	V. Fine	Unc.
1795 Small eagle	$300.00	475.00	650.00
1795 Large or heraldic eagle	500.00	900.00	1,800.00
1796 over 95 Small eagle	300.00	450.00	650.00
1797 over 95 Large or heraldic eagle	650.00	850.00	1,250.00

[145]

HALF EAGLES

15 Stars

16 Stars

	Fine	V. Fine	Unc.
1797 15 stars Small eagle on rev	$550.00	800.00	1,250.00
1797 16 stars Small eagle on rev	550.00	800.00	1,250.00
1798 Small eagle (5 known)			
1798 Large or heraldic eagle, small 8 in date	125.00	150.00	225.00
1798 Large eagle, large 8 in date, 13 star reverse	150.00	250.00	450.00
1798 Large eagle, large 8 in date, 14 star reverse	175.00	400.00	650.00

1799	125.00	185.00	290.00
1800	110.00	175.00	260.00

1802 over 1

1803 over 2

1802 over 1	110.00	170.00	260.00
1803 over 2	110.00	170.00	260.00

Small 8

Large 8

1804 Small 8	115.00	180.00	275.00
1804 Large 8	115.00	180.00	275.00
1805	115.00	180.00	275.00

HALF EAGLES

Pointed 6

Round Top 6

	Fine	V. Fine	Unc.
1806 Pointed top 6	$110.00	165.00	250.00
1806 Round top 6	110.00	165.00	250.00
1807	110.00	165.00	250.00

Liberty Facing Left—Round Cap—Smaller Eagle
Value 5D. Used for First Time

1807	100.00	165.00	275.00

1808 over 7

Normal Date

1808 over 7	100.00	165.00	275.00
1808	100.00	160.00	210.00
1809 over 8	100.00	160.00	210.00
1809	100.00	160.00	210.00

Small Date

Small 5

1810 Small date, small 5	100.00	160.00	210.00
1810 Small date, tall 5	100.00	160.00	210.00

HALF EAGLES

Large Date

Tall 5

	Fine	V. Fine	Unc.
1810 Large date	$ 100.00	155.00	210.00
1811 Small 5	100.00	155.00	210.00
1811 Large 5	100.00	155.00	210.00
1812	100.00	155.00	210.00

NEW TYPE — Larger Head

1813	125.00	165.00	275.00
1814	115.00	190.00	290.00
1815			3,500.00
1818	135.00	200.00	375.00
1819			2,000.00

Curve Based 2

Square Based 2

Small Letters

Large Letters

1820 Curve-base 2, small letters	200.00	300.00	425.00
1820 Curve-based 2, large letters	225.00	325.00	450.00
1820 Square-based 2	155.00	275.00	375.00
1821	550.00	750.00	1,050.00

1822 (3 Known)			
1823	185.00	275.00	500.00
1824			

[148]

HALF EAGLES

1825 over 21

1825 over 24

	Fine	V. Fine	Unc.
1825 over 21	$ 550.00	750.00	1,200.00
1825 over 24	—	—	1,500.00
1826	600.00	850.00	1,600.00
1827	1,500.00	2,100.00	3,000.00

1828 over 27

1828 over 27	—	—	—
1828	950.00	1,400.00	2,000.00

Small Date

Large Date

1829 Small date	—	—	—
1829 Large date	—	—	—

Small 5D

Large 5D

1830 Small 5 D	275.00	400.00	600.00
1830 Large 5 D	275.00	400.00	600.00
1831	300.00	425.00	650.00

[149]

HALF EAGLES

12 Stars,
Curve-Based
2

13 Stars,
Square-Based
2

	Fine	V. Fine	Unc.
1832 Curve-based 2, 12 stars			
1832 Square-based 2, 13 stars	$900.00	1,500.00	2,500.00
1833	285.00	400.00	650.00

Plain 4   Crosslet 4

1834 Plain 4	325.00	425.00	650.00
1834 Crosslet 4	375.00	500.00	800.00

No Motto on Reverse

Like the quarter dollar of 1831, the motto E PLURIBUS UNUM was omitted from the new, reduced size half-eagle in 1834, presumably for lack of space. The new motto IN GOD WE TRUST was nevertheless artistically added to the reverse in the form of a scroll in 1866.

1834 Plain 4	23.00	35.00	55.00
1834 Crosslet 4	85.00	140.00	200.00
1835	27.50	40.00	60.00
1836	23.00	35.00	50.00
1837	27.50	40.00	60.00
1838	30.00	40.00	60.00
1838C	75.00	130.00	250.00
1838D	75.00	130.00	250.00

New Type—Smaller Head with Coronet

HALF EAGLES

	Fine	Very Fine	Unc.		Fine	Very Fine	Unc.
1839	$27.00	40.00	60.00	1840D	$60.00	100.00	140.00
1839C	60.00	105.00	150.00	1840O	25.00	50.00	75.00
1839D	60.00	100.00	165.00	1841	25.00	50.00	75.00
1840	24.00	35.00	55.00	1841C	40.00	75.00	110.00
1840C	60.00	90.00	150.00	1841D	40.00	80.00	100.00
				1841O (2 Known)	—	—	—

Small Letters   Large Letters

	V. Fine	Unc.		V. Fine	Unc.	Proof
1842 Small letters	$60.00	130.00	1850D	$75.00	110.00	
1842 Large letters	40.00	80.00	1851	23.00	45.00	
1842C Small date	60.00	95.00	1851C	55.00	90.00	
1842C Large date	65.00	90.00	1851D	75.00	110.00	
1842D Small date	55.00	80.00	1851O	37.50	75.00	
1842D Large date	65.00	100.00	1852	23.00	45.00	
1842O	50.00	95.00	1852C	60.00	110.00	
1843	22.50	45.00	1852D	60.00	110.00	
1843C	50.00	85.00	1853	23.00	40.00	
1843D	60.00	100.00	1853C	45.00	70.00	
1843O Small letters	25.00	60.00	1853D	45.00	70.00	
1843O Large letters	27.50	60.00	1854	23.00	45.00	
1844	22.00	45.00	1854C	50.00	80.00	
1844C	60.00	100.00	1854D	65.00	90.00	
1844D	45.00	80.00	1854O	40.00	90.00	
1844O	23.00	50.00	1854S	3,250.00		
1845	23.00	50.00	1855	23.00	45.00	850.00
1845D	65.00	100.00	1855C	80.00	110.00	
1845O	30.00	65.00	1855D	60.00	110.00	
1846	23.00	45.00	1855O	45.00	90.00	
1846C	75.00	110.00	1855S	25.00	60.00	
1846D	60.00	100.00	1856	23.00	40.00	750.00
1846O	25.00	50.00	1856C	50.00	85.00	
1847	23.00	45.00	1856D	60.00	90.00	
1847C	45.00	70.00	1856O	45.00	90.00	
1847D	70.00	100.00	1856S	25.00	45.00	
1847O	42.50	90.00	1857	23.00	45.00	750.00
1848	23.00	45.00	1857C	60.00	110.00	
1848C	70.00	110.00	1857D	70.00	120.00	
1848D	50.00	80.00	1857O	40.00	80.00	
1849	23.00	45.00	1857S	25.00	45.00	
1849C	50.00	80.00	1858	40.00	65.00	650.00
1849D	60.00	95.00	1858C	45.00	75.00	
1850	23.00	45.00	1858D	95.00	115.00	
1850C	60.00	100.00				

[151]

HALF EAGLES

	V.Fine	Unc.	Proof		V. Fine	Unc.	Proof
1858S	$ 30.00	60.00		1861D	$300.00	450.00	
1859	40.00	80.00	500.00	1861S	30.00	60.00	
1859C	45.00	85.00		1862	50.00	100.00	400.00
1859D	75.00	120.00		1862S	45.00	90.00	
1859S	35.00	75.00		1863	90.00	175.00	450.00
1860	35.00	75.00	400.00	1863S	25.00	60.00	
1860C	70.00	100.00		1864	70.00	150.00	475.00
1860D	50.00	90.00		1864S	75.00	150.00	
1860S	30.00	60.00		1865	125.00	250.00	475.00
1861	23.00	45.00	350.00	1865S	25.00	55.00	
1861C	125.00	275.00		1866S	55.00	110.00	

MOTTO ABOVE EAGLE

1866	40.00	80.00	300.00	1877S	27.50	55.00	
1866S	25.00	60.00		1877CC	35.00	80.00	
1867	40.00	90.00	250.00	1878	23.00	35.00	450.00
1867S	25.00	55.00		1878S	23.00	35.00	
1868	45.00	100.00	400.00	1878CC	40.00	70.00	
1868S	25.00	45.00		1879	22.00	30.00	250.00
1869	100.00	200.00	375.00	1879S	22.00	30.00	
1869S	25.00	45.00		1879CC	40.00	95.00	
1870	45.00	90.00	375.00	1880	19.00	25.00	220.00
1870S	25.00	50.00		1880S	22.00	30.00	
1870CC	45.00	90.00		1880CC	35.00	60.00	
1871	50.00	100.00	385.00	1881	19.00	24.00	185.00
1871S	25.00	45.00		1881S	19.00	24.00	
1871CC	35.00	75.00		1881CC	35.00	70.00	
1872	90.00	175.00	350.00	1882	19.00	24.00	185.00
1872S	23.00	45.00		1882S	19.00	24.00	
1872CC	35.00	75.00		1882CC	30.00	45.00	
1873 Closed 3	35.00	75.00	325.00	1883	19.00	24.00	185.00
1873 Open 3	20.00	35.00		1883S	20.00	30.00	
1873S	23.00	45.00		1883CC	38.00	75.00	
1873CC	35.00	75.00		1884	19.00	24.00	425.00
1874	45.00	100.00	385.00	1884S	22.00	28.00	
1874S	25.00	50.00		1884CC	30.00	60.00	
1874CC	35.00	70.00		1885	19.00	24.00	175.00
1875	300.00	600.00	800.00	1885S	19.00	24.00	
1875S	40.00	85.00		1886	19.00	24.00	
1875CC	40.00	80.00		1886S	19.00	24.00	
1876	75.00	150.00	275.00	*1887 Proofs only			900.00
1876S	50.00	90.00		1887S	19.00	24.00	
1876CC	35.00	90.00		1888	30.00	60.00	175.00
1877	125.00	200.00	400.00				

*Beware removed mintmark (buffed).

HALF EAGLES

	V. Fine	Unc.	Proof		V. Fine	Unc.	Proof
1888S	$ 21.00	28.00		1898	$21.00	27.00	165.00
1889	100.00	200.00	300.00	1898S	21.00	27.00	
1890	100.00	200.00	250.00	1899	20.00	25.00	140.00
1890CC	27.50	50.00		1899S	20.00	25.00	
1891	25.00	35.00	150.00	1900	20.00	25.00	140.00
1891CC	20.00	35.00		1900S	20.00	25.00	
1892	22.00	32.00	150.00	1901	20.00	25.00	140.00
1892O	50.00	100.00		1901S	20.00	25.00	
1892S	22.00	30.00		1902	22.00	32.00	140.00
1892CC	23.00	40.00		1902S	20.00	27.00	
1893	21.00	27.00	165.00	1903	21.00	30.00	140.00
1893O	26.00	40.00		1903S	20.00	27.00	
1893S	21.00	30.00		1904	23.00	28.00	140.00
1893CC	30.00	42.00		1904S	40.00	60.00	
1894	21.00	27.00	200.00	1905	20.00	25.00	140.00
1894O	35.00	65.00		1905S	20.00	25.00	
1894S	23.00	35.00		1906	20.00	25.00	150.00
1895	21.00	27.00	150.00	1906S	20.00	25.00	
1895S	23.00	30.00		1906D	20.00	25.00	
1896	23.00	38.00	150.00	1907	20.00	25.00	150.00
1896S	22.00	32.00		1907D	20.00	25.00	
1897	21.00	27.00	150.00	1908	20.00	25.00	140.00
1897S	21.00	27.00					

Indian Head Type

This type conforms to the quarter eagle of the same date. The incuse designs and lettering make this a unique series, along with the quarter eagle, in our United States coinage.

The scarcer mintmarks, when well struck command higher prices.

	Very Fine	Unc.	Matte Proof		Very Fine	Unc.	Matte Proof
1908	$ 20.00	25.00	140.00	1911D	$ 75.00	150.00	
1908S	60.00	150.00		1912	20.00	24.00	135.00
1908D	21.00	30.00		1912S	22.00	38.00	
1909	21.00	30.00	160.00	1913	20.00	24.00	160.00
*1909O	190.00	275.00		1913S	23.00	40.00	
1909S	24.00	45.00		1914	21.00	27.00	150.00
1909D	18.00	22.50		1914S	24.00	40.00	
1910	19.00	24.00	125.00	1914D	22.00	32.00	
1910S	22.00	35.00		1915	21.00	24.00	175.00
1910D	21.00	32.00		1915S	23.00	45.00	
1911	21.00	25.00	140.00	1916S	22.00	43.00	
1911S	23.00	35.00		1929	260.00	400.00	

*Beware spurious "O" mintmark.

[153]

EAGLES ($10.00 Gold Pieces)

Coinage authority including specified weights and fineness of the eagle conform to that of the half-eagle. The small eagle reverse was used until 1797 when the large, heraldic eagle replaced it. The early dates have variations in the number of stars, the rarest date being 1798. No eagles were struck from 1805 to 1837. Proofs prior to 1855 are known to exist of some dates, and all are rare.

Small Eagle

	Very Fine	Fine	Unc.		Very Fine	Fine	Unc.
1795	$400.00	525.00	850.00	1797 Small eagle	$325.00	475.00	900.00
1796	350.00	500.00	750.00				

Large Eagle

	Fine	V. Fine	Unc.
1797 Large eagle	$260.00	350.00	475.00
1798 over 97, 9 stars left, 4 right	600.00	800.00	1,000.00

[154]

EAGLES

	Fine	V. Fine	Unc.
1798 over 97, 7 stars left, 6 right (Rare)	$1,500.00	2,000.00	3,500.00

	Fine	Very Fine	Unc.		Fine	Very Fine	Unc.
1799	$210.00	290.00	450.00	1803	$200.00	300.00	450.00
1800	200.00	275.00	425.00	1804	250.00	350.00	600.00
1801	200.00	275.00	425.00				

Reduced Size

In 1838 the weight and diameter of the eagle were reduced and the obverse and reverse were redesigned. Liberty now faces left and the word LIBERTY is placed on the coronet. A more natural appearing eagle is used on the reverse. The value, TEN D., is shown for the first time on this denomination.

1838	150.00	200.00	290.00	1839 Small letters	95.00	150.00	275.00
1839 Large letters	90.00	140.00	260.00				

EAGLES

	V. Fine	Unc.	Proof		V. Fine	Unc.	Proof
1840	$50.00	100.00		1855	$30.00	65.00	1,400.00
1841	40.00	80.00		1855O	40.00	85.00	
1841O	125.00	250.00		1855S	75.00	150.00	
1842 Small date	40.00	80.00		1856	30.00	85.00	900.00
1842 Large date	40.00	80.00		1856O	42.50	100.00	
1842O	42.50	90.00		1856S	30.00	65.00	
1843	35.00	60.00		1857	35.00	85.00	900.00
1843O	37.50	60.00		1857O	100.00	200.00	
1844	75.00	150.00		1857S	40.00	75.00	
1844O	35.00	65.00		*1858	2,500.00	4,500.00	—
1845	40.00	95.00		1858O	40.00	75.00	
1845O	35.00	70.00		1858S	47.50	90.00	
1846	40.00	80.00		1859	37.50	85.00	700.00
1846O	35.00	65.00		1859O	125.00	250.00	
1847	30.00	60.00		1859S	60.00	120.00	
1847O	30.00	60.00		1860	45.00	90.00	600.00
1848	30.00	60.00		1860O	45.00	90.00	
1848O	35.00	70.00		1860S	75.00	150.00	
1849	30.00	60.00		1861	27.50	60.00	450.00
1849O	32.00	75.00		1861S	50.00	100.00	
1850	30.00	60.00		1862	55.00	100.00	450.00
1850O	32.00	70.00		1862S	52.50	105.00	
1851	30.00	60.00		1863	125.00	250.00	550.00
1851O	32.50	60.00		1863S	55.00	90.00	
1852	30.00	60.00		1864	85.00	175.00	475.00
1852O	40.00	85.00		1864S	100.00	300.00	
1853	30.00	60.00		1865	75.00	150.00	475.00
1853O	32.50	70.00		1865S	45.00	90.00	
1854	30.00	70.00		1865S over inv. 186			
1854O	32.50	70.00		1866S	60.00	125.00	
1854S	32.50	70.00		*Beware — removed mintmark.			

MOTTO ABOVE EAGLE

1866		80.00	150.00	425.00	1871S	40.00	90.00	
1866S		50.00	100.00		1871CC	60.00	120.00	
1867		90.00	135.00	375.00	1872	110.00	185.00	425.00
1867S		55.00	110.00		1872S	45.00	90.00	
1868		50.00	100.00	450.00	1872CC	80.00	160.00	
1868S		45.00	90.00		1873	150.00	300.00	600.00
1869		115.00	185.00	450.00	1873S	45.00	90.00	
1869S		52.50	100.00		1873CC	85.00	170.00	
1870		90.00	165.00	350.00	1874	35.00	70.00	575.00
1870S		50.00	100.00		1874S	50.00	100.00	
1870CC		75.00	150.00		1874CC	50.00	100.00	
1871		110.00	185.00	375.00				

EAGLES

	V. Fine	Unc.	Proof		V. Fine	Unc.	Proof
1875	$350.00	700.00	1,100.00	1891	$25.00	42.50	275.00
1875CC	60.00	120.00		1891CC	28.50	50.00	
1876	175.00	350.00	550.00	1892	25.00	35.00	250.00
1876S	50.00	100.00		1892O	40.00	65.00	
1876CC	80.00	160.00		1892S	30.00	45.00	
1877	150.00	300.00	700.00	1892CC	40.00	70.00	
1877S	32.50	75.00		1893	25.00	35.00	275.00
1877CC	90.00	175.00		1893O	45.00	75.00	
1878	26.00	60.00	700.00	1893S	30.00	45.00	
1878S	27.00	50.00		1893CC	50.00	100.00	
1878CC	90.00	175.00		1894	25.00	35.00	300.00
1879	25.00	47.50	400.00	1894O	30.00	55.00	
1879O	250.00	400.00		1894S	45.00	90.00	
1879S	25.00	40.00		1895	25.00	35.00	275.00
1879CC	135.00	250.00		1895O	30.00	55.00	
1880	25.00	40.00	350.00	1895S	35.00	55.00	
1880O	45.00	90.00		1896	25.00	40.00	225.00
1880S	25.00	35.00		1896S	25.00	40.00	
1880CC	42.50	90.00		1897	25.00	35.00	250.00
1881	25.00	35.00	300.00	1897O	35.00	55.00	
1881O	50.00	100.00		1897S	25.00	36.00	
1881S	25.00	35.00		1898	25.00	40.00	265.00
1881CC	37.50	80.00		1898S	25.00	35.00	
1882	25.00	35.00	300.00	1899	25.00	35.00	240.00
1882O	37.50	75.00		1899O	40.00	70.00	
1882S	25.00	40.00		1899S	25.00	35.00	
1882CC	60.00	100.00		1900	25.00	35.00	225.00
1883	25.00	35.00	300.00	1900S	30.00	45.00	
1883O	475.00	750.00		1901	25.00	35.00	250.00
1883S	25.00	50.00		1901O	30.00	55.00	
1883CC	45.00	80.00		1901S	25.00	35.00	
1884	25.00	45.00	300.00	1902	30.00	45.00	225.00
1884S	25.00	40.00		1902S	25.00	35.00	
1884CC	50.00	90.00		1903	25.00	37.50	235.00
1885	25.00	36.00	275.00	1903O	25.00	45.00	
1885S	25.00	38.00		1903S	25.00	35.00	
1886	25.00	36.00	275.00	1904	30.00	40.00	225.00
1886S	25.00	36.00		1904O	25.00	55.00	
1887	30.00	55.00	240.00	1905	25.00	35.00	250.00
1887S	25.00	36.00		1905S	25.00	35.00	
1888	25.00	36.00	250.00	1906	25.00	40.00	250.00
1888O	40.00	70.00		1906D	25.00	35.00	
1888S	25.00	35.00		1906O	30.00	42.50	
1889	75.00	150.00	300.00	1906S	25.00	35.00	
1889S	25.00	40.00		1907	25.00	35.00	275.00
1890	30.00	55.00	250.00	1907D	25.00	35.00	
1890CC	40.00	70.00		1907S	25.00	37.50	

INDIAN HEAD TYPE

Augustus Saint-Gaudens, considered by many the greatest of modern sculptors, introduced a new high standard of art in United States coins evidenced by his eagle and double-eagle types of 1907. The obverse of the eagle shows the

EAGLES

head of Liberty crowned with an Indian War bonnet while an impressively majestic eagle dominates the reverse side. A departure from older standards is found on the edge of the piece where 46 raised stars are arranged signifying the states of the Union, instead of a lettered or reeded edge. (48 stars 1912 and later.)

The first eagles struck had no motto IN GOD WE TRUST as did the later issues starting in 1908. President Theodore Roosevelt personally objected to the use of the Deity's name on coins. The motto was restored to the coins by Act of Congress in 1908.

| | 1907 | | No Motto | | 1908 | | With Motto | |

	V. Fine	Unc.	Proof		V. Fine	Unc.	Matte Proof
1907 Wire edge (rim) Periods before and after legends		$475.00	900.00	1910D	$29.00	35.00	
				1910S	32.00	40.00	
				1911	29.00	35.00	275.00
1907 Same, no stars on edge (unique)..		—		1911D	55.00	90.00	
				1911S	50.00	75.00	
1907 Rolled edge, Periods		850.00		1912	29.00	35.00	235.00
				1912S	31.00	45.00	
1907 No periods	32.50	55.00		1913	29.00	35.00	240.00
1908 No Motto	32.50	55.00		1913S	60.00	75.00	
1908D No Motto	30.00	55.00		1914	30.00	37.50	290.00
With Motto IN GOD WE TRUST				1914D	30.00	37.50	
	Very Fine	Unc.	Matte Proof	1914S	30.00	40.00	
				1915	30.00	37.50	240.00
1908	29.00	42.50	240.00	1915S	75.00	90.00	
1908D	30.00	55.00		1916S	45.00	65.00	
1908S	42.50	75.00		1920S	400.00	1,000.00	
1909	27.00	40.00	275.00	1926	30.00	35.00	
1909D	31.00	50.00		1930S	675.00	1,350.00	
1909S	28.00	42.50		1932	30.00	35.00	
1910	26.00	37.50	190.00	1933	600.00	1,250.00	

DOUBLE EAGLES ($20.00 Gold Pieces)
1849-1933

This largest of all regular United States issues, was authorized to be coined by the Act of March 3, 1849. Its weight was 516 grains, 900 fine. The 1849 double-eagle is a unique pattern and reposes in the Mint collection. The rarest date obtainable is 1883. The 1861S reverse designed by Paquet was withdrawn soon after striking. Very few specimens are known.

DOUBLE EAGLES

1861S Paquet Reverse

	V. Fine	Unc.	Proof
1849 Unique — U.S. Mint Collection			
1850	$ 80.00	250.00	
1850O	110.00	200.00	
1851	65.00	125.00	
1851O	100.00	185.00	
1852	60.00	125.00	
1852O	100.00	185.00	
1853	65.00	125.00	
1853O	125.00	250.00	
1854	65.00	125.00	
1854O	300.00	600.00	
1854S	100.00	200.00	
1855	65.00	125.00	
1855O	150.00	300.00	
1855S	75.00	135.00	
1856	75.00	120.00	
1856O	450.00	700.00	
1856S	70.00	110.00	
1857	70.00	120.00	
1857O	140.00	235.00	
1857S	70.00	110.00	
1858	80.00	130.00	1,100.00
1858O	130.00	220.00	
1858S	$ 70.00	120.00	
1859	125.00	240.00	1,000.00
1859O	170.00	260.00	
1859S	75.00	125.00	
1860	65.00	110.00	1,000.00
1860O	190.00	375.00	
1860S	70.00	110.00	
1861	70.00	110.00	950.00
1861O	175.00	325.00	
1861S	70.00	120.00	
1861—A.C. Paquet Rev. (Ex. Rare)			
1861S—A.C. Paquet Rev. (Tall Letters)			(Ex. Rare)
1862	80.00	140.00	950.00
1862S	75.00	125.00	
1863	80.00	120.00	950.00
1863S	70.00	110.00	
1864	85.00	135.00	950.00
1864S	80.00	125.00	
1865	85.00	135.00	1,050.00
1865S	80.00	115.00	
1866S	300.00	650.00	

MOTTO ABOVE EAGLE

| 1866 | 75.00 | 120.00 | 1,050.00 | 1867 | 75.00 | 115.00 | 925.00 |
| 1866S | 75.00 | 110.00 | | 1867S | 75.00 | 110.00 | |

[159]

DOUBLE EAGLES

	V. Fine	Unc.	Proof		V. Fine	Unc.	Proof
1868	$ 80.00	135.00	1,000.00	1873 (Closed 3)	$100.00	500.00	1,300.00
1868S	60.00	95.00		1873 (Open 3)	55.00	80.00	
1869	70.00	140.00	1,000.00	1873S	55.00	80.00	
1869S	60.00	95.00		1873CC (Closed 3)	125.00	220.00	
1870	80.00	130.00	1,000.00	1874	60.00	85.00	1,150.00
1870S	55.00	95.00		1874S	60.00	85.00	
1870CC	1,250.00	—		1874CC	75.00	120.00	
1871	80.00	140.00	975.00	1875	60.00	100.00	1,150.00
1871S	55.00	95.00		1875S	55.00	87.50	
1871CC	150.00	275.00		1875CC	70.00	125.00	
1872	70.00	105.00	985.00	1876	55.00	85.00	800.00
1872S	60.00	100.00		1876S	55.00	90.00	
1872CC	130.00	240.00		1876CC	70.00	115.00	

TWENTY DOLLARS

	V. Fine	Unc.	Proof		V. Fine	Unc.	Proof
1877	50.00	85.00	1,150.00	1885	165.00	310.00	1,300.00
1877S	50.00	80.00		1885S	50.00	77.50	
1877CC	70.00	130.00		1885CC	105.00	205.00	
1878	50.00	80.00	1,150.00	1886	160.00	300.00	1,100.00
1878S	50.00	80.00		1887 Proofs Only.			1,750.00
1878CC	90.00	175.00		1887S	50.00	85.00	
1879	50.00	85.00	900.00	1888	50.00	80.00	1,200.00
1879O	170.00	375.00		1888S	45.00	75.00	
1879S	50.00	80.00		1889	70.00	115.00	900.00
1879CC	105.00	210.00		1889S	45.00	75.00	
1880	65.00	115.00	850.00	1889CC	80.00	140.00	
1880S	50.00	80.00		1890	60.00	110.00	1,100.00
1881	160.00	310.00	850.00	1890S	45.00	80.00	
1881S	50.00	80.00		1890CC	70.00	120.00	
1882	255.00	425.00	950.00	1891	125.00	210.00	900.00
1882S	50.00	80.00		1891S	45.00	77.50	
1882CC	75.00	135.00		1891CC	120.00	240.00	
1883 Proofs Only.			2,500.00	1892	80.00	135.00	1,250.00
1883S	50.00	80.00		1892S	45.00	75.00	
1883CC	67.50	125.00		1892CC	95.00	150.00	
1884 Proofs Only.			2,500.00	1893	65.00	95.00	1,000.00
1884S	50.00	80.00		1893S	47.50	75.00	
1884CC	65.00	130.00		1893CC	97.50	165.00	

DOUBLE EAGLES

	V. Fine	Unc.	Proof		V. Fine	Unc.	Proof
1894	$ 47.50	67.50	1,350.00	1901S	$ 53.00	70.00	
1894S	47.50	67.50		1902	85.00	155.00	750.00
1895	53.00	75.00	1,000.00	1902S	53.00	70.00	
1895S	52.00	70.00		1903	60.00	85.00	950.00
1896	52.00	70.00	1,000.00	1903S	50.00	67.50	
1896S	52.00	70.00		1904	45.00	65.00	950.00
1897	53.00	70.00	1,000.00	1904S	45.00	65.00	
1897S	52.00	70.00		1905	67.00	110.00	950.00
1898	55.00	85.00	1,000.00	1905S	50.00	70.00	
1898S	53.00	70.00		1906	67.00	100.00	950.00
1899	53.00	70.00	1,250.00	1906D	53.00	75.00	
1899S	53.00	70.00		1906S	53.00	70.00	
1900	53.00	70.00	925.00	1907	53.00	70.00	950.00
1900S	52.00	70.00		1907D	53.00	70.00	
1901	60.00	95.00	800.00	1907S	53.00	70.00	

SAINT-GAUDENS TYPE

Few deny that this beautifully designed coin by the noted sculptor Saint-Gaudens marks the farthest advance in artistic effect produced on any United States coin.

It is significant that this coin was struck from the first dies to be completely engraved by the Janvier engraving machine.

The first few specimens known as the "high relief" variety were trial pieces and not a regular issue. Each coin was struck ten times on a medal press and annealed between each impression. Several minor differences in design distinguish the first from the succeeding issues.

The obverse on the first issues, both high and low relief, have the date in Roman numerals, and without the motto IN GOD WE TRUST. Later in the first year of issue, 1907, the date was changed to the Arabic style of numeral. The motto was added in 1908, by Act of Congress. There were two distinct types of edges, the wire edge and the modified or flat edge, in the Roman Numeral issues of 1907.

There are 46 stars on the obverse from 1907 to 1911. This was changed to 48 stars on the coins from 1912 to 1933 in recognition of the addition of Arizona and New Mexico to the Union in 1912.

1907 Ex. High Relief plain edge (Unique).......................
1907 Ex. High Relief Lettered Edge —
    Kreisberg-Schulman Sale, 1961............................$18,250.00

	V. Fine	Unc.	Proof
1907 Date Roman Num. (MCMVII) Wire Edge...	$300.00	400.00	1,600.00
1907 Same, Flat Edge.........................	300.00	385.00	1,600.00

DOUBLE EAGLES

Arabic Numerals

No Motto

	V. Fine	Unc.
1907 Large Letters on Edge (Proof only) Unique		
1907 Small Letters on Edge	$72.50	95.00
1908	55.00	70.00
1908D	55.00	75.00

With Motto
IN GOD WE TRUST
←

	V. Fine	Unc.	Matte Proof
1908	$ 50.00	75.00	950.00
1908D	52.00	75.00	
1908S	100.00	175.00	
1909 over 8	90.00	120.00	
1909	70.00	100.00	1,000.00
1909D	75.00	125.00	
1909S	53.00	67.50	
1910	50.00	60.00	900.00
1910D	65.00	80.00	
1910S	53.00	70.00	
1911	53.00	70.00	950.00
1911D	53.00	70.00	
1911S	53.00	72.00	
1912	60.00	90.00	1,000.00
1913	53.00	65.00	1,000.00
1913D	65.00	85.00	
1913S	90.00	175.00	
1914	65.00	80.00	1,050.00
1914D	60.00	75.00	
1914S	60.00	75.00	
1915	60.00	70.00	1,100.00
1915S	60.00	75.00	
1916S	90.00	120.00	
1920	52.00	67.50	

	V. Fine	Unc.
1920S	$175.00	375.00
1921	400.00	750.00
1922	55.00	75.00
1922S	135.00	250.00
1923	55.00	75.00
1923D	53.00	65.00
1924	53.00	60.00
1924D	100.00	150.00
1924S	250.00	360.00
1925	53.00	75.00
1925D	225.00	500.00
1925S	135.00	200.00
1926	58.00	75.00
1926D	550.00	950.00
1926S	200.00	400.00
1927	55.00	65.00
1927D	550.00	950.00
1927S	250.00	490.00
1928	55.00	65.00
1929	275.00	650.00
1930S	450.00	950.00
1931	450.00	750.00
1931D	500.00	950.00
1932	375.00	650.00
1933 None in circulation.		

[162]

COMMEMORATIVE COINS

Commemorative coins have been popular since the days of the Greeks and Romans. In the beginning they served to record and honor important events and in the absence of newspapers they proved highly useful in passing along news of the day.

Many modern nations have issued commemorative coins and such pieces are highly esteemed by collectors. Yet no nation has surpassed our own country when it comes to commemorative coins and in this we have reason to be proud.

The unique position occupied by commemoratives in United States coinage is largely due to the fact that with few exceptions they are the only coins that have a real historical significance. The progress and advance of people in the New World are presented in an interesting and instructive manner on the commemorative issues. Such a record of facts artistically presented on our gold and silver memorial issues, appeals strongly to the collector who favors the historical side of numismatics. It is the historical features of the commemoratives, in fact, which create interest among many people who would otherwise have little interest in coins.

Commemorative issues are considered for coinage by two committees of Congress—The Committee on Banking and Currency of the Senate, and the Committee on Coinage, Weights and Measures of the House. Congress is guided to a great extent by the reports of these committees when passing upon bills authorizing commemorative coins.

These special coins are usually issued either to commemorate events or to help pay for monuments or celebrations that commemorate historical persons, places or things. The commemorative coins are offered in most instances by a commission in charge of the event to be commemorated, and sold at a price in advance of the face value of the piece.

During a half century over fifty different types of commemorative coins have been issued in the United States. A complete set of commemorative half dollars comprises forty-eight types, and with the addition of mint mark varieties a total of 142 coins to the series.

No commemorative coins were struck from 1940 to 1945, and none since 1954.

The coinage figures given represent the total outstanding coinage. In many cases, larger quantities were minted but were not all sold. The unsold coins were usually returned to the mint and melted, although some were placed in circulation at face value.

SILVER COMMEMORATIVE COINS

COLUMBIAN EXPOSITION HALF DOLLAR

The first United States commemorative coin was the Columbian half dollar. C. E. Barber designed the obverse showing the bust of Columbus; and G. T. Morgan designed the reverse having a representation of Columbus' flagship the Santa Maria above two hemispheres. The coins were sold for $1.00 each at the World's Columbian Exposition in Chicago during 1893. A great many remained unsold and a substantial quantity was later released for circulation at face value.

			Ex. Fine	Unc.
1892	Columbian Exposition, Chicago	950,000	$2.00	4.50
1893	Same type	1,550,405	1.50	3.50

ISABELLA QUARTER DOLLAR

In 1893 the Board of Lady Managers of the Columbian Exposition petitioned for a souvenir quarter-dollar. Authority was granted March 3, 1893. The coin known as the Isabella quarter was designed by C. E. Barber. These souvenir quarters were sold for $1.00. The obverse has the crowned bust of Queen Isabella of Spain. The kneeling female on the reverse with distaff and spindle is emblematic of woman's industry.

1893	Columbian Exposition, Chicago	24,214	$27.50	42.50

LAFAYETTE DOLLAR

The heads of Washington and Lafayette appear on this commemorative issue, which was the first commemorative coin of one dollar denomination, and the first authorized United States coin to bear a portrait of one of our presidents. The dies were prepared by C. E. Barber. The statue on the reverse is similar to the monument of General Lafayette which was erected in Paris as a gift of the American people. The coins were sold by the Lafayette Memorial Commission for $2.00 each.

SILVER COMMEMORATIVE COINS

			Ex. Fine	Unc.
1900	Lafayette Dollar	36,000	$35.00	57.50

PANAMA-PACIFIC EXPOSITION

This half dollar was designed by C. E. Barber. The exposition held in San Francisco in 1915 celebrated the opening of the Panama Canal. The coins were struck at the San Francisco Mint and were sold at $1.00 each during the exposition. The Panama-Pacific coins have the distinction of being the first commemorative coins to carry the mottoes. IN GOD WE TRUST appears above the eagle. A representation of Columbia with the golden gate in the background is the principal feature of the obverse.

1915S	Panama-Pacific Exposition	27,134	$37.50	56.00

ILLINOIS CENTENNIAL

The obverse was designed by G. T. Morgan and the reverse by J. R. Sinnock. The obverse shows the head of Lincoln taken from the statue by Andrew O'Connor in Springfield, Illinois. The reverse is based on the Illinois State Seal. This coin was authorized to commemorate the one hundredth anniversary of the admission of Illinois into the Union, the first souvenir piece for such an event.

1918	Illinois Centennial	100,058	$7.00	13.50

COMMEMORATIVE HALF DOLLARS

MAINE CENTENNIAL

Congress authorized the Maine Centennial half dollar May 10, 1920, to be sold at the Centennial celebration at Portland. They were received too late for this event and were sold by the state Treasurer until all were sold. Anthony de Francisci modeled this coin according to specifications furnished him. The latin word DIRIGO means: I direct. The obverse device is the arms of the state of Maine.

			Ex. Fine	Unc.
1920	Maine Centennial	50,028	$7.50	15.00

PILGRIM TERCENTENARY

To commemorate the landing of the Pilgrims at Plymouth, Massachusetts in 1620, Congress authorized a special half dollar May 12, 1920. Cyrus E. Dallin, a Boston sculptor, executed the designs furnished him by the Commission. The obverse has a portrait of Governor Bradford. The reverse shows the "Mayflower." The first issue had no date on the obverse. The coins struck in 1921 show that date in addition to 1620-1920. There was a large coinage of both issues and not all were sold. A total of 148,000 were returned to the mint and melted.

1920	Pilgrim Tercentenary	152,112	$3.00	6.00

1921	Same type	20,053	$6.00	12.00

COMMEMORATIVE HALF DOLLARS

MISSOURI CENTENNIAL

The one hundredth anniversary of the admission of Missouri to the Union was celebrated at Sedalia during August, 1921. To mark the occasion Congress authorized the coinage of a fifty-cent piece. Robert Aitken designed the piece which shows the bust of a frontiersman on the obverse, and another frontiersman and Indian on the reverse. The first coins struck show 2★4 incused, indicating that Missouri was the twenty-fourth star in the flag. The type without the star was struck later, but was the first to be sold.

			Ex. Fine	Unc.
1921	Missouri Centennial 2★4 in field of obverse	5,000	$57.50	90.00
1921	Missouri Centennial, no 2★4..............	15,428	55.00	82.50

ALABAMA CENTENNIAL

The Alabama half dollars were authorized in 1920 for the centennial which was celebrated in 1919, but they were not struck until 1921. The coins, designed by Laura Gardin Fraser, were offered first during President Harding's visit to Birmingham, October 26, 1921. The St. Andrews cross, an emblem on the state flag, appears on a part of the issue between the figures 22 indicating the twenty-second state of the Union. The obverse has busts of W. W. Bibb, first governor of Alabama, and T. E. Kilby, governor at the time of the centennial. This is the first instance of the use of a living person's portrait on a United States coin.

1921	Alabama Centennial, with 2 x 2 in field of obverse........................	6,006	$27.50	49.00
1921	Alabama Centennial, no 2 x 2..........	59,038	25.00	47.50

[167]

COMMEMORATIVE HALF DOLLARS
GRANT MEMORIAL

This coin was struck during 1922 as a centenary souvenir of Ulysses S. Grant's birth. A star which appeared on the first issues was later removed to create a second variety. The star has no particular significance. Laura Gardin Fraser designed both the Grant half dollar and gold dollar. The reverse shows a log cabin in Point Pleasant, Ohio, where Grant lived as a boy.

			Ex. Fine	Unc.
(Fake stars have flattened spot on reverse.)				
1922	Grant Memorial. Star in obverse field...	4,256	$80.00	125.00
1922	Same, no star.....................	67,405	7.50	13.50

MONROE DOCTRINE CENTENNIAL

The motion picture industry promoted this issue in conjunction with a motion picture exposition in June 1923. The obverse shows the heads of James Monroe and John Quincy Adams who were identified with the Monroe Doctrine. The Western Hemisphere is portrayed on the reverse by two female figures. Chester Beach prepared the models for this coin.

| 1923S | Monroe Doctrine Centennial........... | 274,077 | $6.00 | 11.50 |

HUGUENOT-WALLOON TERCENTENARY

Settling of the Huguenots and Walloons in the New World was the occasion commemorated by this issue. New Netherlands now New York was founded in 1624 by a group of Dutch colonists. The persons represented on the obverse were not directly concerned with the occasion, however. They are Admiral Coligny and William the Silent. The reverse shows the vessel "Nieu Nederland." G. T. Morgan prepared the models for this coin.

| 1924 | Huguenot-Walloon Tercentenary....... | 142,080 | $7.50 | 12.50 |

[168]

COMMEMORATIVE HALF DOLLARS

LEXINGTON-CONCORD SESQUICENTENNIAL

The two famous battles fought in 1775 are commemorated on this coin. A statue of the familiar Minute Man is depicted on the obverse, and the old Belfry at Lexington is the reverse device. Chester Beach designed the coin. The famous statue by Daniel Chester French located in Concord was used for the design.

			Ex. Fine	Unc.
1925	Lexington-Concord Sesquicentennial....	162,013	$4.50	8.00

STONE MOUNTAIN MEMORIAL

The models for this coin were prepared by Gutzon Borglum. The first coins were struck at Philadelphia January 21, 1925, General Thomas "Stonewall" Jackson's birthday. General Robert E. Lee and Jackson, mounted, are shown on the obverse. The reverse has an eagle and the words MEMORIAL TO THE VALOR OF THE SOLDIER OF THE SOUTH. The funds received from the sale of this large issue of half dollars were devoted to the expense of carving figures of Confederate leaders and soldiers on Stone Mountain in Georgia. The work was never completed.

1925   Stone Mountain Memorial............1,314,709 $3.00   5.50

CALIFORNIA DIAMOND JUBILEE

The California half dollar was designed by Jo Mora, a noted California sculptor. The obverse bears a kneeling figure of a forty-niner. The reverse shows a walking grizzly bear, the state emblem. The celebration for which these coins were struck marked the seventy-fifth anniversary of the admission of California into the Union. The jubilee was held in 1925.

1925S   California Diamond Jubilee............ 86,594 $7.50   13.50

[169]

COMMEMORATIVE HALF DOLLARS

FORT VANCOUVER CENTENNIAL

Dr. John McLaughlin, shown on the obverse of this coin, built Fort Vancouver, on the Columbia River in 1825. The sale of the coins at $1.00 each helped to finance the pageant staged for the celebration. Laura Gardin Fraser prepared the models for this coin, which was minted in San Francisco. The S Mint mark was omitted. The reverse has a pioneer settler in buckskin suit with a musket in his hands. Fort Vancouver is in the background.

			Ex. Fine	Unc.
1925	Fort Vancouver Centennial	14,994	$40.00	75.00

SESQUICENTENNIAL OF AMERICAN INDEPENDENCE

The one hundred and fiftieth anniversary of the signing of the Declaration of Independence was the occasion for an International Fair held in Philadelphia in 1926. To help raise funds for financing the fair special issues of half dollars and quarter-eagles were authorized by Congress. For the first time a portrait of a president appeared on a coin struck during his lifetime. President Coolidge and Washington are depicted on the obverse of the half-dollar. The reverse bears an accurate model of the Liberty Bell. John R. Sinnock, Chief Engraver of the United States mint, designed the sesquicentennial coins. The dies were in very low relief causing much loss of detail in the coin.

1926	Sesquicentennial of American Independence	141,120	$6.50	11.50

OREGON TRAIL MEMORIAL

This memorial coin was struck in commemoration of the Oregon trail and in memory of the pioneers many of whom lie buried along the famous 2,000 mile highway of history. James Earle Fraser and his wife,

COMMEMORATIVE HALF DOLLARS

Laura Gardin Fraser, prepared the designs. The original issue was struck at Philadelphia and San Francisco in 1926. The coin was reissued in 1928 (released in 1933), 1933, 1934, 1936, and 1938. The 1933 half dollar was the first commemorative coin struck at the Denver Mint.

			Ex. Fine	Unc.
1926	Oregon Trail Memorial	48,030	$ 2.50	6.50
1926S	Same type, S mint	86,354	2.00	6.25
1928	Oregon Trail Memorial (same as 1926)	6,028		10.00
1933D	Oregon Trail Memorial, same type, D mint	5,008		12.50
1934D	Oregon Trail Memorial, same type, D mint	7,006		8.00
1936	Oregon Trail Memorial, (same as 1926)	10,006		6.50
1936S	Same type S mint	5,006		12.50
1937D	Oregon Trail Memorial, D mint (same as 1926)	12,008		6.50
1938	Oregon Trail Memorial (same as 1926)	6,006		
1938D	Same type D mint	6,005	Set	22.50
1938S	Same type S mint	6,006		
1939	Oregon Trail (same as 1926)	3,004		
1939D	Same type D mint	3,004	Set	80.00
1939S	Same type S mint	3,005		

VERMONT SESQUICENTENNIAL

This souvenir issue commemorates the 150th Anniversary of the Battle of Bennington and the Independence of Vermont. Authorized in 1925 it was not coined until 1927. The models were prepared by Charles Keck. The obverse shows the head of Ira Allen, founder of Vermont. The reverse bears a catamount on a pedestal.

1927   Vermont Sesquicentennial (Bennington) 28,142 $19.00   30.00

HAWAIIAN SESQUICENTENNIAL

This small issue was struck to commemorate the 150th anniversary of the rediscovery of the Hawaiian Islands by Captain James Cook in 1778. The design was sketched by Juliette May Fraser of Honolulu and executed by Chester Beach. Captain Cook is shown on the obverse and a native chief on the reverse. The coins were distributed in 1928 and sold for $2.00 each, the highest initial sale price up to that time.

1928	Hawaiian Sesquicentennial	10,008	$150.00	240.00
1928	Hawaiian Sesquicentennial — Sandblast Proof Presentation Piece—50 struck			500.00

[171]

COMMEMORATIVE HALF DOLLARS

MARYLAND TERCENTENARY

The three hundredth anniversary of the founding of the Maryland Colony by Cecil Calvert known as Lord Baltimore was the occasion for this special coin. The profits from the sale of this issue were used to finance the celebration in Baltimore during 1934. Hans Schuler designed the coin which shows the facing head of Lord Baltimore on the obverse and the arms of Maryland on the reverse, reminiscent of the Maryland colonial pieces.

			Ex. Fine	Unc.
1934	Maryland Tercentenary	25,015	$10.00	18.00

TEXAS CENTENNIAL

This issue commemorated the independence of Texas. The first of several dates was offered in 1934. The later dates were struck at all three mints. The models were prepared by Pompeo Coppini. The reverse shows the kneeling figure of winged Victory, and on each side, medallions with portraits of General Sam Houston and Stephen Austin, founders of the Republic and State of Texas. The large five-pointed star behind the eagle on the obverse carries out the "Lone star" tradition.

1934	Texas Centennial	61,350		$ 8.50
1935	Texas Centennial (same as 1934)	9,994		
1935D	Same type D mint	10,007	Set	21.00
1935S	Same type S mint	10,008		
1936	Texas Centennial (same as 1934)	8,911		
1936D	Same type D mint	9,039	Set	21.00
1936S	Same type S mint	9,064		
1937	Texas Centennial (same as 1934)	6,571		
1937D	Same type D mint	6,605	Set	22.50
1937S	Same type S mint	6,637		
1938	Texas Centennial (same as 1934)	3,780		
1938D	Same type D mint	3,775	Set	62.50
1938S	Same type S mint	3,816		

COMMEMORATIVE HALF DOLLARS

DANIEL BOONE BICENTENNIAL

This coin, issues for which covered several dates, was struck to commemorate the two hundredth anniversary of the famous frontiersman's birth. The commemorative date, 1934, was removed after the first issue. The change of date to 1935 for the next year's coinage brought about the addition of 1934 above the words PIONEER YEAR. Coinage covered several years similar to the schedule for the Texas issues. The models for this coin were prepared by Augustus Lukeman. The obverse bears a portrait of Daniel Boone. The reverse shows Boone with Chief Black Fish.

			Unc.
1934	Daniel Boone Bicentennial	10,007	$9.00
1935	Same type	10,010	8.00
1935D	Same type D mint	5,005	11.00
1935S	Same type S mint	5,005	11.00

1935	Daniel Boone Bicentennial same as 1934 but small 1934 added on reverse	10,008	$ 8.00
1935D	Same type D mint	2,003 ⎫ Pair	300.00
1935S	Same type S mint	2,004 ⎭	
1936	Daniel Boone Bicentennial (same as 1934)	12,012	7.50
1936D	Same type D mint	5,005	11.00
1936S	Same type S mint	5,006	11.00
1937	Daniel Boone Bicentennial, same as 1934	9,810	7.50
1937D	Same type D mint	2,506 ⎫ Pair	215.00
1937S	Same type S mint	2,506 ⎭	
1938	Daniel Boone (same as 1934)	2,100 ⎫	
1938D	Same type D mint	2,100 ⎬ Set	340.00
1938S	Same type S mint	2,100 ⎭	

COMMEMORATIVE HALF DOLLARS

CONNECTICUT TERCENTENARY

In commemoration of the three hundredth anniversary of the founding of the Colony of Connecticut a souvenir half dollar was struck. Henry Kreiss designed the coin. The famous "Charter Oak" is the main device on the obverse. According to tradition the Royal Charter was secreted in the tree during the reign of James II who wished to revoke it. The Charter was produced after the king's overthrow in 1688 and the Colony continued under its protection.

			Ex. Fine	Unc.
1935	Connecticut Tercentenary	25,018	$20.00	35.00

ARKANSAS CENTENNIAL

This souvenir issue marked the one hundredth anniversary of the admission of Arkansas into the Union. Edward Everett Burr designed the piece and models were prepared by Emily Bates of Arkansas. Although 1936 was the centennial year the first of several issues was brought out in 1935 from all three mints. During 1936 a new design was authorized by Congress. The late Senator Joseph T. Robinson consented to have his portrait placed on the obverse side of the coins which were struck in January 1937 at the Philadelphia Mint. The 1937 and 1938 issues were the same as those of 1935 except for the dates. They were sold by the distributors at $8.75 per set of three coins. The obverse shows accolated heads of an Indian chief of 1836 and an American girl of 1936.

1935	Arkansas Centennial	13,012	$7.50
1935D	Same type D mint	5,505	9.00
1935S	Same type S mint	5,506	9.00
1936	Arkansas Centennial, same as 1935— date 1936 on rev	9,660	
1936D	Same type D mint	9,660 Set	21.00
1936S	Same type S mint	9,662	
1937	Arkansas Centennial (same as 1935)	5,505	
1937D	Same type D mint	5,505 Set	24.00
1937S	Same type S mint	5,506	

COMMEMORATIVE HALF DOLLARS

			Ex. Fine	Unc.
1938	Arkansas Centennial (same as 1934)	3,156 ⎫		
1938D	Same type D mint	3,155 ⎬ Set		$65.00
1938S	Same type S mint	3,156 ⎭		
1939	Arkansas (same as 1935)	2,104 ⎫		
1939D	Same type D mint	2,104 ⎬ Set		300.00
1939S	Same type S mint	2,105 ⎭		

HUDSON, NEW YORK SESQUICENTENNIAL

This souvenir half dollar marked the one hundred and fiftieth anniversary of the founding of Hudson, New York, which was named after the explorer Hendrick Hudson. The designs by Chester Beach show Hudson's flagship the "Half Moon" on the obverse and the seal of the City of Hudson on the reverse. Details of the seal include representations of Neptune with trident on a spouting whale and a mermaid blowing a conch shell.

| 1935 | Hudson, N. Y. Sesquicentennial | 10,008 | $60.00 | 115.00 |

CALIFORNIA-PACIFIC EXPOSITION

Congress approved the coinage of souvenir half dollars for the exposition May 3, 1935. Robert Aitken designed the coin which was struck at the San Francisco Mint. The same type with date 1936 was struck at the Denver Mint, under authority of the special Recoinage Act of May 6, 1936, which specified that 180,000 pieces could be recoined with the date 1936 irrespective of the year of issue. The obverse displays a seated female with spear and a bear in the left background. The reverse shows the observation tower and the State of California building at the Exposition.

| 1935S | San Diego, California-Pacific Exp. S mint | 70,132 | $5.50 | 9.00 |
| 1936D | San Diego, California-Pacific Expo. D mint same as 1935 | 30,092 | 5.75 | 11.00 |

COMMEMORATIVE HALF DOLLARS

OLD SPANISH TRAIL

This coin commemorated the four hundredth anniversary of the overland trek of the Cabeza de Vaca Expedition through the gulf states in 1535. L. W. Hoffecker designed the coin models which were prepared by Edmund J. Senn. The explorer's name literally translated means "head of a cow," therefore this device was chosen for the obverse. The reverse bears a yucca tree and a map showing the Old Spanish Trail.

			Ex. Fine	Unc.
1935	Old Spanish Trail 1535-1935	10,008	$40.00	75.00

PROVIDENCE RHODE ISLAND TERCENTENARY

The three hundredth anniversary of Roger Williams' founding of Providence was the occasion for this special half dollar in 1935. The designs were the work of Arthur Graham Carey and John Howard Benson. The obverse shows Roger Williams in a canoe being welcomed by an Indian. The reverse has the anchor of Hope with a shield and mantling in the background. Although the founding of Providence was being celebrated, no mention of the city is to be found on the coin.

1936	Rhode Island Tercentenary	20,013		
1936D	Same type D mint	15,010	Set	$30.00
1936S	Same type S mint	15,011		

CLEVELAND GREAT LAKES EXPOSITION

A special coinage of fifty-cent pieces was authorized in commemoration of the centennial celebration of Cleveland, Ohio on the occasion of the Great Lakes Exposition held there in 1936. The designs were prepared by

COMMEMORATIVE HALF DOLLARS

Brenda Putnam. Although half the coinage was struck in 1937 all were dated 1936. The obverse has a bust of Moses Cleaveland and the reverse displays a map of the Great Lakes region with a compass pointed at Cleveland. Nine Great Lakes cities are marked by stars.

			Ex. Fine	Unc.
1936	Cleveland, Great Lakes Exposition	50,030	$3.50	6.50

WISCONSIN TERRITORIAL CENTENNIAL

The one hundredth anniversary of the Wisconsin Territorial government was the occasion for a special half dollar issue. The original design was made by David Parsons, a University of Wisconsin student. Benjamin Hawkins, a New York artist, made changes to conform with technical requirements. The obverse has the Territorial Seal, which includes a forearm holding a pickaxe over a mound of lead ore, and the inscription 4th DAY OF JULY ANNO DOMINI 1836. The reverse shows a badger on a log typifying the early fur trade, and the state emblem.

1936	Wisconsin Centennial	25,015	$ 7.50	16.00

CINCINNATI MUSICAL CENTER

Although the head of Stephen Foster, "America's Troubadour," dominates the obverse of this special issue the anniversary celebrated bears no relation to him. The coins, designed by Constance Ortmayer of Washington, D. C., were struck to commemorate the fiftieth anniversary in 1936 of Cincinnati as a center of music. The coins were struck at the three mints and were sold only in sets at $7.75, the highest initial cost of a new type.

1936	Cincinnati Musical Center	5,005		
1936D	Same type D	5,005	Set	$110.00
1936S	Same type S	5,006		

LONG ISLAND TERCENTENARY

This souvenir issue was authorized to commemorate the three hundredth anniversary of the first white settlement on Long Island which was at Jamaica Bay by Dutch colonists. The design was prepared by

[177]

COMMEMORATIVE HALF DOLLARS

Howard Kenneth Weinman, son of the sculptor A. A. Weinman, who designed the regular Liberty standing type half dollar. Accoladed heads depicting a Dutch settler and an Indian are shown on the obverse, while a Dutch sailing vessel is the reverse device. This was the first issue for which a date was specified (1936) irrespective of the year minted or issued.

			Ex. Fine	Unc.
1936	Long Island Tercentenary	81,773	$4.50	8.50

YORK COUNTY, MAINE TERCENTENARY

A souvenir half dollar was authorized by Congress upon the three hundredth anniversary of the founding of York County, Maine. Brown's Garrison on the Saco River was the site of a town which was settled in 1636. The designs were made by Walter H. Rich of Portland. The reverse design shows a stockade and the obverse has an adaptation of the York County seal. The oversize border inscriptions have been the basis for much adverse criticism.

1936	York County, Maine Centennial	25,015	$6.50	13.50

BRIDGEPORT, CONNECTICUT CENTENNIAL

In commemoration of the one hundredth anniversary of the incorporation of the city of Bridgeport a special fifty-cent piece was authorized May 15, 1936. Henry Kreiss designed this coin which somewhat resembles the Connecticut Tercentenary issue. The head of P. T. Barnum, who was Bridgeport's best known citizen, occupies the obverse. An ultra-modernistic eagle dominates the reverse.

1936	Bridgeport, Conn., Centennial	25,015		$20.00

COMMEMORATIVE HALF DOLLARS

LYNCHBURG, VIRGINIA SESQUICENTENNIAL

The issuance of a charter to the city of Lynchburg in 1786 was commemorated in 1936 by a special coinage of half dollars. The models for the coin were prepared by Charles Keck. The obverse bears a portrait of Senator Carter Glass, a native of Lynchburg and former Secretary of the Treasury, who objected to the idea of using portraits of living men on coins. Despite his protests his likeness was incorporated on the coin. The reverse shows Liberty standing, with the old Lynchburg courthouse in the background.

			Ex. Fine	Unc.
1936	Lynchburg, Va., Sesquicentennial	20,013	$9.00	20.00

ELGIN, ILLINOIS CENTENNIAL

The one hundredth anniversary of the founding of Elgin was marked by a special issue of half dollars in 1936. The proceeds were devoted to financing a Pioneer Memorial statue, which is depicted on the reverse of the coin. The year 1673 bears no relation to the event but refers to the year in which Joliet and Marquette entered Illinois Territory. The designs were prepared by Trygve Rovelstad who also designed the Memorial.

1936	Elgin, Illinois, Centennial	20,015	$10.00	20.00

ALBANY, NEW YORK CHARTER

The two hundred and fiftieth anniversary of the granting of a charter to the city of Albany was the occasion for a commemorative half dollar. The reverse design shows Governor Dongan, Peter Schuyler and Robert Livingston. The obverse has a beaver which is gnawing on a maple branch. Gertrude K. Lathrop of Albany was the designer.

1936	Albany, New York	16,887	$15.00	32.50

[179]

COMMEMORATIVE HALF DOLLARS

SAN FRANCISCO-OAKLAND BAY BRIDGE

The opening of the Oakland Bay Bridge was the occasion for a special souvenir fifty-cent piece. The designs were the work of Jacques Schnier, a San Francisco artist. A California grizzly bear dominates the obverse. The famous bridge is shown on the reverse. The coins were struck at the San Francisco Mint in November 1936. The bear depicted was Monarch II.

		Ex. Fine	Unc.
1936 San Francisco-Oakland Bay Bridge S mint...	71,369	$8.00	12.50

COLUMBIA, SOUTH CAROLINA SESQUICENTENNIAL

Souvenir half dollars were authorized to help finance the extensive celebrations marking the sesquicentennial of the founding of Columbia in 1786. A. Wolfe Davidson designed the coin which was struck at all three mints and sold only in sets. The obverse bears the figure of Justice with sword and scales. At the left is the Capitol of 1786 and at the right the Capitol of 1936. A palmetto tree, the state emblem, is the reverse device.

1936	Columbia, S. C., Sesquicentennial..........	9,007		
1936D	Same type D mint........................	8,009	Set	$62.50
1936S	Same type S mint........................	8,007		

ARKANSAS CENTENNIAL-ROBINSON

A new obverse design for the Arkansas Centennial coin was authorized by the Act of June 26, 1936. Senator Joseph T. Robinson is the subject for the new issue designed by Henry Kreiss. The reverse, designed by Everett Burr, was unchanged. The law specified a change in the reverse, because of the fact that the obverse side is that which bears the date. From a numismatic viewpoint, however, the side which has the portrait is usually considered the obverse. Thus in this instance, the side with the eagle device is considered the reverse.

1936	Arkansas Centennial (Robinson)...........	25,265	$13.50

COMMEMORATIVE HALF DOLLARS

DELAWARE TERCENTENARY

The three hundredth anniversary of the landing of the Swedes in Delaware was the occasion for a souvenir issue of half dollars. The colonists landed on a spot which is now Wilmington and established a church which is the oldest Protestant church still used for worship. Their ship "Kalmar Nyckel" is shown on the reverse of the coin and the old Swedes church is on the obverse. Designs were chosen from a competition which was won by Carl L. Schmitz. This coin was authorized in 1936, struck in 1937 and dated 1938 on the reverse and 1936 on the obverse. The anniversary was celebrated in 1938 both in Sweden and America. A two kroner coin was issued in Sweden to commemorate the same event.

			Ex. Fine	Unc.
1936	Delaware Tercentenary	25,015	$12.00	21.00

BATTLE OF GETTYSBURG

On June 16, 1936 Congress authorized a coinage of fifty-cent pieces in commemoration of the Battle of Gettysburg. The models were prepared by Frank Vittor, a Philadelphia sculptor. Portraits of a Union and a Confederate veteran are shown on the obverse. Two shields representing the Union and Confederate armies separated by a double-bladed fasces are on the reverse.

| 1936 | Battle of Gettysburg 1863-1938 | 26,928 | $27.50 |

NORFOLK, VIRGINIA BICENTENNIAL

To provide funds for the celebration of Norfolk's anniversary of its growth from a township in 1682 to a royal borough in 1736, Congress first passed a law for the striking of medals. The proponents, however, being dissatisfied finally succeeded in winning authority for commemorative half dollars. William Marks Simpson and his wife Marjorie Emory Simpson designed the piece. The obverse shows the Seal of the City of Norfolk with a

[181]

COMMEMORATIVE HALF DOLLARS

three-masted ship as the central device. The reverse features the Royal Mace of Norfolk which had been presented by Lieutenant Governor Dinwiddie in 1753.

			Ex. Fine	Unc.
1936	Norfolk, Va., Bicentennial	15,000	$16.00	35.00

ROANOKE ISLAND, NORTH CAROLINA

A celebration was held in Old Fort Raleigh in 1937 to commemorate the three hundred and fiftieth anniversary of Sir Walter Raleigh's "Lost Colony" and the birth of Virginia Dare, the first white child born on the American Continent. A special half dollar was minted for the occasion which was designed by William Marks Simpson of Baltimore. The obverse bears a portrait of Sir Walter Raleigh and the reverse has a figure representing Eleanor Dare holding the child Virginia Dare.

1937	Roanoke Island, N. C., 1587-1937	29,030	$9.00	15.00

BATTLE OF ANTIETAM

A souvenir half dollar was designed by William Marks and struck in 1937 to commemorate the seventy-fifth anniversary of the famous Civil War battle over possession of Burnside Bridge. The opposing generals McClellan and Lee are featured on the obverse while the Burnside Bridge is shown on the reverse. The Battle of Antietam was one of the bloodiest single-day battles of the war. Approximately 25,000 men were killed during the fighting which occurred September 17, 1862.

1937	Battle of Antietam 1862-1937	18,028	$45.00

NEW ROCHELLE, NEW YORK

To observe the founding of New Rochelle in 1688 by French Huguenots, a special half dollar was issued in 1938. The title to the land which the Huguenots purchased from John Pell provided that a fattened calf be

[182]

COMMEMORATIVE HALF DOLLARS

given away every year on June 20th. This will explain the appearance of the calf and figure representing John Pell on the obverse of the coin. The fleur-de-lis which is shown on the reverse is adopted from the Seal of the city. Both sides of the coin were designed by Gertrude K. Lathrop.

			Ex. Fine	Unc.
1938	New Rochelle, N. Y. 1688-1938	15,266	$18.00	36.00

IOWA CENTENNIAL

This half dollar, commemorating the one hundredth anniversary of Iowa's statehood, was designed by Adam Pietz of Philadelphia. The obverse shows the Iowa state seal and the reverse has the first stone capitol building at Iowa City. This issue was sold first to the residents of Iowa and only a small remainder to others. The entire issue was disposed of in a few weeks.

1946	Iowa Centennial	100,057	$6.00	12.50

BOOKER T. WASHINGTON MEMORIAL

The great Negro educator was memorialized in this half dollar. Issued from all mints, it received wide distribution from the start. The reverse has the legend FROM SLAVE CABIN TO HALL OF FAME. His log cabin birthplace is shown beneath. Designed by Isaac Scott Hathaway, as was the Washington-Carver half dollar issued under the same authority.

1946 Booker T.		Unc.	1949	6,004 ⎫	Unc.
Washington	1,000,546	$2.00	1949D	6,004 ⎬ Set	$22.50
1946D	200,113	2.25	1949S	6,004 ⎭	
1946S	500,279	2.00	1950	6,004 ⎫	
1947	100,017 ⎫		1950D	6,004 ⎬ Set	22.50
1947D	100,017 ⎬ Set	9.50	1950S	512,091 ⎭	
1947S	100,017 ⎭		1951	510,082 ⎫	
1948	8,005 ⎫		1951D	7,004 ⎬ Set	16.00
1948D	8,005 ⎬ Set	13.50	1951S	7,004 ⎭	
1948S	8,005 ⎭				

COMMEMORATIVE HALF DOLLARS
WASHINGTON-CARVER

1951...110,018		Unc.
1951D..10,004	Set	$11.00
1951S..10,004		
1952..2,006,292		
1952D. 8,006	Set	15.00
1952S.. 8,006		
1953... 8,003		
1953D. 8,003	Set	15.00
1953S..108,020		
1954... 12,006		
1954D.. 12,006	Set	10.00
1954S.. 122,024		

GOLD COMMEMORATIVE COINS
LOUISIANA PURCHASE EXPOSITION

The first souvenir gold coins were authorized for the Louisiana Purchase Exposition held in St. Louis in 1904. There are two varieties of gold dollars—one with the head of Jefferson who was president when the Louisiana Territory was purchased from France; and the other President William McKinley who sanctioned the Exposition. The reverse is the same for each variety. The designs were by C. E. Barber.

	Ex. Fine	Unc.
1903 Louisiana Purchase Jefferson Dollar 17,375	$30.00	52.50
1903 Louisiana Purchase McKinley Dollar 17,375	30.00	52.50

LEWIS AND CLARK EXPOSITION

The Lewis and Clark Centennial Exposition was held in Portland, Oregon in 1905. A souvenir issue of gold dollars was struck to mark the event with the dates 1904 and 1905. The two famous explorers are represented on each side of the coin which was designed by C. E. Barber. A bronze memorial of the Indian guide, Sacagawea, who assisted in the famous expedition was erected in Portland, Oregon and financed by the sale of these coins.

1904 Lewis and Clark Exposition Dollar 10,025	125.00	235.00
1905 Lewis and Clark Exposition Dollar 10,041	125.00	235.00

PANAMA-PACIFIC EXPOSITION

Charles Keck designed the gold dollar the obverse of which has the head of a man representing a Panama Canal laborer. Two dolphins encircle ONE DOLLAR on the reverse.

The quarter-eagle was the work of Charles E. Barber and George T. Morgan. It was the first commemorative coin of this denomination. The obverse shows Columbia with a caduceus in her right hand seated on a hippocampus typifying the use of the Panama Canal. An American eagle with raised wings is shown on the reverse.

1915S Panama Pacific Exposition Dollar 25,000	$20.00	36.00

GOLD COMMEMORATIVE COINS

	Ex. Fine	Unc.
1915S Panama Pacific Exposition $2.50	6,750 $115.00	175.00

The fifty-dollar gold piece was designed by Robert Aitken and was issued in round and octagonal form. The obverse bears the helmeted head of Minerva, and the owl, symbol of wisdom, on the reverse. The octagonal issue has eight dolphins in the angles on both sides. The devices are smaller on the octagonal variety.

1915S Panama Pacific $50 Round...............	483	3300.00
1915S Panama Pacific $50 Octagonal............	645	2700.00

GOLD COMMEMORATIVE COINS

McKINLEY MEMORIAL GOLD DOLLARS

The sale of the McKinley dollars aided in paying for a memorial building at Niles, Ohio, the martyred president's birthplace. The obverse showing a profile of McKinley was designed by C. E. Barber and the reverse with the memorial building was designed by G. T. Morgan.

			Ex. Fine	Unc.
1916	McKinley Memorial Dollar	9,977	$21.00	42.50
1917	McKinley Memorial Dollar	10,000	25.00	50.00

GRANT MEMORIAL GOLD DOLLARS

Like the half-dollar commemorative coins the gold dollars were issued first with a star which was removed for the later issues. The designs by Laura Gardin Fraser are the same as for the half-dollar coinage.

1922	Grant Memorial Dollar with star	5,016	85.00	130.00
1922	Grant Memorial Dollar without star	5,000	100.00	165.00

PHILADELPHIA SESQUICENTENNIAL QUARTER EAGLES

The obverse of this special gold issue has a standing female figure symbolic of Liberty, holding in one hand a scroll representing the Declaration of Independence and in the other the Torch of Freedom. The reverse bears a representation of Independence Hall in Philadelphia. The coin was designed by J. R. Sinnock.

1926	Philadelphia Sesquicentennial $2.50	46,019	25.00	36.00

BIBLIOGRAPHY

Bullowa, David M., The Commemorative Coinage of the U. S. 1938.
Mosher, Stuart, U. S. Commemorative Coins (1892-1939), 1940.

PROOF COINS

A "proof" is a specimen striking of coinage for presentation, souvenir, exhibition and/or numismatic purposes. Proofs come only from the Philadelphia Mint.

A proof coin has a glittering, mirror-like, perfect appearance. Regular production coins in mint state have a coruscating, frosty lustre with small detail and lettering larger-spread and not always in full relief.

Matte proofs have a sandblast surface instead of the mirror one. Matte cent, nickel and gold proofs were issued from 1908 to 1916; a few 1921 and 1922 matte silver dollars are known.

"*New-die-proofs*" are the first impressions off regular production dies. They are the best examples from long periods of mintage when there were no specimen proof strikings and of issues from branch mints which never coin regular proofs.

HOW A PROOF COIN IS MADE

Carefully selected metal blanks free of imperfections are washed with a solution of Cream of Tartar, rinsed in water and dipped in alcohol.

The dies for proofs receive a special polish resulting in a mirror-like surface not unlike the finished brilliant proof coin and are occasionally wiped with an oily cloth to retain a clean, polished surface. Unlike ordinary coinage produced by mechanical pressure at the rate of 90 to 130 coins per minute, proofs are struck by hydraulic pressure at a slower rate. The coins are carefully placed in cellophane immediately, never allowed to come in contact with other coins.

Proof coins struck prior to 1855 are very rare. Because they are offered infrequently, they are not listed in this catalog.

Collectors should beware of coins which have been buffed to look like proofs and should use a magnifying glass. Buffed coins have myriad hair lines and lack perfect detail.

MODERN PROOF COINS

After a lapse of twenty years proof coins were struck at the Philadelphia Mint from 1936 to 1942 inclusive. They are issued primarily as collection pieces and souvenirs. An extra charge is made at the mint for each coin struck in proof condition. During the period mentioned, coins were usually purchased in sets for which the mint charged $1.81 for one each of the cent, five-cent piece, dime, quarter and half dollar. In 1942 when the content of the five-cent piece was changed, there were two types of this denomination available to collectors. The striking of proof coins was temporarily suspended from 1942 to 1950. The present cost of proof sets is $2.10 postpaid.

RECENT PROOF SETS

Cent—Nickel—Dime—Quarter—Half

1936 (3,837)	$385.00	1954 (233,300)	$12.50
1937 (5,542)	160.00	1955 (378,200)	11.00
1938 (8,045)	75.00	1956 (669,384)	7.50★
1939 (8,795)	60.00	1957 (1,247,952)	4.50★
1940 (11,246)	50.00	1958 (875,652)	9.00★
1941 (15,287)	39.00	1959 (1,149,291)	4.75★
1942 with both nickels (21,120)	37.50	1960 Large Date Cent	3.50★
1950 (51,386)	62.50	1960 Small Date Cent	
1951 (57,500)	35.00	(1,691,602 both kinds)	20.00★
1952 (81,980)	26.00	1961	3.00★
1953 (128,800)	15.00	★Speculative	

Figures in parentheses represent the total number of full sets minted.

PRIVATE OR TERRITORIAL GOLD COINS

The words "Private Gold," used with reference to coins struck outside of the United States Mint, are a general term. In the sense that no state or territory had authority to coin money, private gold simply refers to those interesting necessity pieces of various shapes, denominations and degrees of intrinsic worth which were circulated in isolated areas of our country by individuals, assayers, bankers, etc. Some will use the words "Territorial" and "State" to cover certain issues because they were coined and circulated in a Territory or State. While the state of California properly sanctioned the ingots stamped by F. D. Kohler as state assayer, in no instance were any of the gold pieces struck by authority of any of the territorial governments.

The stamped ingots put out by Augustus Humbert, the United States assayer of gold, were not recognized at the United States Mint as an official issue of coins, but simply as ingots, though Humbert placed the value and fineness on the pieces as an official agent of the federal government.

Private coins were circulated in most instances because of a shortage of regular coinage. Gold pieces whether in the form of bars, octagonal slugs or circular discs were primarily pieces of metal bearing an accurate appraisal of their values, sometimes in terms of weight and fineness, stamped upon them by individuals or firms.

The underlying principle of the private gold issues is expressed in the following words written centuries ago by the famous Greek philosopher Aristotle:

"...not all the necessaries of life are easy of carriage; wherefore, to effect their exchanges, men contrived something to give and take among themselves, which, being valuable in itself, had the advantage of being easily passed from hand to hand for the needs of life; such as iron or silver or something else of that kind, of which they first determined merely the size and weight, but eventually put a stamp on it in order to save the trouble of weighing, and this stamp became the sign of its value."

In the western states particularly, money became so scarce that the very commodity which the pioneers had come so far to acquire was converted into a local medium of exchange. The inability of the government to immediately supply an official circulating medium brought about an emergency which was remedied by the citizens with traditional pioneer resourcefulness.

Ephraim Brasher's New York doubloon of 1787 described on page 39 also falls into this class.

BIBLIOGRAPHY
Private Gold Coinage

Adams, Edgar H., Private Gold Coinage of California.................1913
Adams, Edgar H., Official Premium Lists, Private Territorial Gold.....1909
Griffin, Clarence, The Bechtlers and Bechtler Coinage and Gold
    Mining in North Carolina (1814-1830).........................1929
Lee, Ed. M., California Gold Quarters, Halves and Dollars............1932
Renz, Dr. Russell H., Private Gold Coinage of The United States......1938

TEMPLETON REID
Georgia 1830

Gold pieces were struck by Templeton Reid, Assayer, in Lumpkin County, Georgia, in 1830. The designs and denominations of these coins were well known, but almost nothing has been learned about Templeton Reid. Denominations struck were $2.50, $5.00 and $10.00.

The scarcity of the Templeton Reid Georgia pieces has been attributed to the fact that their high-grade gold content created a greater bullion value than their face value. For that reason most of these coins were melted and lost to the numismatic world.

A reference to the coinage of Templeton Reid of Georgia appeared in the National Gazette of Philadelphia, January 11, 1831, as follows: "GOLD.— Upward of $200,000 in gold are said to have been coined in Georgia the present season in $2.50, $5.00 and $10.00 pieces. On one side is 'Templeton Reid, Assayer'; on the other 'Georgia Gold.'" Templeton Reid was known to have been an expert gunsmith, a skill which would easily qualify him for the craft of making coins.

Obverse: A circle within which is GEORGIA GOLD. The date 1830 is in the center.

Reverse: T. REID at the top ASSAYER below. 2.50 is in the center. Milled border.

	Fine
1830 $2.50	$650.00
1830 $5	———

1830 TEN DOLLARS.. ———

TEMPLETON REID—GEORGIA

Fine

(No Date) TEN DOLLARS.................................. ———

TEMPLETON REID
San Francisco, Calif. 1849

The later Templeton Reid issues were made in California in 1849. It is supposed that he moved his coining equipment to California when gold was discovered there. The California issues were in denominations of ten and twenty-five dollars. The twenty-five-dollar issue is unique in design and denomination.

1849 TEN DOLLAR GOLD (Mint Collection Unique)........... ———

1849 TWENTY-FIVE DOLLARS GOLD...................... ———

The only specimen known of this piece was stolen from the Cabinet of the U. S. Mint on August 16, 1858. It was never recovered.

The illustration for the $25 piece is from a copper trial piece of unknown origin, and is probably somewhat different from the original, though similar.

[190]

THE BECHTLERS
Rutherford County, N. C. 1830-1852

Two skilled German metallurgists, Christopher Bechtler and his son, August Bechtler, and later Christopher Bechtler, Junior, a nephew of Christopher the elder, operated a "private" mint at Rutherfordton, North Carolina. Rutherford county in which Rutherfordton is located was the principal source of the nation's gold supply from 1790 to 1840.

There was but a scant supply of federal currency in the area during that period, and gold dust was the principal medium of exchange. Miners did not care to risk transportation of their gold by rough and poorly marked trails to the distant Philadelphia mint, so the metal remained in the locality in which it was mined passing from hand to hand. The Bechtlers who were natives of the Grand Duchy of Baden in Germany, came to Rutherford County in 1830. They soon offered a solution to the problem by advertising on July 2, 1831, that they were ready to coin the products of the mines. At first only $2.50 and five-dollar pieces were struck. The dollars were first coined in 1832.

Christopher Bechtler, the elder, was a gunsmith and goldsmith of some reputation. He was known to be a rather mystical, imaginative and superstitious person who was extremely reticent and seldom indulged in lengthy conversation.

Augustus Bechtler, his son, was quite the opposite, being possessed of a friendly, cheerful disposition. Christopher, Junior, was a heavy smoker and spent a great deal of time in a convenient tavern. He did not adhere to the high standards set by his elder namesake, for his gold pieces were worth less than the nominal value marked on them.

The honesty of Christopher, the elder, and Augustus was never questioned. They died poor and respected by all.

The coins minted by the Bechtlers were of only three denominations, but they cover a wide variety of weights and sizes. These variations are due to the fact that some gold contained foreign metals, and to conform exactly to the gold standard, such coins were made heavier.

The one-dollar coins are divided into three sets: 27 grains, 28 grains and 30 grains. The thirty-grain dollar was believed to have been the first struck. The Bechtlers have the distinction of producing the first gold dollar in the United States. The government mint did not release the first regular series until 1849.

Bechtler coins were passed at face value throughout the southeast for many years. At the outbreak of The War Between the States, Bechtler coins were carefully hoarded, and many contracts specified payment in Bechtler gold coins rather than Confederate States currency. These pieces were in reality only "tokens," yet they received the same consideration as though they were government specie. Local banks accepted them at face value for many years.

Christopher Bechtler's books showed that from 1831 to 1840 $2,241,850.50 was coined. Considering the great quantity coined, it may seem strange that this money should now be so rare. This can be understood when we realize that many holders of these coins had them recoined into United States specie when the branch mint was established at Charlotte in 1837. All gold passing through banks also was recoined at the nearest mint.

The inscription "Aug. 1, 1834" on one variety of the five-dollar piece has a special significance. The law reducing the weight and value of gold was passed in 1834. The Secretary of the Treasury recommended to the Director of the Mint that the gold coins of the reduced weight bear the date "Aug. 1, 1834." Instead of this, however, a new U. S. Gold design was used (the motto was omitted). Christopher Bechtler evidently acted on the official recommendation to avoid any difficulty with Treasury authorities.

CHRISTOPHER BECHTLER

                Fine   Unc.

ONE DOLLAR CAROLINA,
   28 gr. N reversed...$37.50 $77.50

ONE DOLLAR N. CAROLINA,
   28 gr., without star.187.50 500.00
ONE DOLLAR N. CAROLINA,
   28 gr., with star....75.00 150.00

ONE DOLLAR N. CAROLINA,
   30 gr..............80.00 152.50

$2.50 CAROLINA,
   67 gr. 21 carats....147.50 245.00

$2.50 CAROLINA,
   70 gr. 20 carats.... 197.50 360.00

$2.50 GEORGIA,
   64 gr. 22 carats.. 137.50   225.00
$2.50 GEORGIA, 64 gr.
   22 carats—even 22 350.00   650.00

                Fine   Unc.

$2.50 NORTH CAROLINA,
   75 gr. 20 carats. RUTHER-
   FORD in a circle..$510.00 $850.00
$2.50 NORTH CAROLINA
   without 75 G......405.00 625.00

$2.50 NORTH CAROLINA, 20 carats
   on obv. 75 gr. on rev.... 1,100.00

5 DOLLARS CAROLINA,
   RUTHERFORD, 140 gr. 20 carats.
   Date August 1, 1834 152.50 290.00

5 DOLLARS CAROLINA,
   RUTHERF. 140 gr. 20 carats. Date
   August 1, 1834.... 145.00 287.50

5 DOLLARS CAROLINA,
   134 gr. 21 carats... 135.00 275.00

THE BECHTLERS

AUGUST BECHTLER
1842-1852

                        Fine   Unc.

5 DOLLARS GEORGIA,
128 gr. 22 carats,
RUTHERFORD..$140.00 $285.00

5 DOLLARS GEORGIA,
128 gr. 22 carats,
RUTHERF...... 132.50 275.00

                        Fine   Unc.

1 DOLLAR CAROLINA,
27 gr. 21 carats.... $42.50 $92.50

5 DOLLARS, Obv. C. Bechtler,
Rev. A. Bechtler (Unique)
(A.N.A. 1956 Sale E. F.) 5000.00

5 DOLLARS CAROLINA,
128 gr. 22 carats.... 135.00 270.00

Without 150 G

5 DOLLARS NORTH CAROLINA, 150 gr. 20 carats..... 480.00 910.00
5 DOLLARS. Same as last variety without 150 G........ 1300.00 1950.00

5 DOLLARS CAROLINA,
134 gr. 21 carats... 132.50 270.00

5 DOLLARS CAROLINA,
141 gr. 20 carats... 132.50 270.00

[193]

CALIFORNIA GOLD

In the days following the discovery of gold in California, the lack of a convenient circulating medium proved to be the greatest obstacle to ordinary business transactions. Isolated from the great centers of commerce as they were, the citizens of California were placed at a great disadvantage. They applied for months for relief from the government with little success.

Conditions in those days and the situation which brought about private coinages were well explained in a Memorial forwarded by influential businessmen of San Francisco to Thomas Corwin, Secretary of the Treasury, Washington, D. C., in September, 1852. A portion of this important communication is quoted herewith:

"Chief among the evils experienced by the citizens of California engaged in mercantile transactions after the discovery of gold was the absence of a circulating medium. A country prior to and during its occupation by the American forces had known no other representatives of value than its hides and cattle, whose imports were so limited as to afford employment to only a dozen vessels annually, at once became the resort of all the unemployed vessels on the Pacific, and when the stimulant of so important a discovery was communicated to our Atlantic and the European cities, a thousand vessels entered the port of San Francisco the year succeeding, freighted with valuable cargoes, to supply the host that had embarked for the theatre of profitable labor.

"Under the administration of the military government of the Territory the impossibility of collecting duties in the coin prescribed by law was so apparent as to leave the officers of collection no other alternative than to receive gold-dust on deposit as a security of the ultimate payment in coin of the amounts due on the importation. These deposits were subsequently sold at public auction, and gold the known value of which approximated $18 per ounce realized but from $6 to $8 per ounce. The extreme low rates at which gold was purchased by the holders of the limited amount of coin then in the country induced importations from the South American republics of the debased currency of those countries, and for a brief period supplied the demand so painfully experienced for a medium of circulation other than the native gold used in the ordinary transactions of trade.

"Upon the establishment of the Collective District, of which this city is the great centre, the instructions of the Department being imperative, the newly appointed revenue officers exacted the payment of all public dues either in the National mint issue or in those of foreign governments at the rates prescribed by the Act of Congress. All the coin in a short time was absorbed by the Treasury, and resort was had to numerous private coinages, the evils of which were only checked by the Act authorizing the appointment of an Assayer, and instructions from the Department permitting the receipt of the Assay Office ingots in payment of the revenue. The result was most beneficial, not only to the mercantile community, but was more especially felt by the miners, the price of gold-dust advancing from the current rate of $16 an ounce, at which value it was used in barter, to $17 and $17.50 per ounce; a circulating medium was furnished, the baser coin of foreign countries driven comparatively from circulation, and the private coining establishments compelled to discontinue operations. The confidence with which a coinage attested by an officer of the United States was regarded withdrew from their hoarding places the National emission, and the State at large was provided with a currency bearing the same value in all parts and for all uses.

"It is true the people of California were not wholly contented with the substitute for a mint coinage, and have loudly called for the establishment of a mint; yet the issue of the Assay Office was productive of so many advantages as to be gratefully received as an earnest of the greater benefits soon to be conferred upon the youngest sister of the Confederation."

ANONYMOUS GOLD INGOT
Probably the first such piece struck in California.

	Fine
TEN DOLLARS San Francisco 1849 (Unique)...............	———

NORRIS, GRIEG AND NORRIS
San Francisco 1849

Edgar H. Adams considered this piece the first of the California private gold coins. A newspaper account dated May 31, 1849, described a five-dollar gold coin, struck at Benicia City, though with the imprint San Francisco. It mentioned the private stamp of Norris, Grieg and Norris. The initials N. G. and N. were not identified until 1902 when the coins of Augustus Humbert were sold. An uncirculated gold piece of this type was found wrapped in a sheet of paper with the words "From my friends, Norris, Grigg and Norris." The second name was evidently misspelled by Humbert as newspaper accounts had spelled the name Grieg.

1849 HALF EAGLE—Plain Edge
Fine....$200.00   Unc.....$500.00
1849 HALF EAGLE—Reeded Edge
Fine....$240.00   Unc.....$500.00

A recently discovered specimen is dated 1850, with STOCKTON beneath date.
1850 HALF EAGLE (Unique)
....

MEYERS & COMPANY

The exact location of this firm is presently unknown, as is the date of issue. However, its manufacture is almost certainly believed contemporaneous with the Moffat & Co. $9.43, $14.25 and $16.00 ingots which appeared in the summer of 1849 in San Francisco. Edgar H. Adams mentions a copper trial for a ¼ oz. piece, bearing almost identical wording, issued by this firm, on p. 102 of his "Private Gold Coinage." Except for the rounded corners, this ingot appears almost identical to the Moffat issues.

$18.00 Ingot (Unique)... ———

MOFFAT & CO.
San Francisco 1849-1853

The firm of Moffat and Company was perhaps the most important of the California private coiners. Operating for a longer period than any of the others, its issues were never questioned. The assay office they conducted was semi-official in character. The successors to this firm, Curtis, Perry and Ward, later established the United States Branch mint of San Francisco.

John L. Moffat, a New York assayer, arrived in California in early 1849. He was associated with Joseph R. Curtis, P. H. W. Perry and Samuel H. Ward in the business of assaying and smelting. They were gold brokers at first and shipped much of the metal to the East.

In June or July, 1849, Moffat & Co. began to issue small rectangular pieces of gold owing to lack of coin in the locality, in values from $9.43 to $264. The $9.43, $14.25 and $16.00 varieties are the only types known today.

$14.25 Ingot 1849

The only specimen known of the $9.43 ingot is in the National Coin Collection. The illustration of the $16.00 ingot is reproduced from a photograph furnished by courtesy of the Smithsonian Institution.

	Fine	Unc.
$9.43 Ingot (Unique)		
$14.25 Ingot (Unique) A.N.A. 1956 Sale (Very Fine)		$9250.00
$16.00 Ingot	$1200.00	2250.00

The dies for the $10 piece were cut by a Bavarian, Albert Kuner. This piece closely resembles the United States eagle, the chief difference being that the words MOFFAT & CO. appear on the coronet of Liberty instead of the word LIBERTY.

1849 TEN DOL.	150.00	350.00
1849 TEN D.	150.00	350.00

MOFFAT & CO.

	Fine	Unc.
1849 FIVE DOL.	$60.00	$135.00
1850 FIVE DOL.	65.00	147.50

The Moffat coins were accepted in trade with confidence by everyone and on the whole were exchanged at par, whereas other privately issued gold coins were discredited and disposed of at a loss after a short time. Moffat & Co. was the only California private mint to redeem its coins. The others never did so. Many of the private mints ceased to operate in 1850. In that year Moffat & Co. received a government contract to "assay and fix the value of gold in grains and lumps, etc., indicating the fineness and value of each ingot."

United States Assay Office
AUGUST HUMBERT
U. S. Assayer 1851

Augustus Humbert, a New York watch-case maker, was appointed United States Assayer, and he placed his name and the government stamp on the ingots of gold issued by Moffat & Co. The assay office was a temporary expedient to accommodate the Californians until the establishment of a permanent branch mint. The price of gold dust as a result of this action immediately became stabilized. Moffat & Co. upon taking the contract ceased to issue private coins. They moved to new quarters and soon after the arrival of Humbert January 30, 1851, turned out the first fifty-dollar octagonal gold pieces. It is stated by Edgar H. Adams in his book "Private Gold Coinage of California" that the dies for this piece were probably engraved in New York by C. C. Wright and that Humbert did not expect to make coins but simply to use this stamp on such ingots as might be issued at the assay office. The fact that the reverse of the fifty-dollar pieces contains an engine-turned device, such as usually appeared on watch cases of that day, would lead to the belief that this embellishment was an afterthought which as a watchmaker Humbert was perfectly capable of carrying into execution.

The fifty-dollar piece was at first gratefully received by the Californians as they badly needed a medium which would be accepted at the Custom House where gold dust and private gold coins were refused. It was accepted as legal tender on a par with standard U. S. gold coins and was known variously as a slug, quintuple eagle or five-eagle piece. It was officially termed an ingot.

MOFFAT—HUMBERT
Lettered Edge Varieties

                                                                               Fine   Unc.

1851 50 D C 880 THOUS. No 50 on Reverse. Sunk in Edge:
AUGUSTUS HUMBERT UNITED STATES
ASSAYER OF GOLD CALIFORNIA 1851..........$1025.00 $4300.00

1851 50 D C Similar to last variety, but 50 on Reverse... 1125.00   4300.00

1851 Similar to last variety, but 887 THOUS............1125.00   4300.00
1851 50 D C 887 THOUS. No 50 on Reverse.............1050.00   4100.00

[198]

MOFFAT—HUMBERT

                                                                                                   Fine   Unc.

1851 50 D C 880 THOUS. Rev. Rays from central star. (Unique)

Reeded Edge Varieties

1851 FIFTY DOLLS 880 THOUS. "Target" Reverse.... $975.00 $2900.00

1851 FIFTY DOLLS 887 THOUS. "Target" Reverse.... 975.00   2750.00

MOFFAT—HUMBERT

	Fine	Unc.
1852 FIFTY DOLLS. 887 THOUS.	$1000.00	$2900.00

The withdrawal of the discredited private coins of $5, $10 and $20 denomination as a result of the new U. S. Assay operations, caused a new turn of affairs for Californians. The new $50 slug was the only gold coin in circulation and it was too large a denomination for ordinary transactions. Two to three percent was charged for changing one of them and Moffat & Co. soon were criticized by the tradespeople and citizens. The company asked for permission from the Secretary of the U. S. Treasury to supply pieces of smaller denomination on April 14, 1851, but were refused in a communication dated July 9, 1851.

The money question was the most predominant in California at that time as it affected the lives of everyone. On August 26th Moffat & Co. again asked authority from the Treasury Department to relieve the citizens of California from an intolerable situation, but again authority was withheld.

The fractional currency coins of almost every nation were pressed into service by the Californians, but the supply was too small to help to any extent. During this monetary crisis agitation for a branch mint received strong impetus. Moffat & Co. in their monthly reports to the Treasury constantly drew attention to the necessity of being allowed to produce ingots of smaller denominations. Finally on December 9, 1851, William L. Hodge, assistant Secretary of the Treasury, gave authority to make ingots of $10 and $20 valuation, but the authority was immediately revoked on December 10.

The local businessmen and bankers, however, had so urgently requested Moffat & Co. to relieve the currency situation that the company proceeded in January, 1852, to issue a new ten-dollar piece bearing the stamp **MOFFAT & CO.** to the amount of $300,000.

Ten Dollars 1852

Obverse: Head of Liberty facing left, surrounded by thirteen stars. **MOFFAT & CO.** on the coronet. 1851 below.

Reverse: Eagle beneath a scroll with 880 THOUS. thereon. Around border, 264 GRS. CALIFORNIA GOLD TEN D.

MOFFAT—HUMBERT

	Fine	Unc.
1852 TEN D. MOFFAT & CO.	$170.00	$340.00

Government authority for issue of ingots in values of $10 and $20 was finally received at the United States Assay Office early in February, 1852.

Twenty Dollars 1852

Obverse: Eagle same as for $50 piece, except eagle holds olive branch in right talon instead of arrows. UNITED STATES OF AMERICA around the border, TWENTY DOLS. below. 884 THOUS. on a scroll above eagle.

Reverse: Rectangular space in center inscribed AUGUSTUS HUMBERT/ UNITED STATES ASSAYER/OF GOLD CALIFORNIA./ 1852. Beaded border and reeded edge.

The twenty-dollar piece was the first put out by the U. S. Assay Office. The date is struck 1852 over 1851. The dies were probably produced late in 1851 in anticipation of the authority and were dated before the close of the year. The long delayed permission, finally granted February 11, 1852, gave little time to make an entire new die so the figure 2 was sunk over the 1 in 1851.

1852 TWENTY DOLS. 1852 over 1	625.00	1050.00

1852 TEN DOLS. 1852 over 1	182.50	325.00
1852 TEN DOLS.	130.00	275.00

UNITED STATES ASSAY OFFICE OF GOLD
1852

The firm of Moffat & Co. dissolved at about this time and a new reorganized company known as the United States Assay Office of Gold, composed of Curtis, Perry and Ward took over the contract. The dissolution actually took place December 24, 1851. The remaining partners retained the right to use the name, Moffat & Co.

Early in the autumn of 1852 a new crisis arose as owing to a technicality concerning the fineness of gold (standard being .900 fine) the customhouse repudiated the assay office ingots. The merchants offered the Collector of Customs a guaranty against loss through continued free acceptance of the assay office ingots, which was believed to have been accepted. Curtis, Perry and Ward then began to issue their gold pieces in the standard fineness of .900 which apparently settled the matter. No fifty-dollar ingots were made by them after 1852. The scarcity of this denomination is probably a result of the fact that they were worth more than face value and were remelted for profit.

	Fine	Unc.
1852 FIFTY DOLLS. 887 THOUS.	$925.00	$2850.00
1852 FIFTY DOLLS. 900 THOUS.	900.00	2800.00

UNITED STATES ASSAY OFFICE

	Fine	Unc.
1852 TEN DOLS 884 THOUS.	$145.00	$285.00
1853 TEN D. 884 THOUS.	145.00	285.00
1853 TEN D. 900 THOUS.	140.00	275.00
1853 TWENTY D. 884 THOUS.	225.00	450.00

UNITED STATES ASSAY OFFICE

	Fine	Unc.
1853 TWENTY D. 900 THOUS.	$185.00	$425.00

UNITED STATES ASSAY OFFICE DISKS

A Humbert issued coin-like medium of exchange, used for conversion of raw gold dust into a standard medium, having an accepted monetary value predicated upon fluctuating gold value in various areas. The modern counterpart of this issue is the 1945-47 Saudi-Arabian discs made by, and bearing the stamp of the Philadelphia Mint. The piece illustrated is the only known example.

1853—1 (OUNCE) 900 (THOUS) .... ———

U. S. ASSAY—MOFFAT

The last Moffat issue was the 1853 Twenty-dollar piece which is very similar to the U. S. Double Eagle of that period. It was struck after the retirement of Mr. Moffat from the Assay Office.

1853 TWENTY D. 190.00 425.00

[204]

CINCINNATI MINING & TRADING CO.

The only known reference to a company from Cincinnati, which could possibly have been the private coiners, was contained in a letter printed July 7, 1849, in the "Cincinnati Gazette." The letter was written by a member of a party which left Cincinnati March 10, 1849, on the steamer *Bay State* for St. Louis. They started overland from there on March 18. The letter was written from Fort Childs, 300 miles west of Independence, Missouri and reads in part: "We left behind the wagon that we purchased for carrying corn, which cost $210; blacksmith tools, consisting of anvil, forge, sledgehammers, etc.; about 200 mule shoes; several extra axletrees, and came very near leaving the coining apparatus, most of the company being in favor of so doing, it being very heavy."

A news article in the Nashville Banner (May, 1948) sent us by Wesly R. Meier HMC USN tells about a $5 piece owned by the descendants of Morris Fischel one of the organizers of the Cincinnati Mining & Trading Co. Jacob Fischel, a son now over 84 years old, recalls the piece as a gift from his father in 1877, and later finding a $10 piece which was sold to Virgil Brand. The $5 piece was brought to light once more in 1919 while cleaning out a safe, and is now owned by a grandson.

	Fine	Unc.
1849 FIVE DOLLARS		
1849 TEN DOLLARS		
1849 TWENTY DOLLARS (Copper)		

MASSACHUSETTS AND CALIFORNIA COMPANY
San Francisco 1849

The history of this firm is very obscure. Edgar H. Adams in his book on California private gold coinage mentions an old newspaper article printed in Massachusetts in May, 1849. This article stated that a party had "gone from North Hampton, Mass., taking with them a mint, or, rather, all the implements necessary for coining gold and silver, and a competent assayer." They intended to establish a private mint, buy gold and coin it. The plant was to have had a capacity of $10,000 a day, and curiously it was "said to have the sanction of the government."

Henry Chapman, cataloger of the A. C. Nygren collection of pioneer gold coins April 29, 1924, has this to say of the Massachusetts and California Company five-dollar piece of 1849, "organized at Northhampton, Mass., with a capital of $6,000 increased it to $50,000. Josiah Hayden was President; S. S. Wells, Miles G. Moies and others, Directors. It sent Rev. F. P. Tracy and W. Hayden to California, accompanied by coining Machinery." A very fine specimen in silver sold in this sale for $510.00, rated excessively rare.

A San Francisco paper contained an article which mentioned that a five-dollar piece of the Massachusetts and California Company was understood to have been struck in the East. This is very likely as the piece contained copper, while native gold, with a percentage of silver but no copper, was used for nearly all other California private gold coins. There were several patterns prepared, suggesting that an extensive coinage was contemplated. These were struck in silver and copper, including one for a $10.00 coin. The only variety in gold known to Adams is described by him as follows:

Five Dollars 1849

"Obverse, a shield bearing a mounted vaquero in the act of throwing a lasso. Supporters, on the right a stag, and on the left a bear, both rampant. On a ribbon scroll directly underneath, ALTA (upper). Crest, an arm, with the hand holding an arrow. Around the border of the field are thirteen stars, the whole forming a very handsome design. Reverse, in the field a wreath enclosing in two lines, FIVE D. Around the border is the legend, MASSA-CHUSETTS & CALIFORNIA CO. Below is the date, 1849." They are all struck in a low grade gold.

	Fine	Unc.
1849 FIVE D	$4000.00	———
1849 TEN D (Brass)	———	———

MINERS' BANK
San Francisco 1849

The institution of Wright & Co. exchange brokers located in Portsmouth Square, San Francisco, was known as the Miners' Bank. On August 7, 1849,

MINERS' BANK

they asked state authorities for permission to issue gold coins of $5 and $10 denomination. They wanted to make the coins available for payment of duties, and to afford a circulating medium for business transactions in the area. The request was rejected.

A ten-dollar piece was issued in the autumn of 1849, but the coins were not readily accepted because they were worth less than face value. The firm dissolved January 14, 1850. Unlike most issues, the gold in these coins was alloyed with copper.

	Fine	Unc.
(1849) TEN. D.	$850.00	$1800.00

J. S. ORMSBY
Sacramento 1849

The initials J. S. O. which appear on certain issues of California privately coined gold pieces represent the firm of J. S. Ormsby & Co. They struck both five- and ten-dollar denominations, and are undated.

There are 31 stars on the $10 piece which coincide with the number of states in the Union upon the admission of California in 1850. This fact would indicate that the coins were minted in 1850 although some authorities state all of them were minted in 1849.

The firm Ormsby & Co. was composed of Dr. J. S. and Major William M. Ormsby. They operated an assay office and mint on K Street in Sacramento. Dr. Ormsby was a member of the California legislature in 1858. Major Ormsby was a Nevada pioneer having once owned a house in Eagle Valley where Carson City is now situated. Ormsby County in Nevada was named for him. He was killed during a fight with Indians near Pyramid Lake in 1860.

	Fine	Unc.
(1849) 5 DOLLS..	—	—
(1849) 10 DOLLS.	—	—

PACIFIC COMPANY
San Francisco 1849

The origin of the Pacific Co. is very uncertain. All data regarding the firm is based on conjecture.

There was a Virginia firm called the "Pacific Mining and Trading Co." organized in 1849 with 115 members. They sailed, according to a newspaper account, April 7, 1849, from Richmond and it was said to be the first expedition from that state. This may have been the company who produced the gold coins, now very rare, of one-dollar, $2.50, five- and ten-dollar denominations, all dated 1849.

There is also a record of a company of 30 members known as "The Pacific Company," which organized in Boston, Mass., and sailed for California February 20, 1849.

There is no proof that either of these groups was responsible for the gold pieces bearing the title "The Pacific Company."

Edgar H. Adams wrote that he believed that the coins bearing the stamp of the Pacific Company were produced by the coining firm of Broderick and Kohler. The coins were probably handstruck, with the aid of a sledgehammer.

	Fine	Unc.
1849 1 DOLLAR (known in silver and tin)	___	___
1849 2½ DOLLARS (known in silver only)	___	$575.00

1849 5 DOLLARS.... ___   ___

Fine	Unc.
1849 10 DOLLARS	___	___

[208]

F. D. KOHLER
California State Assayer 1850

The State Assay office was the outgrowth of a meeting of citizens in San Francisco July 22, 1848. A resolution, addressed to Military Governor Richard B. Mason, called for assayers to test the quality of mined gold, and that such gold be converted into ingots and be stamped with the weight and fineness and the name of the person furnishing the gold.

No legislative action was taken, however, until April 12, 1850, when a law was passed providing for an office of State Assayer, melter and refiner of gold.

Section nine of the act reads in part "The state assayer shall regularly number and stamp upon the ingots or bars thus made a true value in dollars and cents, and the correct weight and carat fineness thereof—also the letters 'CAL.,' the date, and his own initials—."

Other provisions of the act specified that the bars were to be accepted in payment of all state and county dues, taxes and assessments, at the value expressed thereon; that when the United States government established a branch mint within the state, the office of State Assayer was to be abolished.

Governor Burnett appointed O. P. Sutton as Director and Frederick D. Kohler as Assayer for the state. Upon accepting this office Mr. Kohler sold his private assaying business to Baldwin and Company.

A branch office was soon established in Sacramento June 28, 1850. John Bigler, afterward governor of California, was appointed as director. Kohler was named assayer at this office also.

The ingots issued ranged from $36.55 to $150. They were also known as "slugs." They were actually worth more than U. S. gold.

The State Assay office was discontinued at the time the United States Assay Office was established February 1, 1851.

The State Assay Office ingots are excessively rare. The $45.34 ingot of 1850 illustrated herewith is typical.

	Fine
36.55 Sacramento	———
40.07 San Francisco	———
37.31 San Francisco	———
45.34 San Francisco	———
50.00 San Francisco	———
54.09 San Francisco	———

BLAKE & AGNELL, ASSAYERS
Sacramento 1855

Gorham Blake and —— Agnell conducted an assaying and gold-smelting plant at 52 J Street in Sacramento, in and after 1854. Mr. Agnell died a few days after Christmas in 1855.

1855 $25.00 Ingot (Unique) ———

BLAKE & AGNELL, ASSAYERS

1855 $23.30 Ingot
(Unique) ———

BLAKE & COMPANY
Sacramento 1855

The twenty-dollar piece shown herewith, was undoubtedly made during the last days of December, 1855. The piece illustrated is by far the finer of only two known specimens. There are also known, in copper or brass, trial pieces for a conventional appearing double eagle dated 1856, and bearing the legend "Blake & Co."

1855 $20.00.. ———

DUBOSQ & COMPANY
San Francisco 1850

Theodore Dubosq, senior member of the firm, was a jeweler in Philadelphia. According to a news item in the Philadelphia Evening Bulletin of January 18, 1849, the names of Theodore Dubosq, Sr., Theodore Dubosq, Jr., and Henry A. Dubosq appear on the passenger list of the *Gray Eagle*. The account goes on to say that "Mr. Theodore Dubosq, jeweler, North Second Street, we understand takes out with him the machinery for melting and coining gold, and stamping it with a private mark, so as to establish a currency which will afford the greater convenience and facility for dealing in the raw material."

On May 31, 1849, an item in the "Alta California" published in San Francisco reads, "We learn that Mr. Theodore Dubosq, a jeweler from Philadelphia, who recently arrived in the 'Gray Eagle,' has brought with him the necessary machinery for striking private coins."

Although the five- and ten-dollar gold pieces were circulated generally they are very rare. Dies for trial pieces with T. DUBOSQ 1849 on the obverse were supposedly engraved before going west. These are known to exist only in copper of $2.50 and five-dollar denominations.

DUBOSQ & COMPANY

1849 2½ DOL. Trial Piece (copper)... _____

             Fine   Unc.

1849 FIVE DOLS. Trial piece (copper)..... _____ _____

                         Fine   Unc.

1850 TEN D. _____ _____
1850 FIVE D Similar to TEN D.... _____ _____

BALDWIN & COMPANY
San Francisco 1850

George C. Baldwin and Thomas S. Holman were in the jewelry business in San Francisco and were known as Baldwin & Co. They were the successors to F. D. Kohler & Co., taking over their machinery and other equipment in May, 1850.

The output of this firm was very large, even exceeding that of the U. S. Assay Office in the first three months of 1851. Baldwin & Co. struck $590,000 worth of gold coins during that period.

The quality of these coins, however, left much to be desired. An assay of specimens conducted by August Humbert disclosed the fact that all of the Baldwin coins had an intrinsic value below their face value.

The *Pacific News* printed an editorial April 9, 1851, headed "The Gold Coin Swindle." The article suggested that the public refuse to accept the coin since Baldwin's establishment imposed a penalty of 5% on a citizen who had presented two Baldwin $20 pieces for redemption in silver.

On April 17 the same newspaper reported that the manufacturers of the Baldwin coin had left in the steamer *Panama* for the Atlantic states.

Two denominations, Five and Ten Dollars, were issued in 1850. The dies were cut by Albert Kuner.

Horseman Type   Fine   Unc.   Fine   Unc.
1850 TEN DOLLARS $1350.00 $2350.00 1850 FIVE DOL..$300.00 $600.00

BALDWIN & COMPANY

          Fine   Unc.
1851 TEN D..$2000.00 $4000.00

The Baldwin & Co. $20 piece was the first of that denomination issued in California.

Baldwin coins were believed to have contained about twenty-thousandths copper alloy.

                                                      Fine   Unc.
1851 TWENTY D.................................$2300.00 $4700.00

JAMES KING OF WILLIAM & COMPANY
San Francisco 1851

James King of William was one of the first California pioneers. After finding out that he was not physically able to work in the gold fields, he made his way to Sacramento. In the fall of 1849 he went to San Francisco and opened an "Exchange and Deposit Office" in partnership with Jacob R. Snyder. In 1851, the firm's name was changed to James King of William & Company. Three years later, King sold out to Adams & Co., which organization failed in 1855. Later that year, he became editor and publisher of a San Francisco newspaper, and immediately crusaded against the baser elements in the city. For his pains, he was shot down on May 14, 1856, by James Casey, a local politician.

It is believed that the twenty-dollar piece illustrated below was struck in 1851. This specimen is presently the only one known, having been discovered in 1955.

(1851) 20 DOLLARS .... (Unique)..

SCHULTZ & COMPANY
San Francisco 1851

The firm located in back of Baldwins' establishment conducted a brass foundry beginning in 1851. Judge G. W. Schultz and William T. Garratt were partners in the enterprise.

According to a biographical sketch of Mr. Garratt in "Builders of a Great City," published in San Francisco in 1891, this firm made all the dies for private coinage in San Francisco except those of Moffat & Co. Albert Kuner did the engraving of these dies. Besides the actual manufacture of the dies the firm also coined five-dollar pieces. Machinery was made for coining both five- and ten-dollar pieces but only five-dollar coins are known. The company discontinued operations when the state legislature passed a law placing private coiners on a banking basis.

Five Dollars 1851

Obverse: Head of Liberty facing left surrounded by thirteen stars. SHULTS & CO. (Misspelled by the engraver with an S instead of Z.) Date 1851 below.

Reverse: Eagle with outstretched wings and shield on its breast, holding arrows and olive branch in its talons. Above, PURE CALIFORNIA GOLD; below, FIVE D.

	Fine	Unc.
1851 FIVE D	$1350.00	$2300.00

DUNBAR & COMPANY
San Francisco 1851

Edward E. Dunbar conducted the California Bank in San Francisco. At the time when Baldwin & Co. coins were being refused, a Dunbar advertisement appeared offering to redeem the coins. Baldwin & Co. ceased to strike coins at about this time and Dunbar supposedly took over the machinery from the former firm. Five dollars was the only denomination issued.

Mr. Dunbar later returned to New York and organized the famous Continental Bank Note Co.

1851 FIVE D	1750.00	3500.00

WASS, MOLITOR & COMPANY
San Francisco 1852-1855

The gold smelting and assaying plant of Wass, Molitor & Co. was composed of two Hungarian patriots Count S. C. Wass and A. P. Molitor. They maintained an excellent laboratory and complete apparatus for analysis and coinage of gold.

The firm at first did not undertake to strike coins, but offered to pay over the proceeds in any coin that was current at the banks.

During the latter part of 1851 the only coins struck in that area were the Augustus Humbert octagonal fifty-dollar pieces, and gold pieces of small denomination were hoarded for custom house payments on foreign shipments. As stated in the history of Moffat & Co. the businessmen of San Francisco petitioned for gold coins of smaller size. Wass Molitor took the initiative by bringing out on January 8, 1852, their first gold coin, a five-dollar piece.

	Fine	Unc.
1852 FIVE DOLLARS	$150.00	$250.00

The company struck five-, ten-, twenty- and fifty-dollar coins. In 1852 in addition to the five-dollar piece illustrated above they produced a ten-dollar piece similar in design to the five-dollar denomination. The difference is in the reverse legend which reads: SMV (Standard Mint Value) CALIFORNIA GOLD TEN D.

1852 TEN D. Large Head	240.00	525.00

1852 TEN D. Small Head	725.00	1450.00

WASS, MOLITOR & COMPANY

No pieces were coined in 1853 or 1854, but they brought out the twenty-dollar and fifty-dollar pieces in 1855. A considerable number of the fifty-dollar coins were made. At one time they were produced at the rate of $38,000 a day. There was a ten-dollar piece issued in 1855 also, with a somewhat different design of the Liberty head.

	Fine	Unc.
1855 TEN D.	$150.00	$360.00
1855 TWENTY DOL. Large Head	1900.00	3500.00
1855 TWENTY DOL. Small Head	600.00	1075.00

WASS, MOLITOR & COMPANY

	Fine	Unc.
1855 50 DOLLARS	$2300.00	$7500.00

KELLOGG & COMPANY
San Francisco 1854-1855

John G. Kellogg came to San Francisco October 12, 1849, from Auburn, New York. At first he was employed by Moffat and Company, and remained with that organization when control passed to Curtis, Perry and Ward. When the United States Assay Office was discontinued December 14, 1853, Mr. Kellogg became associated with G. F. Richter who had been an assayer in the government assay office. These two set up business as Kellogg & Richter December 19, 1853.

When the U. S. Assay Office ceased operations a period ensued during which no private firm was striking gold. The new San Francisco branch mint did not produce coins for some months after Curtis & Perry took the contract for the government. The lack of coin was again keenly felt by business men who petitioned Kellogg & Richter to "supply the vacuum" by issuing private coin.

Their plea was soon answered, for on February 9, 1854, Kellogg & Co. placed their first twenty-dollar piece in circulation.

1854 TWENTY D. 175.00   415.00

The 1855 twenty-dollar piece is similar to that dated 1854. The letters on the reverse side are larger and the arrows longer on one 1854 variety. There are several die varieties of both issues.

KELLOGG & COMPANY

	Fine	Unc.
1855 TWENTY D	$180.00	$440.00

Although the branch mint began operations shortly thereafter, production was very slow. The responsibility for supplying coins therefore fell upon Kellogg & Richter, a job which the publication "Prices Current" characterized as "important . . . in preventing any disarrangement of our financial matters."

The firm dissolved late in 1854 and reorganized as Kellogg & Humbert. The latter partner was Augustus Humbert for some time identified as U. S. Assayer.

Regardless of the fact that the branch mint was then producing coins, Kellogg & Humbert issued coins in 1855 in a quantity greater than before.

Fifty Dollars 1855

Obverse: Head of Liberty surrounded by thirteen stars. KELLOGG & CO. on the coronet. 1855 beneath. In small letters F. GRUNER at truncation of bust of Liberty. (Ferdinand Gruner.)

Reverse: An eagle similar to that on Octagonal $50 piece, U. S. shield and arrows in left talon. Beak holds a ribbon, 1309 GRS 887 THOUS. inscribed on flowing ribbon. Around border, SAN FRANCISCO CALIFORNIA FIFTY DOLLS. Reeded edge.

1855 FIFTY DOLLS..................................$6000.00 ———

KELLOGG & COMPANY

Edgar H. Adams believed that the above type and denomination designed by Ferdinand Gruner was never issued in quantity for he could find no records of any but the Wass, Molitor & Co. issued during the period referred to. Thirteen specimens are known to exist. The dies are still in existence.

E. R. Kellogg, a son of the pioneer coiner, stated in a letter to Frank Doughty May 6, 1891, that about 60,000 were struck of the $50 Kellogg piece. The letter came to light many years later and was printed in the February 1921 *Numismatist*. Mr. Kellogg, the elder, died April 21, 1886, having dissolved partnership with Augustus Humbert in 1860.

CALIFORNIA SMALL DENOMINATION GOLD PIECES

California Gold quarters, halves and dollars were issued in many cases by the same parties who coined the larger denominations. Others were made by jewelers and merchants. So-called jewelers' pieces have the word EUREKA or a bear on them, and are relatively common. None of these small denomination gold pieces can be attributed with certainty to any individual or firm.

Specimens are found in both round and octagonal shape. They were coined as late as 1882. Some pieces are without dates. The genuine have the denomination spelled DOL. or DOLLAR.

	Fine	V. Fine	Unc.
25c Octagonal	$ 11.50	$ 15.75	$ 19.00
25c Round	11.50	15.75	19.00
50c Octagonal	13.50	16.50	21.50
50c Round	13.50	16.50	21.50
$1.00 Octagonal	32.50	40.00	50.00
$1.00 Round	125.00	155.00	195.00

OREGON EXCHANGE COMPANY
Oregon City, 1849

The Beaver Coins of Oregon

The early settlers of the Oregon Territory took over a wild and uninhabited country without the aid or protection of any government. There industries were chiefly agriculture, lumbering and trapping. The beaver was the principal fur-bearing animal and the pelts were used widely in the earliest days as a medium of exchange. Wheat also was of standard value and used for swapping of commodities.

The provisional territory government passed an act December 10, 1845, providing that "treasury drafts, approved orders on solvent merchants and good merchantable wheat at the market value . . . shall be lawful tender for payment of taxes and judgments rendered in the courts. . . ."

Upon the discovery of gold in California there was a great exodus of settlers who joined in the hunt for the precious metal. Soon returning gold seekers offered their gold dust, which became the accepted medium of exchange.

OREGON EXCHANGE COMPANY

Like other western areas of that time the uncertain qualities of the gold and weighing devices tended to irk the tradespeople and petitions were made to the legislature for a standard gold coin issue.

On February 16, 1849, the legislature passed an act providing for a mint and specified five- and ten-dollar gold coins without alloy. Oregon City, the largest city in the territory with a population of about 1000, was designated as the location for the mint. At the time this act was passed Oregon had been brought into the United States as a territory by act of Congress. When the new governor arrived March second, he declared the coinage act unconstitutional.

The public-spirited people, however, continued to work for a convenient medium of exchange and soon took matters into their own hands by starting a private mint. Eight men of affairs whose names were Kilborne, Magruder, Taylor, Abernethy, Willson, Rector, Campbell and Smith set up the Oregon Exchange Company.

Hamilton Campbell was employed to engrave the five-dollar dies. Thomas Powell, a blacksmith, forged the machinery which was said to have been made from old wagon tires and the like. The coins struck were of virgin gold as specified in the original act. Ten-dollar dies were made later, and were of finer design and workmanship.

Five Dollars 1849

Obverse: Initials of the members of the Oregon Exchange Co. KMTAWRGS. The initial G was an error and was supposed to have been a C for Campbell. Center, a beaver facing right on a log. Below T. O. another error which should have read O. T. (Oregon Territory). Date at bottom, 1849.

Reverse: OREGON EXCHANGE CO. In the center, 130 G NATIVE GOLD, 5D.

	Fine	Unc.
1849 5 D	$700.00	$1250.00

Ten Dollars 1849

The ten-dollar dies were engraved by Victor Wallace and were similar to the five-dollar denomination. Errors mentioned in the above description were corrected, but the initials for Abernethy and Willson were eliminated for reasons unknown.

Since the coins contained about eight per cent more gold than was necessary, they were bought up and remelted, causing a great scarcity of these issues. These interesting coins are known as the "Beaver Coins of Oregon."

OREGON EXCHANGE COMPANY

	Fine	Unc.
1849 TEN D	$3500.00	$6000.00

MORMON GOLD PIECES
Salt Lake City, Utah 1849-1860

The first name given to the organized Mormon Territory was the "State of Deseret," the latter word meaning "honey bee." The beehive, which is shown on the reverse of the five-dollar 1860 piece, was a favorite device of the followers of Joseph Smith and Brigham Young. The clasped hands appear on most Mormon coins and exemplify strength in unity. "Holiness to the Lord" was an inscription frequently used.

Brigham Young was the instigator of the coinage system and personally supervised the mint which was housed in a little adobe building in Salt Lake City.

The mint was inaugurated late in 1849 as a public convenience. As in other gold mining sections there was much trouble in payment of small sums in the form of gold dust.

Obverse: Eye of Providence and bishop's mitre. Legend around border, HOLINESS TO THE LORD.

Reverse: Clasped hands in center, 1849 beneath. In circle G.S.L.C.P.G. (Great Salt Lake City Pure Gold.)

1849 TWO AND HALF DO............................ 350.00   700.00

1849 FIVE DOLLARS................................ 240.00   500.00

[220]

MORMON GOLD PIECES

                                                                     Fine   Unc.
1849 TEN DOLLARS............................$2500.00 $4400.00

1849 TWENTY DOLLARS 1200.00   2000.00
    The Mormon twenty-dollar piece was the first of that denomination to be coined in this country.

1850 FIVE DOLLARS... 275.00   600.00

Five Dollars 1860

    Obverse: Lion facing left, surrounded by legend in the Mormon alphabet. HOLINESS TO THE LORD. 1860 beneath.
    Reverse: Beehive with eagle holding a laurel branch and arrows in its talons. Around border, DESERET ASSAY OFFICE PURE GOLD. Below is 5D.

              Fine   Unc.
1860 5.D........ $550.00 $950.00

COLORADO GOLD PIECES
Clark Gruber & Co.—Denver 1860-1861

Clark, Gruber and Co. was a well-known private minting firm in Denver, Colo., in the early sixties.

Austin M. and Milton E. Clark, brothers, and E. H. Gruber composed the firm, which organized a banking business in Leavenworth, Kansas, in 1858. As gold dust and nuggets were coming in from the Denver country they decided to establish a bank in Denver also. They had made heavy purchases of gold dust and were obliged to ship it to the states to have it coined into money. This procedure took from three weeks to three months as only stage coaches and pony express were available for transportation. High insurance and shipping rates added greatly to the cost so the idea for establishing a mint in connection with the bank was not long in becoming a reality.

The Bank and Mint was established in July, 1860. The dies and presses were purchased in Boston and were delivered overland to Denver by ox or mule team from Missouri River points, heavily guarded from Indian attacks.

Clark & Co. 1860

	Fine	Unc.
1860 2½ D	$80.00	$190.00
1860 5D	90.00	225.00

Clark Gruber & Co. 1860

1860 TEN D	450.00	950.00
1860 TWENTY D	$1850.00	$3250.00

CLARK GRUBER & COMPANY

The $2.50 and five-dollar pieces of 1861 follow closely the designs of the 1860 issues. The main difference is found in the legends. The reverse side now has CLARK GRUBER & CO. DENVER, PIKES PEAK is on the coronet of Liberty.

	Fine	Unc.
1861 2½D	$ 80.00	$200.00
1861 FIVE D	80.00	200.00
1861 TEN D	157.50	325.00

1861 TWENTY D.................................... 825.00   1400.00

JOHN PARSONS & COMPANY

Tarryall Mines
Colorado 1861

Very little is known regarding the mint of John Parsons and Co., although it is reasonably certain that it operated in the South Park of Colorado, near Tarryall, in the summer of 1861.

The coins are undated, but the *Weekly News* of Denver, and the *Miner's Record* issued at Tarryall carried news items in 1861 concerning the J. Parsons and Co. gold coinage.

Although the spelling of the name is correct with the final "s," the omission on the coins was probably owing to a mistake by the engraver.

1860 20 DOLS. Gold Ingot...

[223]

JOHN PARSONS & COMPANY

Obverse: Quartz stamp mill device in the center, J. PARSON & CO. above ORO below.

Reverse: An eagle with wings outstretched and a shield on its breast. A laurel wreath is held in the left talon, three arrows in the other. PIKES PEAK GOLD in circle above, 2½ D or Five D, below.

	Fine	Unc.
(1861) Undated 2½ D	$1500.00	$2500.00
(1861) Undated FIVE D	2500.00	4500.00

J. J. CONWAY & COMPANY
Georgia Gulch—Colorado, 1861

Records show that the Conway Mint operated for a short while in 1861. As in all gold mining areas the value of gold dust caused disagreement among the merchants and the miners. The firm of J. J. Conway & Co. solved this difficulty by bringing out their gold pieces in August, 1861.

A news item about this company appeared in the *Rocky Mountain News,* August 21, 1861, as follows: "There is a mint in Georgia Gulch, conducted by J. J. Conway & Co., jewelers and bankers. Their machinery seems to be as fine as that of Clark, Gruber & Co., and their five- and ten-dollar gold pieces look as nice and rich as Uncle Sam himself could get up."

	Fine	Unc.
(1861) Undated 2½ DOLL'S	$1900.00	$3500.00
(1861) Undated FIVE DOLLARS	1650.00	4000.00
(1861) Undated FIVE DOLLARS, Similar. Variety without numeral 5 on reverse	—	—

(1861) Undated TEN DOLLARS..... —

[224]

LESHER REFERENDUM DOLLARS

Coined by Joseph Lesher in 1900 and 1901 at Victor, Colorado. Used in trade to some extent, and stocked by various merchants who redeemed them in goods. Coins were numbered and a blank space left at bottom of 1901 issues, in which were stamped names of businessmen who bought them. All are quite rare, many varieties extremely rare.

1900   1901

		V. Fine	Unc.
1900	First Type, no business name	$140.00	$225.00
1900	A.B. Bumstead, with scrolls	127.50	195.00
1900	A.B. Bumstead, no scrolls	95.00	155.00
1900	Bank Type (5 known)	275.00	400.00
1901	Imprint Type, no name	147.50	195.00
1901	J. M. Slusher, Cripple Creek, Colo.	125.00	180.00
1901	Sam Cohen, Victor, Colo.	225.00	350.00
1901	D. W. Klein & Co., Pueblo, Colo.	370.00	550.00
1901	George Mullen, Victor, Colo.	220.00	325.00
1901	Boyd Park, Denver, Colo.	125.00	190.00
1901	W. C. Alexander, Salida, Colo.	300.00	450.00
1901	Goodspeeds & Co., Pikes Peak Ave. (3 known)	425.00	———
1901	W. F. White, Grand Junction, Colo.	365.00	———
1901	J. E. Nelson & Co., Holdredge, Nebr. (Only 3 known)	425.00	———

HARD TIME TOKENS
1834-1844

In addition to the coins issued by the United States government, numismatists include in their collections the Hard Times and Civil War tokens which circulated as money during two periods in this country's history when nearly all the minor coin was hoarded.

The Hard Times tokens were issued in the period 1834-1844 and are the size of the large U. S. cent. They were generally struck in copper and are of two general groups: political tokens whose theme centered around President Jackson's fight against the United States Bank, and those issued by merchants (tradesman's cards). Many different varieties exist. The most common pieces are generally valued at 75¢ good to $3.00 Unc.

[225]

CIVIL WAR TOKENS
1861-1864

Civil War Tokens are generally divided into two groups; tradesmen's coins, and anonymously issued pieces with political or patriotic themes. They came into existence only because of the scarcity of government coins and disappeared as soon as the bronze coins of 1864 met the public demand for small copper change.

From the outset of the Civil War, government cents were insufficient in number, widely hoarded and worth a premium over all other currencies. As a result of this scarcity of cent pieces, private copper coins were issued by many individuals. Their wide circulation was made possible by the scarcity of copper-nickel cents and the public dislike of fractional paper money.

The tradesmen's tokens were issued by various firms to provide change and advertise the dealers' wares. They usually bore an implied or an explicit promise of redemption in goods or money. The second type were simply unauthorized substitutes for government coins, produced at a profit by private manufacturers and put into general circulation through various agencies.

These tokens are of great variety in composition and design. A number were more or less faithful imitations of the copper-nickel cent. A few of this type have the word "NOT" in very small letters above the words "ONE CENT."

Many pieces, especially of the tradesmen token type, were individual in device and size, representing any caprice of design or slogan that appealed to the maker. Some were political or patriotic in character, carrying the likeness of some military leader such as McClellan or bearing such inscriptions as "Millions for contractors, not one cent for the widows." An estimated 50,000,000 or more of these pieces were issued. Approximately 10,000 different varieties have been recorded.

The legal status of the Civil War Tokens was uncertain. Mint Director Pollock thought they were illegal; however, there was no law prohibiting the issue of tradesmen's tokens or of private coins not in imitation of United States coins. A law was passed on April 22, 1864 prohibiting the issue of any one or two-cent coins, tokens, or devices for use as money, and on June 8 another law was passed which abolished private coinage of every kind.

	Fine	V. Fine	Unc.
Copper or Brass Tokens	$ .50	$1.00	$ 2.00
Nickel or German Silver Tokens	1.50	3.00	6.00
White Metal Tokens	2.00	4.00	8.00
Copper-Nickel Tokens	1.50	3.00	6.00
Silver Tokens	5.00	7.50	15.00

CONFEDERATE STATES OF AMERICA
Confederate 1861 Half Dollar

The half dollar struck by the Confederacy was unknown to collectors until 1879. A specimen of the coin and both dies were found in the possession of Dr. B. F. Taylor of New Orleans. Mr. E. Mason, Jr., of Philadelphia purchased Dr. Taylor's specimen and the reverse die and later sold them to J. W. Scott and Company of New York.

CONFEDERATE STATES OF AMERICA—1861

Five hundred genuine 1861 half dollars from the New Orleans mint were acquired by J. W. Scott and Company. The reverses were planed off and then restamped with the Confederate die. These are known as restrikes. The restrikes have flattened obverses.

According to records only four originals were struck. These were made on a hand press. Original silver half dollar planchets were used, as well as the original obverse die. One of the coins was given to the Secretary of the Confederacy Memminger who passed it on to President Jefferson Davis for his approval. Another was given to Prof. Biddle of the University of Louisiana. Dr. E. Ames of New Orleans received a third specimen, the last being kept by Chief Coiner Taylor, who sold it later as mentioned above.

Lack of bullion prevented the Confederate government from proceeding with any coinage plans that might have been made.

J. W. Scott struck some tokens in white metal using the Confederate reverse die and a special die bearing the inscription
4 ORIGINALS STRUCK BY ORDER OF C. S. A. IN NEW ORLEANS 1861 ******* REV. SAME AS U. S. (FROM ORIGINAL DIE SCOTT)

Confederate Reverse **Scott Obverse**

	V. Fine	Unc.
1861 HALF DOL. (Ex. Rare)	—	—
1861 HALF DOL. Restrike	$290.00	$485.00
1861 Scott Token, obverse. Confederate reverse	40.00	70.00

The Confederate Cent

An order to make cents for the Confederacy was placed with Mr. Robert Lovett Jr., an engraver and die-sinker of Philadelphia, by a jewelry firm of that city. Fearing arrest by the United States government for giving assistance to the enemy, Mr. Lovett decided against delivering the coins to the Confederate government and hid the coins and dies in his cellar.

The original dies were later purchased by Capt. John W. Haseltine who made restrikes from the dies.

	Proof
1861 Cent Original (copper-nickel) 12 struck	$550.00
1861 Cent Restrike (copper) 55 struck	350.00
1861 Cent Restrike (gold) 7 struck	1500.00
1861 Cent Restrike (silver) 12 struck	550.00

COINS AND TOKENS OF HAWAII

The first official coins of Hawaii were the copper cents of 1847 issued by King Kamehameha III. The five cent piece of 1881 and the eighth dollar piece of 1883 are patterns. In 1883 Kalakaua I issued silver dimes, quarters, halves and dollars bearing his bust and showing the Hawaiian coat of arms on the reverse. The plantation tokens listed here were all used as small change on the Islands.

One Cent—1847

Ten Cents 1883

	Fine	V. Fine	Ex. Fine	Unc.	Proof
1847 Cent	$30.00	$40.00	$55.00	$100.00	——
1881 Five Cents	——	——	——	325.00	$400.00
1883 Ten Cents	7.50	10.00	15.00	57.50	187.50
1883 Eighth Dollar (12½¢)	60.00	80.00	110.00	150.00	200.00
1883 Quarter Dollar	6.00	9.00	12.50	20.00	185.00
1883 Half Dollar	13.00	17.50	25.00	100.00	185.00
1883 Dollar	35.00	47.50	60.00	200.00	260.00

HAWAIIAN TOKENS

Thomas Hobron Token—1879

Haiku Plantation—1882

Wailuku Plantation—1871

Wailuku Plantation—1880

	Fine	Ex. Fine
Waterhouse Token 1862. Bust of Kamehameha IV	$225.00	$375.00
Wailuku Plantation Token 1871	70.00	90.00
Wailuku Plantation Token 1880	90.00	150.00
Thomas Hobron Token 1879	75.00	125.00
Haiku Plantation Token	50.00	75.00
Grove Ranch Plantation Token 1886	125.00	175.00

See Coinage Figures on Page 251

ALASKA RURAL REHABILITATION CORPORATION
TOKENS OF 1935

These tokens were issued by the U. S. Government for the use of the colonists of the Matanuska Valley Colonization Project to supply them with much needed Federal aid. They were redeemable only at the ARRC stores. The "Bingles" as they were called, were in use only about six months during 1935-1936 after which they were redeemed for regular U. S. money and destroyed. They were issued on a basis of family dependents. Each token is the size of the corresponding U. S. coin with the exception of the one cent piece which is octagonal. The design is the same on both sides of each denomination.

	V. Fine	Unc.
1¢ Aluminum	$ 8.00	$12.50
5¢ Aluminum	8.00	12.50
10¢ Aluminum	8.00	12.50
25¢ Aluminum	10.00	15.00
50¢ Aluminum	10.00	20.00
$1.00 Aluminum	20.00	30.00
$5.00 Brass	30.00	35.00
$10.00 Brass	40.00	45.00

See Coinage Figures on Page 251

PHILIPPINES UNDER SOVEREIGNTY OF THE U. S.

The 1903-19 issues were struck at Philadelphia and San Francisco. 1920 and after were struck at Manila. Due to World War II the 1944-46 coins were minted at Philadelphia, Denver and San Francisco. The 1946 coins were never released.

Bronze

	Unc.
½ Centavo 1903-08	$ .35
1 Centavo 1903-36	.15

Copper-Nickel

5 Centavos 1903-28	.20
5 Centavos 1918 Rev. of 20 Centavos (Error)	—

Reduced Size

5 Centavos 1930-35	.15

Silver

10 Centavos 1903-06	.25
20 Centavos 1903-06	.50
50 Centavos 1903-06	1.50
1 Peso 1903-06	5.00

Size Reduced

	Unc.
10 Centavos 1907-35	$ .20
20 Centavos 1907-29	.40
20 Centavos 1928 Rev. of 5 Centavos (Error)	—
50 Centavos 1907-21	1.00
1 Peso 1907-12	4.00

Bronze

Centavo 1937-45	.10

Copper-Nickel

5 Centavos 1937-41	.25

Nickel-Silver
Same Type as Cop.-Nic.

5 Centavos 1944-46	.15

Silver

10 Centavos 1937-46	.15
20 Centavos 1937-46	.25
50 Centavos 1944-46	1.00

PHILIPPINES UNDER SOVEREIGNTY OF THE U.S.

Silver Coins Commemorating the Establishment of the Commonwealth of the Philippines, 1935

Murphy and Quezon Facing Each Other

	Unc.
50 Centavos 1936	$3.50

Gov. Gen. Murphy and Quezon   Roosevelt and Quezon

	Unc.		Unc.
1 Peso 1936	$10.00	1 Peso 1936	$10.00

MINTS AND MINT MARKS

Coins struck at Philadelphia (excepting 1942 and later silver five-cent pieces) do not carry a mint mark. The mint mark is found only on coins struck at the branch mints. It is a small letter, usually found on the reverse side (the Lincoln cent is one exception to the rule; there are other exceptions, too). The letters to signify the various mints are as follows:

"C" for Charlotte, North Carolina (on gold coins only).
"CC" for Carson City, Nevada.
"D" for Dahlonega, Georgia (gold coins only, 1838 to 1861).
"D" for Denver, Colorado (from 1906 to date).
"O" for New Orleans, Louisiana.
"P" for Philadelphia, Pennsylvania.
"S" for San Francisco, California.

Location of Mint Marks

The mint mark is of utmost importance to collectors due to the fact that the coinage at the branch mints has usually been much smaller than at Philadelphia and many of the branch mint pieces are very scarce.

MINTS AND MINT MARKS

Half Cents—All coined at Philadelphia, no mint mark.
Large Cents—All coined at Philadelphia, no mint mark.
Flying Eagle Cents—All coined at Philadelphia, no mint mark.
Indian Cents—1908 and 1909, under the wreath on reverse side.
Lincoln Cents—Under the date.
Two Cents, Three Cent Nickels—All coined at Philadelphia, no mint mark.
Three Cents Silver—All coined at Philadelphia, except 1851 New Orleans mint—reverse side.

Shield Nickels—All coined at Philadelphia, no mint mark.

Liberty Nickels—All coined at Philadelphia except 1912 S and D—reverse side to left of word CENTS.

Buffalo Nickels—Reverse side under words FIVE CENTS.

Jefferson Nickels—Reverse side at right of the building.

Jefferson Five-Cent Pieces (1942 to 1945 silver)—above dome on reverse.

Half Dimes—Reverse side either within or below the wreath.

Dimes—Old types on reverse side below or within wreath; Mercury type (1916 to 1945) on the reverse to left of fasces. Roosevelt type, left of bottom of torch on reverse.

Twenty Cents—Reverse, under the eagle.

Quarter Dollars—Old types on reverse under eagle; Standing Liberty type obverse to left of date; Washington type on reverse under eagle.

Half Dollars—1838 and 1839 O mint mark above date; other dates to 1915 on reverse under eagle. 1916 on obverse, 1917 on obverse and reverse. After 1917 on lower left reverse. Franklin type, above bell beam.

Dollars—Old types, on reverse under eagle; Peace type (1921 and after) on reverse above eagle's tail feathers.

Trade Dollars—On reverse under eagle.

Gold Dollars—Reverse under wreath.

Quarter Eagles ($2.50)—1838 and 1839 over the date; other dates previous to 1907 on reverse under the eagle; Indian type (1908-29) on reverse lower left.

Three Dollar Pieces—Reverse under the wreath.

Half Eagles ($5.00)—Same as quarter eagles.

Eagles ($10.00)—Reverse under eagle; after 1907 at left of value.

Double Eagles ($20.00)—Old types on reverse under eagle; St. Gaudens (after 1907) above the date.

QUANTITIES OF COINS STRUCK

Collectors are cautioned that mint reports are not always reliable for estimating the rarity of coins. In the early years of the mint, dies of previous years were often used until they became worn or broken.

It should also be emphasized that quantities reported, particularly for gold and silver, cover the number of coins struck and have no reference to the quantity reaching actual circulation. Many issues were deposited in the treasury as backing for paper currency and were later melted. There are other similar examples.

The rarity of gold pieces struck before 1834, particularly half eagles, can be traced to the fact that the gold content was reduced in 1834, making previous issues greater in value than their face, causing extensive melting and reminting.

The quantities reported by the mint of three dollar gold pieces from 1873 to 1877 and half cents from 1832 to 1836 are subject to doubt.

PROOF TOTALS ARE SHOWN IN PARENTHESES

HALF CENTS Date and Mint Mark	Quantity Minted	HALF CENTS Date and Mint Mark	Quantity Minted	HALF CENTS Date and Mint Mark	Quantity Minted
1793........	31,934	1800........	211,530	1806........	356,000
1794........	81,600	1802........	14,366	1807........	476,000
1795........	25,600	1803........	97,900	1808........	400,000
1796........	115,480	1804........	1,055,312	1809........	1,154,572
1797........	107,048	1805........	814,464	1810........	215,000

HALF CENTS

Date and Mint Mark	Quantity Minted
1811........	63,140
1825........	63,000
1826........	234,000
1828........	606,000
1829........	487,000
1831........	2,200
1832........	154,000
Not in mint report, but accepted as correct.	
1833........	(120,000)
mint report	154,000
1834........	(141,000)
mint report	120,000
1835........	(398,000)
mint report	141,000
1836 mint report	398,000
1849........	39,864
1850........	39,812
1851........	147,672
1853........	129,694
1854........	55,358
1855........	56,500
1856........	40,430
1857........	35,180

LARGE CENTS

Date and Mint Mark	Quantity Minted
1793 Wreath	101,156
1793 Lib. Cap	11,056
1794........	918,521
1795........	82,000
1796........	974,700
1797........	897,510
1798........	979,700
1799........	904,585
1800........	2,822,175
1801........	1,362,837
1802........	3,435,100
1803........	2,471,353
1804........	756,838
1805........	941,116
1806........	348,000
1807........	727,221
1808........	1,109,000
1809........	222,867
1810........	1,458,500
1811........	218,025
1812........	1,075,500
1813........	418,000
1814........	357,830
1816........	2,820,982
1817........	3,948,400
1818........	3,167,000
1819........	2,671,000
1820........	4,407,550

LARGE CENTS

Date and Mint Mark	Quantity Minted
1821........	389,000
1822........	2,072,339
1823........	855,730
1824........	1,262,000
1825........	1,461,100
1826........	1,517,425
1827........	2,357,732
1828........	2,260,624
1829........	1,414,500
1830........	1,711,500
1831........	3,359,260
1832........	2,362,000
1833........	2,739,000
1834........	1,855,100
1835........	3,878,400
1836........	2,111,000
1837........	5,558,300
1838........	6,370,200
1839........	3,128,661
1840........	2,462,700
1841........	1,597,367
1842........	2,383,390
1843........	2,428,320
1844........	2,398,752
1845........	3,894,804
1846........	4,120,800
1847........	6,183,669
1848........	6,415,799
1849........	4,178,500
1850........	4,426,844
1851........	9,889,707
1852........	5,063,094
1853........	6,641,131
1854........	4,236,156
1855........	1,574,829
1856........	2,690,463
1857........	333,456

EAGLE CENTS

1857........	17,450,000
1858 (L.L. 80, S.L. 200)..	24,600,000

INDIAN CENTS

1859........	36,400,000
1860 (400)...	20,566,000
1861 (375)...	10,100,000
1862 (450)...	28,075,000
1863 (460)...	49,840,000
1864 cop. nic. (300)..	13,740,000
1864 bronze (150).....	39,233,714
1864L (20)..	Unknown
1865 (500)..	35,429,286

INDIAN CENTS

Date and Mint Mark	Quantity Minted
1866 (725)...	9,826,500
1867 (625)...	9,821,000
1868 (600)...	10,266,500
1869 (600)...	6,420,000
1870 (1,000).	5,275,000
1871 (960)...	3,929,500
1872 (950)...	4,042,000
1873 (600)...	11,676,500
1874 (700)...	14,187,500
1875 (700)...	13,528,000
1876 (1,150).	7,944,000
1877 (510)...	852,500
1878 (2350).	5,799,850
1879 (3200).	16,231,200
1880 (3955).	38,964,955
1881 (3575).	39,211,575
1882 (3100).	38,581,100
1883 (6609).	45,598,109
1884 (3942).	23,261,742
1885 (3790).	11,765,384
1886 (4290).	17,654,290
1887 (2960).	45,226,483
1888 (4582).	37,494,414
1889 (3336).	48,869,361
1890 (2740).	57,182,854
1891 (2350).	47,072,350
1892 (2745).	37,649,832
1893 (2195).	46,642,195
1894 (2632).	16,752,132
1895 (2062).	38,343,636
1896 (1862).	39,057,293
1897 (1938).	50,466,330
1898 (1795).	49,823,079
1899 (2031).	53,600,031
1900 (2262).	66,833,764
1901 (1985).	79,611,143
1902 (2018).	87,376,722
1903 (1790).	85,094,493
1904 (1817).	61,328,015
1905 (2152).	80,719,163
1906 (1725).	96,022,255
1907 (1475).	108,138,618
1908 (1620).	32,327,987
1908S.......	1,115,000
1909.. (2175)	14,370,645
1909S.......	309,000

LINCOLN CENTS

1909 (2198).	72,702,618
1909 V.D.B. (420).....	27,995,000
1909S.......	1,825,000
1909S V.D.B.	484,000
1910 (2405).	146,801,218

LINCOLN CENTS

Date and Mint Mark	Quantity Minted
1910S	6,045,000
1911 (1733)	101,177,787
1911D	12,672,000
1911S	4,026,000
1912 (2145)	68,153,060
1912D	10,411,000
1912S	4,431,000
1913 (2848)	76,532,352
1913D	15,804,000
1913S	6,101,000
1914 (1365)	75,238,432
1914D	1,193,000
1914S	4,137,000
1915 (1150)	29,092,120
1915D	22,050,000
1915S	4,833,000
1916 (1050)	131,833,677
1916D	35,956,000
1916S	22,510,000
1917	196,429,785
1917D	55,120,000
1917S	32,620,000
1918	288,104,634
1918D	47,830,000
1918S	34,680,000
1919	392,021,000
1919D	57,154,000
1919S	139,760,000
1920	310,165,000
1920D	49,280,000
1920S	46,220,000
1921	39,157,000
1921S	15,274,000
1922D	7,160,000
1923	74,723,000
1923S	8,700,000
1924	75,178,000
1924D	2,520,000
1924S	11,696,000
1925	139,949,000
1925D	22,580,000
1925S	26,380,000
1926	157,088,000
1926D	28,020,000
1926S	4,550,000
1927	144,440,000
1927D	27,170,000
1927S	14,276,000
1928	134,116,000
1928D	31,170,000
1928S	17,266,000
1929	185,262,000
1929D	41,730,000
1929S	50,148,000

LINCOLN CENTS

Date and Mint Mark	Quantity Minted
1930	157,415,000
1930D	40,100,000
1930S	24,286,000
1931	19,396,000
1931D	4,480,000
1931S	866,000
1932	9,062,000
1932D	10,500,000
1933	14,360,000
1933D	6,200,000
1934	219,080,000
1934D	28,446,000
1935	245,388,000
1935D	47,000,000
1935S	38,702,000
1936 (5569)	309,637,569
1936D	40,620,000
1936S	29,130,000
1937 (9320)	309,179,320
1937D	50,430,000
1937S	34,500,000
1938 (14734)	156,696,734
1938D	20,010,000
1938S	15,180,000
1939 (13520)	316,479,520
1939D	15,160,000
1939S	52,070,000
1940 (15872)	586,825,872
1940D	81,390,000
1940S	112,940,000
1941 (21100)	887,039,100
1941D	128,700,000
1941S	92,360,000
1942 (32600)	657,828,600
1942D	206,698,000
1942S	85,590,000
1943	684,628,670
1943D	217,660,000
1943S	191,550,000
1944	1,435,400,000
1944D	430,578,000
1944S	282,760,000
1945	1,040,515,000
1945D	226,268,000
1945S	181,770,000
1946	991,655,000
1946D	315,690,000
1946S	198,100,000
1947	190,555,000
1947D	194,750,000
1947S	99,000,000
1948	317,570,000
1948D	172,637,500
1948S	81,735,000

LINCOLN CENTS

Date and Mint Mark	Quantity Minted
1949	217,490,000
1949D	154,370,500
1949S	64,290,000
1950 (51386)	272,686,386
1950D	334,950,000
1950S	118,505,000
1951 (57500)	294,633,500
1951D	625,355,000
1951S	100,890,000
1952 (81980)	186,856,980
1952D	746,130,000
1952S	137,800,004
1953 (128800)	256,883,800
1953D	700,515,000
1953S	181,835,000
1954 (233,300)	71,873,350
1954D	251,552,500
1954S	96,190,000
1955 (378,200)	330,958,200
1955D	563,257,500
1955S	44,610,000
1956 (669,384)	421,414,384
1956D	1,098,201,100
1957 (1,247,952)	283,787,952
1957D	1,051,342,000
1958 (875, 652)	253,400,652
1958D	800,953,000
1959 (1,149,291)	610,864,291
1959D	1,279,760,000
1960 (1,691,602)	588,096,602
1960D	1,580,884,000

2-CENT BRONZE

1864 All kinds	19,847,500
1865	13,640,000
1866	3,177,000
1867	2,938,750
1868	2,803,750
1869	1,546,500
1870	861,250
1871	721,250
1872	65,000
1873	

NICKEL 3-CENT

1865	11,382,000
1866	4,801,000
1867	3,915,000
1868	3,252,000

[234]

NICKEL 3-CENT

Date and Mint Mark	Quantity Minted
1869........	1,604,000
1870........	1,335,000
1871........	604,000
1872........	862,000
1873........	1,173,000
1874........	790,000
1875........	228,000
1876........	162,000
1877 (proofs available)	
1878 Proofs only	2,350
1879 (3200).	41,200
1880 (3955).	24,955
1881 (3575).	1,080,575
1882 (3100).	25,300
1883 (6609).	10,609
1884 (3942).	5,642
1885 (3790).	4,790
1886 (4290)..	4,290
1887 All kinds(2960)	7,961
1888 (4582).	41,083
1889 (3436).	21,561

NICKEL 5-CENT

Date and Mint Mark	Quantity Minted
1866 All kinds, rays through stars	14,742,500
1867 All kinds	30,909,500
1868........	28,817,000
1869........	16,395,000
1870........	4,806,000
1871........	561,000
1872........	6,036,000
1873........	4,550,000
1874........	3,538,000
1875........	2,097,000
1876........	2,530,000
1877 Est. issued (500)	500
1878 (2350).	2,350
1879 (3200).	29,100
1880 (3955).	19,955
1881 (3575).	72,375
1882 (3100).	11,476,600
1883 Shield type (5419)	1,456,919
1883 Liberty, without CENTS (9152)*....	5,479,519
1883 Liberty, with CENTS	16,032,983
1884 (3942).	11,273,942
1885 (3790).	1,476,490
1886 (4290).	3,330,290
1887 (2960).	15,263,652
1888 (4582).	10,720,483
1889 (3336).	15,881,362

All Types*

NICKEL 5-CENT

Date and Mint Mark	Quantity Minted
1890 (2740).	16,259,271
1891 (2350).	16,834,350
1892 (2745).	11,699,642
1893 (2195).	13,370,195
1894 (2632).	5,413,132
1895 (2062).	9,979,884
1896 (1862).	8,842,920
1897 (1938).	20,428,735
1898 (1795).	12,532,087
1899 (2031).	26,029,031
1900 (2262).	27,255,995
1901 (1985).	26,480,213
1902 (2018).	31,480,579
1903 (1790).	28,006,725
1904 (1817).	21,404,984
1905 (2152).	29,827,276
1906 (1725).	38,613,725
1907 (1475).	39,214,800
1908 (1620).	22,686,177
1909 (4763).	11,590,526
1910 (2405).	30,169,353
1911 (1733).	39,559,372
1912 (2145).	26,236,714
1912D......	8,474,000
1912S.......	238,000
1913........	5
1913 Indian head— Type 1—Buffalo on mound.....	30,993,520
1913S Type 1—Buffalo mound*(2594)	2,105,000
1913D Type 1—Buffalo on mound..	5,337,000
1913 Indian head— Type 2—Buffalo on plane......	29,858,700
1913S Type 2—Buffalo on plane...	1,209,000
1913D Type 2—Buffalo on plane...	4,156,000
1914 (1275).	20,665,738
1914D......	3,912,000
1914S......	3,470,000
1915 (1050).	20,987,270
1915D......	7,569,500
1915S......	1,505,000
1916 (600)..	63,498,066
1916D......	13,333,000
1916S.......	11,860,000
1917........	51,424,029
1917D......	9,910,800
1917S.......	4,193,000
1918........	32,086,314
1918D All kinds	8,362,000

NICKEL 5-CENT

Date and Mint Mark	Quantity Minted
1918S.......	4,882,000
1919........	60,868,000
1919D......	8,006,000
1919S.......	7,521,000
1920........	63,093,000
1920D......	9,418,000
1920S.......	9,689,000
1921........	10,663,000
1921S.......	1,557,000
1923........	35,715,000
1923S.......	6,142,000
1924........	21,620,000
1924D......	5,258,000
1924S.......	1,437,000
1925........	35,565,100
1925D......	4,450,000
1925S.......	6,256,000
1926........	44,693,000
1926D......	5,638,000
1926S.......	970,000
1927........	37,981,000
1927D......	5,730,000
1927S.......	3,430,000
1928........	23,411,000
1928D......	6,436,000
1928S......	6,936,000
1929........	36,446,000
1929D......	8,370,000
1929S.......	7,754,000
1930........	22,849,000
1930S.......	5,435,000
1931S.......	1,200,000
1934........	20,213,003
1934D......	7,480,000
1935........	58,264,000
1935D......	12,092,000
1935S.......	10,300,000
1936 (4420)	119,001,420
1936D......	24,418,000
1936S.......	14,930,000
1937 (5769).	79,485,769
1937D......	17,826,000
1937S.......	5,635,000
1938D Buffalo	7,020,000
1938 Jefferson (19365)	19,515,365
1938D Jefferson	5,376,000
1938S Jefferson	4,105,000
1939 (12535)	120,627,535
1939D......	3,514,000
1939S.......	6,630,000
1940 (14158)	176,499,158
1940D......	43,540,000
1940S.......	39,690,000

[235]

NICKEL 5-CENT

Date and Mint Mark	Quantity Minted
1941 (18720)	203,283,720
1941D	53,432,000
1941S	43,445,000
1942 (29600)	49,818,600
1942D	13,938,000

W. T. SILVER 5-c Pc.

Date and Mint Mark	Quantity Minted
1942P (27600)	57,900,600
1942S	32,900,000
1943P	271,165,000
1943D	15,294,000
1943S	104,060,000
1944P	119,150,000
1944D	32,309,000
1944S	21,640,000
1945P	119,408,100
1945D	37,158,000
1945S	58,939,000

REGULAR COMP.

Date and Mint Mark	Quantity Minted
1946	161,116,000
1946D	45,292,200
1946S	13,560,000
1947	95,000,000
1947D	37,822,000
1947S	24,720,000
1948	89,348,000
1948D	44,734,000
1948S	11,300,000
1949	60,652,000
1949D	35,238,000
1949S	9,716,000
1950 (51386)	9,847,386
1950D	2,630,030
1951 (57500)	28,689,500
1951D	20,460,000
1951S	7,776,000
1952 (81980)	64,069,980
1952D	30,638,000
1952S	20,572,000
1953 (128800)	46,772,800
1953D	59,878,600
1953S	19,210,900
1954 (233,300)	47,917,350
1954D	117,183,060
1954S	29,384,000
1955 (378,200)	8,266,200
1955D	74,464,100
1956 (669,384)	35,885,384
1956D	67,222,040
1957 (1,247,952)	39,655,952
1957D	136,828,900

REGULAR COMP.

Date and Mint Mark	Quantity Minted
1958 (875,652)	17,963,652
1958D	168,249,120
1959 (1,149,291)	28,397,291
1959D	160,738,240
1960 (1,691,602)	57,107,602
1960D	192,582,180

SILVER 3-CENT

Date	Quantity Minted
1851	5,447,400
1851O	720,000
1852	18,663,500
1853	11,400,000
1854 Three outlines to star, L.D.	671,000
1855	139,000
1856	1,458,000
1857	1,042,000
1858	1,604,000
1859 Two outlines to star, S.D.	365,000
1860	287,000
1861	498,000
1862	363,550
1863 (460)	21,460
1864 (470)	470
1865 (500)	8,500
1866 (725)	22,725
1867 (625)	4,625
1868 (600)	4,100
1869 (600)	5,100
1870 (1000)	4,000
1871 (960)	4,260
1872 (950)	1,950
1873 (600)	600

HALF DIMES

Date	Quantity Minted
1794, 1795	86,416
1796	10,230
1797	44,527
1800	24,000
1801	33,910
1802 (Rare)	13,010
1803	37,850
1805	15,600
1829	1,230,000
1830	1,240,000
1831	1,242,700
1832	965,000
1833	1,370,000
1834	1,480,000
1835	2,760,000
1836	1,900,000

HALF DIMES

Date and Mint Mark	Quantity Minted
1837	2,276,000
1837 No stars	2,255,000
1838 With stars	2,255,000
1839	1,069,150
1839O	1,096,550
1840	1,344,085
1840O	935,000
1841	1,150,000
1841O	815,000
1842	815,000
1842O	350,000
1843	1,165,000
1844	430,000
1844O	220,000
1845	1,564,000
1846	27,000
1847	1,274,000
1848	668,000
1848O	600,000
1849	1,309,000
1849O	140,000
1850	955,000
1850O	690,000
1851	781,000
1851O	860,000
1852	1,000,500
1852O	260,000
1853	13,345,020
1853O	2,360,000
1854	5,740,000
1854O	1,560,000
1855	1,750,000
1855O	600,000
1856	4,880,000
1856O	1,100,000
1857	7,280,000
1857O	1,380,000
1858	3,500,000
1858O	1,660,000
1859	340,000
1859O	560,000
1860 Stars	100
1860 Legend	799,000
1860O Legend	1,060,000
1861	3,281,000
1862	1,492,550
1863 (460)	18,460
1863S	100,000
1864 (470)	470
1864S	90,000
1865 (500)	13,500
1865S	120,000
1866 (725)	10,725
1866S	120,000

HALF DIMES		DIMES		DIMES	
Date and Mint Mark	Quantity Minted	Date and Mint Mark	Quantity Minted	Date and Mint Mark	Quantity Minted
1867 (625)..	8,625	1842O......	2,020,000	1869S......	450,000
1867S......	120,000	1843........	1,370,000	1870 (1000).	471,500
1868 (600)..	85,900	1843O......	150,000	1870S......	50,000
1868S......	280,000	1844........	72,500	1871 (960)..	753,610
1869 (600)..	208,600	1845........	1,755,000	1871CC.....	20,100
1869S......	230,000	1845O......	230,000	1871S......	320,000
1870 (1000).	536,600	1846........	31,300	1872 (950)..	2,396,450
1871 (960)..	1,488,860	1847........	245,000	1872CC.....	24,000
1871S......	161,000	1848........	451,500	1872S......	190,000
1872 (950)..	2,947,950	1849........	839,000	1873 No Arrows	
1872S All kinds	837,000	1849O......	300,000	(600).....	1,568,600
1873 (600)..	712,600	1850........	1,931,500	1873 Arrows	
1873S......	324,000	1850O......	510,000		(800)2,378,500
		1851........	1,026,500	1873CC No	
DIMES		1851O......	400,000	Arrows....	12,400
1796........	22,135	1852........	1,535,500	1873CC Arrows	18,791
1797 All kinds	25,261	1852O......	430,000	1873S......	455,000
1798 All kinds	27,550	1853	12,173,010	1874 (700)..	2,940,700
1800........	21,760	1853O......	1,100,000	1874CC.....	10,817
1801........	34,640	1854........	4,470,000	1874S......	240,000
1802........	10,975	1854O......	1,770,000	1875 (700)..	10,350,700
1803........	33,040	1855........	2,075,000	1875CC.....	4,645,000
1804........	8,265	1856........	5,780,000	1875S......	9,070,000
1805........	120,780	1856O......	1,180,000	1876 (1150).	11,461,150
1807........	165,000	1856S.......	70,000	1876CC.....	8,270,000
1809........	44,710	1857........	5,580,000	1876S......	10,420,000
1811 11 over 09	65,180	1857O......	1,540,000	1877 (510)..	7,310,510
1814 All kinds	421,500	1858........	1,540,000	1877CC.....	7,700,000
1820 All kinds	942,587	1858O......	290,000	1877S......	2,340,000
1821 All kinds	1,186,512	1858S.......	60,000	1878 (800)..	1,678,800
1822........	100,000	1859	430,000	1878CC.....	200,000
1823 All kinds	440,000	1859O......	480,000	1879 (1100).	15,100
1824........	———	1859S.......	60,000	1880 (1355).	37,355
1825........	510,000	1860S (Stars		1881 (975)..	24,975
1827........	1,215,000	on Obv.)...	140,000	1882 (1100).	3,911,100
1828 All kinds	125,000	1860........	607,000	1883 (1039).	7,675,712
1829 All kinds	770,000	1860O......	40,000	1884 (875)..	3,366,380
1830 All kinds	510,000	1861........	1,924,000	1884S......	564,969
1831 All kinds	771,350	1861S.......	172,500	1885 (930)..	2,533,427
1832........	522,500	1862........	847,550	1885S......	43,690
1833........	485,000	1862S.......	180,750	1886 (886)..	6,377,570
1834 All kinds	635,000	1863 (460)..	14,460	1886S......	206,524
1835........	1,410,000	1863S.......	157,500	1887 (710)..	11,283,939
1836........	1,190,000	1864 (470)..	39,070	1887S......	4,454,450
1837 All kinds	1,042,000	1864S......	230,000	1888 (832)..	5,496,487
1838O......	402,434	1865 (500)..	10,500	1888S......	1,720,000
1838........	1,992,500	1865S.......	175,000	1889 (711)..	7,380,711
1839........	1,053,115	1866 (725)..	8,725	1889S......	972,678
1839O	1,243,272	1866S......	135,000	1890 (590)..	9,911,541
1840 All kinds	1,358,580	1867 (625)..	6,625	1890S......	1,423,076
1840O......	1,175,000	1867S......	140,000	1891 (600)..	15,310,600
1841........	1,622,500	1868 (600)..	466,250	1891O......	4,540,000
1841O......	2,007,500	1868S......	260,000	1891S......	3,196,116
1842........	1,887,500	1869 (600)..	256,600	1892 (1245).	12,121,245

DIMES

Date and Mint Mark	Quantity Minted
1892O	3,841,700
1892S	990,710
1893 (792)	3,340,792
1893O	1,760,000
1893S	2,491,401
1894 (972)	1,330,972
1894O	720,000
1894S	24
1895 (880)	690,880
1895O	440,000
1895S	1,120,000
1896 (762)	2,000,762
1896O	610,000
1896S	575,056
1897 (731)	10,869,264
1897O	666,000
1897S	1,342,844
1898 (735)	16,320,735
1898O	2,130,000
1898S	1,702,507
1899 (846)	19,580,846
1899O	2,650,000
1899S	1,867,493
1900 (912)	17,600,912
1900O	2,010,000
1900S	5,168,270
1901 (813)	18,860,478
1901O	5,620,000
1901S	593,022
1902 (777)	21,380,777
1902O	4,500,000
1902S	2,070,000
1903 (755)	19,500,755
1903O	8,180,000
1903S	613,300
1904 (670)	14,601,027
1904S	800,000
1905 (727)	14,552,350
1905O	3,400,000
1905S	6,855,199
1906 (675)	19,958,406
1906D	4,060,000
1906O	2,610,000
1906S	3,136,640
1907 (575)	22,220,575
1907D	4,080,000
1907O	5,058,000
1907S	3,178,470
1908 (545)	10,600,545
1908D	7,490,000
1908O	1,789,000
1908S	3,220,000
1909 (650)	10,240,650
1909D	954,000

DIMES

Date and Mint Mark	Quantity Minted
1909O	2,287,000
1909S	1,000,000
1910 (551)	11,520,551
1910D	3,490,000
1910S	1,240,000
1911 (543)	18,870,543
1911D	11,209,000
1911S	3,520,000
1912 (700)	19,350,700
1912D	11,760,000
1912S	3,420,000
1913 (622)	19,760,622
1913S	510,000
1914 (425)	17,360,655
1914D	11,908,000
1914S	2,100,000
1915 (450)	5,620,450
1915S	960,000
1916 Old type	18,490,000
1916S Old type	5,820,000
1916 New type (Mercury Head)	22,180,080
1916D New type	264,000
1916S New type	10,450,000
1917	55,230,000
1917D	9,402,000
1917S	27,330,000
1918	26,680,000
1918D	22,674,800
1918S	19,300,000
1919	35,740,000
1919D	9,939,000
1919S	8,850,000
1920	59,030,000
1920D	19,171,000
1920S	13,820,000
1921	1,230,000
1921D	1,080,000
1923	50,130,000
1923S	6,440,000
1924	24,010,000
1924D	6,810,000
1924S	7,120,000
1925	25,610,000
1925D	5,117,000
1925S	5,850,000
1926	32,160,000
1926D	6,828,000
1926S	1,520,000
1927	28,080,000
1927D	4,812,000
1927S	4,770,000

DIMES

Date and Mint Mark	Quantity Minted
1928	19,480,000
1928D	4,161,000
1928S	7,400,000
1929	25,970,000
1929D	5,034,000
1929S	4,730,000
1930	6,770,000
1930S	1,843,000
1931	3,150,000
1931D	1,260,000
1931S	1,800,000
1934	24,080,000
1934D	6,772,000
1935	58,830,000
1935D	10,477,000
1935S	15,840,000
1936 (4130)	87,504,130
1936D	16,132,000
1936S	9,210,000
1937 (5756)	56,865,756
1937D	14,146,000
1937S	9,740,000
1938 (8728)	22,198,728
1938D	5,537,000
1938S	8,090,000
1939 (9321)	67,749,321
1939D	24,394,000
1939S	10,540,000
1940 (11827)	65,361,827
1940D	21,198,000
1940S	21,560,000
1941 (16557)	175,106,557
1941D	45,634,000
1941S	43,090,000
1942 (22329)	205,432,329
1942D	60,740,000
1942S	49,300,000
1943	191,710,000
1943D	71,949,000
1943S	60,400,000
1944	231,410,000
1944D	62,224,000
1944S	49,490,000
1945	159,130,000
1945D	40,245,000
1945S	41,920,000
1946	255,250,000
1946D	61,043,500
1946S	27,900,000
1947	121,520,000
1947D	46,835,000
1947S	31,840,000
1948	74,950,000
1948D	52,841,000

DIMES

Date and Mint Mark	Quantity Minted
1948S	35,520,000
1949	30,940,000
1949D	26,034,000
1949S	13,510,000
1950 (51386)	50,181,500
1950D	46,803,000
1950S	20,440,000
1951 (57500)	103,937,602
1951D	52,191,800
1951S	31,630,000
1952 (81980)	99,122,073
1952D	122,100,000
1952S	44,419,500
1953 (128800)	53,618,920
1953D	136,433,000
1953S	39,180,000
1954 (233300)	114,243,503
1954D	106,397,000
1954S	22,860,000
1955 (378,200)	12,828,381
1955D	13,959,000
1955S	18,510,000
1956 (669,384)	109,309,384
1956D	108,015,100
1957 (1,247,952)	161,407,952
1957D	113,354,330
1958 (875,652)	32,785,652
1958D	136,564,600
1959 (1,149,291)	86,929,291
1959D	164,919,790
1960 (1,691,602)	72,081,602
1960D	200,160,400

20-CENT PIECES

Date and Mint Mark	Quantity Minted
1875 (1200)	39,700
1875CC	133,290
1875S	1,155,000
1876 (1150)	15,900
1876CC	10,000
1877 (510)	510
1878 (600)	600

QUARTER DOLLARS

Date and Mint Mark	Quantity Minted
1796	5,894
1804	6,738
1805	121,394
1806	206,124
1807	220,643
1815	69,232
1818	361,174
1819	144,000
1820	127,440
1821	216,850
1822	64,084
1823 over 2	17,801
1824	—
1825	168,000
1827	4,000
1828	102,000
1831	398,000
1832	320,000
1833	156,000
1834	286,000
1835	1,952,000
1836	472,000
1837	252,400
1838	832,000
1839	491,146
1840O All kinds	425,200
1840	188,127
1841	120,000
1841O	452,000
1842	88,000
1842O	769,000
1843	645,600
1843O	968,000
1844	421,200
1844O	740,000
1845	922,000
1846	510,000
1847	734,000
1847O	368,000
1848	146,000
1849	340,000
1849O	—
1850	190,800
1850O	412,000
1851	160,000
1851O	88,000
1852	177,060
1852O	96,000
1853	15,254,220
1853O	1,332,000
1854	12,380,000
1854O	1,484,000
1855	2,857,000
1855O	176,000
1855S	396,400
1856	7,264,000
1856O	968,000
1856S	286,000
1857	9,644,000
1857O	1,180,000

QUARTER DOLLARS

Date and Mint Mark	Quantity Minted
1857S	82,000
1858	7,368,000
1858O	520,000
1858S	121,000
1859	1,344,000
1859O	260,000
1859S	80,000
1860	805,400
1860O	388,000
1860S	56,000
1861	4,854,600
1861S	96,000
1862	932,550
1862S	67,000
1863 (460)	192,060
1864 (470)	94,070
1864S	20,000
1865 (500)	59,300
1865S	41,000
1866 (725)	17,525
1866S	28,000
1867 (625)	20,625
1867S	48,000
1868 (600)	30,000
1868S	96,000
1869 (600)	16,600
1869S	76,000
1870 (1000)	87,400
1870CC	8,340
1871 (960)	171,232
1871CC	10,890
1871S	30,900
1872 (950)	182,950
1872CC	9,100
1872S	103,000
1873 No Arrows (600)	220,600
1873 Arrows (540)	1,263,700
1873CC No Arrows	4,000
1873CC Arrows	12,462
1873S	156,000
1874 Arrows (700)	471,900
1874S Arrows	392,000
1875 (700)	4,293,500
1875CC	140,000
1875S	680,000
1876 (1150)	17,817,150
1876CC	4,944,000
1876S	8,596,000
1877 (510)	10,911,710
1877CC	4,192,000
1877S	8,996,000

[239]

QUARTER DOLLARS

Date and Mint Mark	Quantity Minted
1878 (800)..	2,260,800
1878CC.....	996,000
1878S......	140,000
1879 (1100).	14,700
1880 (1355).	14,955
1881 (975)..	12,975
1882 (1100).	16,300
1883 (1039).	15,439
1884 (875)..	8,875
1885 (930)..	14,530
1886 (886)..	5,886
1887 (710)..	10,710
1888 (832)..	10,833
1888S......	1,216,000
1889 (711)..	12,711
1890 (590)..	80,590
1891 (600)..	3,920,600
1891O......	68,000
1891S......	2,216,000
1892 (1245).	8,237,245
1892O......	2,640,000
1892S......	964,079
1893 (792)..	5,444,815
1893O......	3,396,000
1893S......	1,454,535
1894 (972)..	3,432,972
1894O......	2,852,000
1894S......	2,648,821
1895 (880)..	4,440,880
1895O......	2,816,000
1895S......	1,764,681
1896 (762)..	3,874,815
1896O......	1,484,000
1896S......	188,039
1897 (731)..	8,140,731
1897O......	1,414,800
1897S......	542,229
1898 (735)..	11,100,735
1898O......	1,868,000
1898S......	1,020,592
1899 (846)..	12,624,846
1899O......	2,644,000
1899S......	708,000
1900 (912)..	10,016,912
1900O......	3,416,000
1900S......	1,858,585
1901 (813)..	8,892,813
1901O......	1,612,000
1901S......	72,664
1902 (777)..	12,197,744
1902O......	4,748,000
1902S......	1,524,612
1903 (755)..	9,670,064
1903O......	3,500,000

QUARTER DOLLARS

Date and Mint Mark	Quantity Minted
1903S......	1,036,000
1904 (670)..	9,588,813
1904O......	2,456,000
1905 (727)..	4,968,250
1905O......	1,230,000
1905S......	1,884,000
1906 (675)..	3,656,435
1906D......	3,280,000
1906O......	2,056,000
1907 (575)..	7,192,575
1907D......	2,484,000
1907O......	4,560,000
1907S......	1,360,000
1908 (545)..	4,232,545
1908D......	5,788,000
1908O......	6,244,000
1908S......	784,000
1909 (650)..	9,268,650
1909D......	5,114,000
1909O......	712,000
1909S......	1,348,000
1910 (551)..	2,244,551
1910D......	1,500,000
1911 (543)..	3,720,543
1911D......	933,600
1911S......	988,000
1912 (700)..	4,400,700
1912S......	708,000
1913 (613)..	484,613
1913D......	1,450,800
1913S......	40,000
1914 (380)..	6,244,610
1914D......	3,046,000
1914S......	264,000
1915 (450)..	3,480,450
1915D......	3,694,000
1915S......	704,000
1916 Old type.	1,788,000
1916D Old type	6,540,800
1916 New type	52,000
1917 Stars at sides of eagle	8,792,000
1917D Stars at sides of eagle......	1,509,200
1917S Stars at sides of eagle......	1,952,000
1917 3 stars below eagle.	13,880,000
1917D 3 stars below eagle.	6,224,400
1917S 3 stars below eagle.	5,552,000
1918........	14,240,000
1918D......	7,380,000

QUARTER DOLLARS

Date and Mint Mark	Quantity Minted
1918S......	11,072,000
1919........	11,324,000
1919D......	1,944,000
1919S.......	1,836,000
1920........	27,860,000
1920D......	3,586,400
1920S......	6,380,000
1921........	1,916,000
1923........	9,716,000
1923S.......	1,360,000
1924........	10,920,000
1924D......	3,112,000
1924S......	2,860,000
1925........	12,280,000
1926........	11,316,000
1926D......	1,716,000
1926S......	2,700,000
1927........	11,912,000
1927D......	976,400
1927S.......	396,000
1928........	6,336,000
1928D......	1,627,600
1928S.......	2,644,000
1929........	11,140,000
1929D......	1,358,000
1929S......	1,764,000
1930........	5,632,000
1930S.......	1,556,000
1932 Washington head...	5,404,000
1932D......	436,800
1932S......	408,000
1934........	31,912,052
1934D......	3,527,200
1935........	32,484,000
1935D......	5,780,000
1935S.......	5,660,000
1936 (3837) .	41,303,837
1936D......	5,374,000
1936S......	3,828,000
1937 (5542) .	19,701,542
1937D......	7,189,600
1937S.......	1,652,000
1938 (8045) .	9,480,045
1938S.......	2,832,000
1939 (8795) .	33,548,795
1939D......	7,092,000
1939S......	2,628,000
1940 (11246)	35,715,246
1940D......	2,797,600
1940S......	8,244,000
1941 (15287)	79,047,287
1941D......	16,714,800
1941S.......	16,080,000

QUARTER DOLLARS

Date and Mint Mark	Quantity Minted
1942 (21123)	102,117,123
1942D	17,487,200
1942S	19,384,000
1943	99,700,000
1943D	16,095,600
1943S	21,700,000
1944	104,956,000
1944D	14,600,000
1944S	12,560,000
1945	74,372,000
1945D	12,341,600
1945S	17,004,001
1946	53,436,000
1946D	9,072,800
1946S	4,204,000
1947	22,556,000
1947D	15,338,400
1947S	5,532,000
1948	35,196,000
1948D	16,766,800
1948S	15,960,000
1949	9,312,000
1949D	10,068,400
1950 (51386)	24,971,512
1950D	21,075,600
1950S	10,284,004
1951 (57500)	43,505,602
1951D	35,354,800
1951S	8,948,000
1952 (81980)	38,862,073
1952D	49,795,200
1952S	13,707,800
1953 (128800)	18,664,920
1953D	56,112,400
1953S	14,016,000
1954 (233,300)	54,645,503
1954D	46,305,500
1954S	11,834,722
1955 (378,200)	18,558,381
1955D	3,182,400
1956 (669,384)	44,813,384
1956D	32,334,500
1957 (1,247,952)	47,779,952
1957D	77,924,160
1958 (875,652)	7,235,652
1958D	78,124,900
1959 (1,149,291)	25,533,291
1959D	62,054,232
1960 (1,691,602)	30,855,602
1960D	63,000,324

HALF DOLLARS

Date and Mint Mark	Quantity Minted
1794	5,300
1795	317,836
1796	?
1797	3,918
1801	30,289
1802	29,890
1803	31,715
1804 (Unknown)	156,519
1805	211,722
1806	839,576
1807 Face to right	301,076
1807 Face to left	750,500
1808	1,368,600
1809	1,405,810
1810	1,276,276
1811	1,203,644
1812	1,628,059
1813	1,241,903
1814 All kinds	1,039,075
1815 (Mint Report for 1816)	47,150
1817 All kinds	1,215,567
1818 All kinds	1,960,322
1819 All kinds	2,208,000
1820 All kinds	751,122
1821	1,305,797
1822	1,559,573
1823 All kinds	1,694,200
1824 All kinds	3,504,954
1825	2,943,166
1826 All kinds	4,004,180
1827 All kinds	5,493,400
1828 All kinds	3,075,200
1829 All kinds	3,712,156
1830 All kinds	4,764,800
1831	5,873,660
1832 All kinds	4,797,000
1833	5,206,000
1834 All kinds	6,412,004
1835	5,352,006
1836 All kinds	6,546,200
1837 All kinds	3,629,820
1838	3,546,000
1838O	(20)
1839 All kinds	3,334,560
1839O	162,976
1840 All kinds	1,435,008
1840O	855,100
1841 All kinds	310,000

HALF DOLLARS

Date and Mint Mark	Quantity Minted
1841O All kinds	401,000
1842 All kinds	2,012,764
1842O	957,000
1843 All kinds	3,844,000
1843O	2,268,000
1844 All kinds	1,766,000
1844O All kinds	2,005,000
1845	589,000
1845O All kinds	2,094,000
1846 All kinds	2,210,000
1846O All kinds	2,304,000
1847 All kinds	1,156,000
1847O All kinds	2,584,000
1848	580,000
1848O	3,180,000
1849 All kinds	1,252,000
1849O	2,310,000
1850	227,000
1850O	2,456,000
1851	200,750
1851O	402,000
1852	77,130
1852O	144,000
1853O	1,328,000
1853 Arrows and rays	3,532,708
1854	2,982,000
1854O	5,240,000
1855	759,500
1855O	3,688,000
1855S	129,950
1856	938,000
1856O	2,658,000
1856S	211,000
1857	1,988,000
1857O	818,000
1857S	158,000
1858	4,226,000
1858O	7,294,000
1858S	476,000
1859	748,000
1859O	2,834,000
1859S	566,000
1860	303,700
1860O	1,290,000
1860S	472,000
1861	2,888,400
1861O Struck by U.S. Govt	330,000

[241]

HALF DOLLARS

Date and Mint Mark	Quantity Minted
1861O For Louisiana...	1,240,000
1861O For Confed.....	962,633
1861S	939,500
1862........	252,350
1862S	1,352,000
1863 (460)..	503,660
1863S......	916,000
1864 (470)..	379,570
1864S......	658,000
1865 (500)..	511,900
1865S......	675,000
1866S......	1,054,000
1866 Motto —"In God We Trust" (725)	745,625
1867 (625)..	424,325
1867S......	1,196,000
1868 (600)..	378,200
1868S......	1,160,000
1869 (600)..	795,900
1869S......	656,000
1870 (1000).	600,900
1870CC.....	54,617
1870S......	1,004,000
1871 (960)..	1,165,360
1871CC.....	139,950
1871S......	2,178,000
1872 (950)..	881,550
1872CC.....	272,000
1872S......	580,000
1873 (600)..	801,800
1873 Arrows (550).....	1,815,700
1873CC No Arrows....	122,500
1873CC Arrows	214,560
1873S No Arrows....	5,000
1873S Arrows	228,000
1874 (700)..	2,360,300
1874CC.....	59,000
1874S......	394,000
1875 (700)..	6,027,500
1875CC.....	1,008,000
1875S......	3,200,000
1876 (1150).	8,419,150
1876CC.....	1,956,000
1876S......	4,528,000
1877 (510)..	8,304,510
1877CC.....	1,420,000
1877S......	5,356,000
1878 (800)..	1,378,400

HALF DOLLARS

Date and Mint Mark	Quantity Minted
1878CC.....	62,000
1878S......	12,000
1879 (1100).	5,900
1880 (1355).	9,755
1881 (975)..	10,975
1882 (1100).	5,500
1883 (1039).	9,039
1884 (875)..	5,275
1885 (930)..	6,130
1886 (886)..	5,886
1887 (710)..	5,710
1888 (832)..	12,833
1889 (711)..	12,711
1890 (590)..	12,590
1891 (600)..	200,600
1892 (1245).	935,245
1892O......	390,000
1892S......	1,029,028
1893 (792)..	1,826,792
1893O......	1,389,000
1893S......	740,000
1894 (972)..	1,148,972
1894O......	2,138,000
1894S......	4,048,690
1895 (880)..	1,835,218
1895O......	1,766,000
1895S......	1,108,086
1896 (762)..	950,762
1896O......	924,000
1896S......	1,140,948
1897 (731)..	2,480,731
1897O......	632,000
1897S......	933,900
1898 (735)..	2,956,735
1898O......	874,000
1898S......	2,358,550
1899 (846)..	5,538,846
1899O......	1,724,000
1899S......	1,686,411
1900 (912)..	4,762,912
1900O......	2,744,000
1900S......	2,560,322
1901 (813)..	4,268,813
1901O......	1,124,000
1901S......	847,044
1902 (777)..	4,922,777
1902O......	2,526,000
1902S......	1,460,670
1903 (755)..	2,278,755
1903O......	2,100,000
1903S......	1,920,772
1904 (670)..	2,992,670
1904O......	1,117,600
1904S......	553,038

HALF DOLLARS

Date and Mint Mark	Quantity Minted
1905 (727)..	662,727
1905O......	505,000
1905S......	2,494,000
1906 (675)..	2,638,675
1906D......	4,028,000
1906O......	2,446,000
1906S......	1,740,154
1907 (575)..	2,598,575
1907D......	3,856,000
1907O......	3,946,600
1907S......	1,250,000
1908 (545)..	1,354,545
1908D......	3,280,000
1908O......	5,360,000
1908S......	1,644,828
1909 (650)..	2,368,650
1909O......	925,400
1909S......	1,764,000
1910 (551)..	418,551
1910S......	1,948,000
1911 (543)..	1,406,543
1911D......	695,080
1911S......	1,272,000
1912 (700)..	1,550,700
1912D......	2,300,800
1912S......	1,370,000
1913 (627)..	188,627
1913D......	534,000
1913S......	604,000
1914 (380)..	124,610
1914S......	992,000
1915 (450)..	138,450
1915D......	1,170,400
1915S.......	1,604,000
1916 New type.......	608,000
1916D on Obv.......	1,014,400
1916S on Obv.......	508,000
1917........	12,292,000
1917D on Obv.....	765,400
1917D on Rev.......	1,940,000
1917S on Obv.......	952,000
1917S on Rev	5,554,000
1918........	6,634,000
1918D......	3,853,040
1918S.......	10,282,000
1919........	962,000
1919D......	1,165,000
1919S.......	1,552,000

HALF DOLLARS

Date and Mint Mark	Quantity Minted
1920	6,372,000
1920D	1,551,000
1920S	4,624,000
1921	246,000
1921D	208,000
1921S	548,000
1923S	2,178,000
1927S	2,392,000
1928S	1,940,000
1929D	1,001,200
1929S	1,902,000
1933S	1,786,000
1934	6,964,000
1934D	2,361,400
1934S	3,652,000
1935	9,162,000
1935D	3,003,800
1935S	3,854,000
1936 (3901)	12,617,901
1936D	4,252,400
1936S	3,884,000
1937 (5728)	9,527,728
1937D	1,760,001
1937S	2,090,000
1938 (8152)	4,118,152
1938D	491,600
1939 (8808)	6,820,808
1939D	4,267,800
1939S	2,552,000
1940 (11279)	9,167,279
1940S	4,550,000
1941 (15412)	24,207,412
1941D	11,248,400
1941S	8,098,000
1942 (21120)	47,839,120
1942D	10,973,800
1942S	12,708,000
1943	53,190,000
1943D	11,346,000
1943S	13,450,000
1944	28,206,000
1944D	9,769,000
1944S	8,904,000
1945	31,502,000
1945D	9,966,800
1945S	10,156,000
1946	12,118,000
1946D	2,151,100
1946S	3,724,000
1947	4,094,000
1947D	3,900,000
1948	3,006,814
1948D	4,028,600
1949	5,714,000

HALF DOLLARS

Date and Mint Mark	Quantity Minted
1949D	4,120,600
1949S	3,744,000
1950 (51386)	7,793,509
1950D	8,031,600
1951 (57500)	16,859,602
1951D	9,475,200
1951S	13,696,000
1952 (81,980)	21,274,073
1952D	25,395,600
1952S	5,526,000
1953 (128800)	2,796,920
1953D	20,900,400
1953S	4,148,000
1954 (233,300)	13,421,503
1954D	25,445,580
1954S	4,993,400
1955 (378,200)	2,876,381
1956 (669,384)	4,701,384
1957 (1,247,952) 6,361,952
1957D	19,966,850
1958 (875,652)	4,917,652
1958D	23,962,412
1959 (1,149,291) 7,349,291
1959D	13,053,750
1960 (1,691,602) 7,715,602
1960D	18,215,812

SILVER DOLLARS

Date	Quantity Minted
1794	1,758
1795	184,013
1796	72,920
1797	7,776
1798	327,536
1799	423,515
1800	220,920
1801	54,454
1802	41,650
1803	66,064
1804	19,570
1840	61,005
1841	173,000
1842	184,618
1843	165,100
1844	20,000
1845	24,500
1846	110,600
1846O	59,000
1847	140,750
1848	15,000
1849	62,600
1850	7,500

SILVER DOLLARS

Date and Mint Mark	Quantity Minted
1850O	40,000
1851	1,300
1852	1,100
1853	46,110
1854	33,140
1855	26,000
1856	63,500
1857	94,000
1858	(80)
1859	256,500
1859O	360,000
1859S	20,000
1860	218,930
1860O	515,000
1861	78,500
1862	12,090
1863 (460)	27,660
1864 (470)	31,170
1865 (500)	47,000
1866 (725)	49,625
1867 (625)	60,325
1868 (600)	182,700
1869 (600)	424,300
1870 (1000)	433,000
1870CC	12,462
1871 (960)	1,115,760
1871CC	1,376
1872 (950)	1,106,450
1872CC	3,150
1872S	9,000
1873 (600)	293,600
1873CC	2,300
1873S	700
1878 All kinds (550)	10,509,550
1878CC	2,212,000
1878S	9,774,000
1879 (1100)	14,807,100
1879CC	756,000
1879O	2,887,000
1879S	9,110,000
1880 (1355)	12,601,355
1880CC	591,000
1880O	5,305,000
1880S	8,900,000
1881 (975)	9,163,975
1881CC	296,000
1881O	5,708,000
1881S	12,760,000
1882 (1100)	11,101,100
1882CC	1,133,000
1882O	6,090,000
1882S	9,250,000
1883 (1039)	12,291,039

[243]

SILVER DOLLARS		SILVER DOLLARS		TRADE DOLLARS	
Date and Mint Mark	Quantity Minted	Date and Mint Mark	Quantity Minted	Date and Mint Mark	Quantity Minted
1883CC.....	1,204,000	1898S......	4,102,000	1875 (700)..	218,900
1883O......	8,725,000	1899 (846)..	330,846	1875CC.....	1,573,700
1883S......	6,250,000	1899O......	12,290,000	1875S......	4,487,000
1884 (875)..	14,070,875	1899S......	2,562,000	1876 (1150).	456,150
1884CC.....	1,136,000	1900 (912)..	8,830,912	1876CC.....	509,000
1884O......	9,730,000	1900O......	12,590,000	1876S......	5,227,000
1884S......	3,200,000	1900S......	3,540,000	1877 (510)..	3,039,710
1885 (930)..	17,787,767	1901 (813)..	6,962,813	1877CC.....	534,000
1885CC.....	228,000	1901O......	13,320,000	1877S......	9,519,000
1885O......	9,185,000	1901S......	2,284,000	1878 (900)..	900
1885S......	1,497,000	1902 (777)..	7,994,777	1878CC.....	97,000
1886 (886)..	19,963,886	1902O......	8,636,000	1878S......	4,162,000
1886O......	10,710,000	1902S......	1,530,000	1879 (1541).	1,541
1886S......	750,000	1903 (755)..	4,652,755	1880 (1987).	1,987
1887 (710)..	20,290,710	1903O......	4,450,000	1881 (960)..	960
1887O......	11,550,000	1903S......	1,241,000	1882 (1097).	1,097
1887S......	1,771,000	1904 (650)..	2,788,650	1883 (979)..	979
1888 (832)..	19,183,833	1904O......	3,720,000	1884 (10)...	10
1888O......	12,150,000	1904S.......	2,304,000	1885 (5)....	5
1888S......	657,000	1921 Mor. T.	44,690,000		
1889 (811)..	21,726,811	1921 D M. T.	20,345,000	GOLD DOLLARS	
1889CC.....	350,000	1921 S M. T.	21,695,000	1849........	688,567
1889O......	11,875,000	1921 Peace type	1,006,473	1849C......	11,634
1889S......	700,000	1922........	51,737,000	1849D......	21,588
1890 (590)..	16,802,590	1922D......	15,063,000	1849O......	215,000
1890CC.....	2,309,041	1922S.......	17,475,000	1850........	481,953
1890O......	10,701,000	1923........	30,800,000	1850C......	6,966
1890S......	8,230,373	1923D......	6,811,000	1850D......	8,382
1891 (650)..	8,694,206	1923S.......	19,020,000	1850O......	14,000
1891CC.....	1,618,000	1924........	11,811,000	1851........	3,317,671
1891O......	7,954,529	1924S.......	1,728,000	1851C......	41,267
1891S......	5,296,000	1925........	10,198,000	1851D......	9,882
1892 (1245).	1,037,245	1925S.......	1,610,000	1851O......	290,000
1892CC.....	1,352,000	1926........	1,939,000	1852........	2,045,351
1892O......	2,744,000	1926D......	2,348,700	1852C......	9,434
1892S......	1,200,000	1926S......	6,980,000	1852D......	6,360
1893 (792)..	378,792	1927........	848,000	1852O......	140,000
1893CC.....	677,000	1927D......	1,268,900	1853........	4,076,051
1893O......	300,000	1927S......	866,000	1853C......	11,515
1893S......	100,000	1928........	360,649	1853D......	6,583
1894 (972)..	110,972	1928S......	1,632,000	1853O......	290,000
1894O......	1,723,000	1934........	954,057	1854 Both large and small...	1,639,445
1894S......	1,260,000	1934D......	1,569,000		
1895 (880)..	12,880	1934S......	1,011,000	1854C......	4
1895O......	450,000	1935........	1,576,000	1854D......	2,935
1895S......	400,000	1935S.......	1,964,000	1854S.......	14,632
1896 (762)..	9,976,762			1855........	758,269
1896O......	4,900,000	TRADE DOLLARS		1855C......	9,803
1896S......	5,000,000	1873 (865)..	397,500	1855D......	1,811
1897 (731)..	2,822,731	1873CC.....	124,500	1855O......	55,000
1897O......	4,004,000	1873S......	703,000	1856........	1,762,936
1897S......	5,825,000	1874 (700)..	987,800	1856D......	1,460
1898 (735)..	5,884,735	1874CC.....	1,373,200	1856S.......	24,600
1898O......	4,440,000	1874S......	2,549,000	1857........	774,789

[244]

GOLD DOLLARS

Date and Mint Mark	Quantity Minted
1857C	13,280
1857D	3,533
1857S	10,000
1858	117,995
1858D	3,477
1858S	10,000
1859	168,244
1859C	5,235
1859D	4,952
1859S	15,000
1860	36,668
1860D	1,566
1860S	13,000
1861	527,499
1861D	
1862	1,326,865
1863	6,250
1864	5,950
1865 (25)	3,725
1866 (30)	7,180
1867 (50)	5,250
1868 (25)	10,525
1869 (25)	5,925
1870 (35)	6,335
1870S	3,000
1871 (30)	3,930
1872 (30)	3,530
1873 (25)	125,125
1874 (20)	198,820
1875 (20)	420
1876 (45)	3,245
1877 (20)	3,920
1878 (20)	3,020
1879 (30)	3,030
1880 (36)	1,636
1881 (40)	7,660
1882 (40)	5,040
1883 (40)	10,840
1884 (976)	6,206
1885 (1049)	12,205
1886 (1016)	6,016
1887 (1043)	8,543
1888 (457)	16,080
1889 (1779)	30,729

QUARTER EAGLES

Date and Mint Mark	Quantity Minted
1796 No stars	897
1796 With stars	66
1797	1,756
1798	614
1802 Over 1	2,612
1804	3,327
1805	1,781
1806	1,616
1807	6,812
1808	2,710
1821	6,448
1824	2,600
1825	4,434
1826 Over 25	760
1827	2,800
1829	3,403
1830	4,540
1831	4,520
1832	4,400
1833	4,160
1834 (Motto)	4,000
1834 (No motto)	112,234
1835	131,402
1836	547,986
1837	45,080
1838	47,030
1838C	7,908
1839	27,021
1839C	18,173
1839D	13,674
1839O	17,781
1840	18,859
1840C	12,838
1840D	3,532
1840O	26,200
1841C	10,297
1841D	4,164
1841O	7,380
1842	2,823
1842C	6,737
1842D	4,643
1842O	19,800
1843	100,546
1843C	26,096
1843D	36,209
1843O	368,002
1844	6,784
1844C	11,622
1844D	17,332
1845	91,051
1845D	19,460
1845O	4,000
1846	21,598
1846C	4,808
1846D	19,303
1846O	66,000
1847	29,814
1847C	23,226
1847D	15,784
1847O	124,000
1848 (Cal. 1389)	8,886

QUARTER EAGLES

Date and Mint Mark	Quantity Minted
1848C	16,788
1848D	13,771
1849	23,294
1849C	10,220
1849D	10,945
1850	252,923
1850C	9,148
1850D	12,148
1850O	84,000
1851	1,372,748
1851C	14,923
1851D	11,264
1851O	148,000
1852	1,159,681
1852C	9,772
1852D	4,078
1852O	140,000
1853	1,404,668
1853D	3,178
1854	596,258
1854C	7,295
1854D	1,760
1854O	153,000
1854S	246
1855	235,480
1855C	3,677
1855D	1,123
1856	384,240
1856C	7,913
1856D	874
1856O	21,100
1856S	71,120
1857	214,130
1857D	2,364
1857O	34,000
1857S	68,000
1858	47,377
1858C	9,056
1858S	1,200
1859	39,444
1859D	2,244
1859S	15,200
1860	22,675
1860C	7,469
1860S	35,600
1861	1,272,518
1861S	24,000
1862	112,353
1862S	8,000
1863	30
1863S	10,800
1864	2,874
1865 (25)	1,545
1865S	23,376

[245]

QUARTER EAGLES

Date and Mint Mark	Quantity Minted
1866 (30)...	3,110
1866S......	38,960
1867 (50)...	3,250
1867S......	28,000
1868 (25)...	3,625
1868S......	34,000
1869 (25)...	4,345
1869S......	29,500
1870 (35)...	4,555
1870S......	16,000
1871 (30)...	5,350
1871S......	22,000
1872 (30)...	3,030
1872S......	18,000
1873 (25)...	178,025
1873S......	27,000
1874 (20)...	3,940
1875 (20)...	420
1875S......	11,600
1876 (45)...	4,221
1876S......	5,000
1877 (20)...	1,652
1877S......	35,400
1878 (20)...	286,260
1878S......	178,000
1879 (30)...	88,900
1879S......	43,500
1880 (36)...	2,996
1881 (40)...	680
1882 (40)...	4,040
1883 (40)...	1,960
1884 (43)...	1,993
1885 (87)...	887
1886 (88)...	4,088
1887 (122)..	6,282
1888 (92)...	16,098
1889 (48)...	17,648
1890 (93)...	8,813
1891 (80)...	11,040
1892 (105)..	2,545
1893 (106)..	30,106
1894 (122)..	4,122
1895 (119)..	6,119
1896 (132)..	19,202
1897 (136)..	29,904
1898 (165)..	24,165
1899 (150)..	27,350
1900 (205)..	67,205
1901 (233)..	91,323
1902 (193)..	133,733
1903 (197)..	201,257
1904 (170)..	160,960
1905 (144)..	217,944
1906 (160)..	176,490

QUARTER EAGLES

Date and Mint Mark	Quantity Minted
1907 (154)..	336,448
1908 (236)..	565,057
1909 (139)..	441,899
1910 (682)..	492,682
1911 (191)..	704,191
1911D......	55,680
1912 (197)..	616,197
1913 (165)..	722,165
1914 (117)..	240,117
1914D......	448,000
1915 (100)..	606,100
1925D......	578,000
1926........	446,000
1927........	388,000
1928........	416,000
1929........	532,000

THREE-DOLLAR GOLD PIECES

Date	Quantity Minted
1854........	138,618
1854D......	1,120
1854O......	24,000
1855........	50,555
1855S.......	6,600
1856........	26,010
1856S.......	34,500
1857........	20,891
1857S.......	14,000
1858........	2,133
1859........	15,638
1860........	7,155
1860S.......	7,000
1861........	6,072
1862........	5,785
1863........	5,039
1864........	2,680
1865 (25)...	1,165
1866 (30)...	4,030
1867 (50)...	2,650
1868 (25)...	4,875
1869 (25)...	2,525
1870 (35)...	3,535
1870S.......	2
1871 (30)...	1,330
1872 (30)...	2,030
1873 (25)...	25
1874 (20)...	41,820
1875 (20)...	20
1876 (45)...	45
1877 (20)...	1,488
1878 (20)...	82,324
1879 (30)...	3,030
1880 (36)...	1,036
1881 (54)...	550

THREE-DOLLAR GOLD PIECES

Date and Mint Mark	Quantity Minted
1882 (76)...	1,540
1883 (89)...	940
1884 (106)..	1,106
1885 (110)..	910
1886 (142)..	1,142
1887 (160)..	6,160
1888 (291)..	5,291
1889 (129)..	2,429

HALF EAGLES

Date	Quantity
1795	8,707
1796........	3,399
1797	6,406
1798........	24,867
1799........	7,451
1800........	11,622
1802........	53,176
1803........	33,506
1804	30,475
1805........	33,183
1806	64,093
1807 Bust facing right	33,496
1807 Bust facing left..	50,597
1808	55,578
1809	33,875
1810	100,287
1811	99,581
1812........	58,087
1813........	95,428
1814........	15,454
1815........	635
1818........	48,588
1819........	51,723
1820	263,806
1821........	34,641
1822........	17,796
1823........	14,485
1824........	17,340
1825	29,060
1826........	18,069
1827	24,913
1828	28,029
1829	57,442
1830	126,351
1831	140,594
1832	157,487
1833........	193,630
1834 Motto..	50,141
1834 No motto	682,028
1835........	371,534
1836........	553,147

[246]

HALF EAGLES

Date and Mint Mark	Quantity Minted
1837........	207,121
1838........	286,588
1838C......	12,913
1838D......	20,583
1839........	118,143
1839C......	23,467
1839D......	18,939
1840........	137,382
1840C......	19,028
1840D......	22,896
1840O......	30,400
1841........	15,833
1841C......	21,511
1841D......	30,495
1841O......	8,350
1842........	27,578
1842C......	27,480
1842D......	59,608
1842O......	16,400
1843........	611,205
1843C......	44,353
1843D......	98,452
1843O......	101,075
1844........	340,330
1844C......	23,631
1844D......	88,982
1844O......	364,600
1845........	417,099
1845D......	90,629
1845O......	41,000
1846........	395,942
1846C......	12,995
1846D......	80,294
1846O......	58,000
1847........	915,981
1847C......	84,151
1847D......	64,405
1847O......	12,000
1848........	260,775
1848C......	64,472
1848D......	47,465
1849........	133,070
1849C......	64,823
1849D......	39,036
1850........	64,491
1850C......	63,591
1850D......	43,950
1851........	377,505
1851C......	49,176
1851D......	62,710
1851O......	41,000
1852........	573,901
1852C......	72,574
1852D......	91,452

Date and Mint Mark	Quantity Minted
1853........	305,770
1853C......	65,571
1853D......	89,678
1854........	160,675
1854C......	39,291
1854D......	56,413
1854O......	46,000
1854S......	268
1855........	117,098
1855C......	39,788
1855D......	22,432
1855O......	11,100
1855S......	61,000
1856........	197,990
1856C......	28,457
1856D......	19,786
1856O......	10,000
1856S......	105,100
1857........	98,188
1857C......	31,360
1857D......	17,046
1857O......	13,000
1857S......	87,000
1858........	15,136
1858C......	38,856
1858D......	15,362
1858S......	18,600
1859........	16,814
1859C......	31,847
1859D......	10,366
1859S......	13,220
1860........	19,825
1860C......	14,813
1860D......	14,635
1860S......	21,200
1861........	639,950
1861C......	6,879
1861D......	1,597
1861S......	18,000
1862........	4,465
1862S......	9,500
1863........	2,472
1863S......	17,000
1864........	4,220
1864S......	3,888
1865 (25)...	1,295
1865S......	27,612
1866 (30)...	6,720
1866S......	43,920
1867 (50)...	6,920
1867S......	29,000
1868 (25)...	5,725
1868S......	52,000
1869 (25)...	1,785

Date and Mint Mark	Quantity Minted
1869S......	31,000
1870 (35)...	4,035
1870CC.....	7,675
1870S......	17,000
1871 (30)...	3,230
1871CC.....	20,770
1871S......	25,000
1872 (30)...	1,690
1872CC.....	16,980
1872S......	36,400
1873 (25)...	112,505
1873CC.....	7,416
1873S......	31,000
1874 (20)...	3,508
1874CC.....	21,198
1874S......	16,000
1875 (20)...	220
1875CC.....	11,828
1875S......	9,000
1876 (45)...	1,477
1876CC.....	6,887
1876S......	4,000
1877 (20)...	1,152
1877CC.....	8,680
1877S......	26,700
1878 (20)...	131,740
1878CC.....	9,054
1878S......	144,700
1879 (30)...	301,950
1879CC.....	17,281
1879S......	426,200
1880 (36)...	3,166,436
1880CC.....	51,017
1880S......	1,348,900
1881 (40)...	5,708,800
1881CC.....	13,886
1881S......	969,000
1882 (40)...	2,514,560
1882CC.....	82,817
1882S......	969,000
1883 (40)...	233,440
1883CC.....	12,958
1883S......	83,200
1884 (18)...	191,048
1884CC.....	16,402
1884S......	177,000
1885 (66)...	601,506
1885S......	1,211,500
1886 (72)...	388,432
1886S......	3,268,000
1887 (87)...	87
1887S......	1,912,000
1888 (94)...	18,296
1888S......	293,900

[247]

HALF EAGLES		HALF EAGLES		EAGLES	
Date and Mint Mark	Quantity Minted	Date and Mint Mark	Quantity Minted	Date and Mint Mark	Quantity Minted
1889 (45)...	7,565	1910D......	193,600	1853........	201,253
1890 (88)...	4,328	1910S......	770,200	1853O......	51,000
1890CC.....	53,800	1911 (139)..	915,139	1854........	54,250
1891 (53)...	61,413	1911D......	72,500	1854O......	52,500
1891CC.....	208,000	1911S......	1,416,000	1854S.......	123,826
1892 (92)...	753,572	1912 (144)..	790,144	1855........	121,701
1892CC.....	82,968	1912S......	392,000	1855O......	18,000
1892O......	10,000	1913 (99)...	916,099	1855S.......	9,000
1892S......	298,400	1913S......	408,000	1856........	60,490
1893 (77)...	1,528,197	1914 (125)..	247,125	1856O......	14,500
1893CC.....	60,000	1914D......	247,000	1856S.......	68,000
1893O......	110,000	1914S......	263,000	1857........	16,606
1893S......	224,000	1915 (75)...	588,075	1857O......	5,500
1894 (75)...	957,955	1915S.......	164,000	1857S.......	26,000
1894O......	16,600	1916S.......	240,000	1858........	2,521
1894S......	55,900	1929........	662,000	1858O......	20,000
1895 (81)...	1,345,936			1858S.......	11,800
1895S......	112,000	EAGLES		1859........	16,093
1896 (103)..	59,063	1795........	2,795	1859O......	2,300
1896S......	155,400	1796........	6,080	1859S.......	7,000
1897 (83)...	867,883	1797	9,177	1860........	11,783
1897S......	354,000	1798........	7,974	1860O......	11,100
1898 (75)...	633,495	1799........	17,483	1860S.......	5,000
1898S......	1,397,400	1800........	25,965	1861........	113,233
1899 (99)...	1,710,729	1801........	29,254	1861S.......	15,500
1899S......	1,545,000	1803........	8,979	1862........	10,995
1900 (230)..	1,405,730	1804........	9,795	1862S.......	12,500
1900S......	329,000	1838........	7,200	1863........	1,248
1901 (140)..	616,040	1839	38,248	1863S.......	10,000
1901S......	3,648,000	1840........	47,338	1864........	3,580
1902 (162)..	172,562	1841........	63,131	1864S.......	2,500
1902S......	939,000	1841O......	2,500	1865 (25)...	4,005
1903 (154)..	227,024	1842........	81,507	1865S.......	16,700
1903S......	1,855,000	1842O......	27,400	1866 (30)...	3,780
1904 (136)..	392,136	1843........	75,462	1866S All	
1904S......	97,000	1843O......	175,162	kinds......	20,000
1905 (108)..	302,308	1844........	6,361	1867 (50)...	3,140
1905S......	880,700	1844O......	118,700	1867S......	9,000
1906 (85)...	348,820	1845........	26,153	1868 (25)...	10,655
1906D......	320,000	1845O......	47,500	1868S......	13,500
1906S......	598,000	1846........	20,095	1869 (25)...	1,855
1907 (92)...	626,192	1846O......	81,780	1869S......	6,430
1907D......	888,000	1847........	862,258	1870 (35)...	2,535
1908 Liberty head. (167)......	421,874	1847O......	571,500	1870CC.....	5,908
		1848........	145,484	1870S......	8,000
1908 Indian head......	578,012	1848O......	35,850	1871 (30)...	1,780
		1849........	653,618	1871CC.....	7,185
1908D......	148,000	1849O......	23,900	1871S......	16,500
1908S......	82,000	1850........	291,451	1872 (30)...	1,650
1909 (78)...	627,138	1850O......	57,500	1872CC.....	5,500
1909D......	3,423,560	1851........	176,328	1872S......	17,300
1909O......	34,200	1851O......	263,000	1873 (25)...	825
1909S......	297,200	1852........	263,106	1873CC.....	4,543
1910 (250)..	604,250	1852O......	18,000	1873S......	12,000

[248]

EAGLES

Date and Mint Mark	Quantity Minted
1874 (20)...	53,160
1874CC.....	16,767
1874S......	10,000
1875 (20)...	120
1875CC.....	7,715
1876 (45)...	732
1876CC.....	4,696
1876S......	5,000
1877 (20)...	817
1877CC.....	3,332
1877S.....	17,000
1878 (20)...	73,800
1878CC.....	3,244
1878S......	26,100
1879 (30)...	384,770
1879CC.....	1,762
1879O......	1,500
1879S......	224,000
1880 (36)...	1,644,876
1880CC.....	11,190
1880O......	9,200
1880S......	506,250
1881 (40)...	3,877,260
1881CC.....	24,015
1881O......	8,350
1881S......	970,000
1882 (40)...	2,324,480
1882CC.....	6,764
1882O......	10,820
1882S......	132,000
1883 (40)...	208,740
1883CC.....	12,000
1883O......	800
1883S......	38,000
1884 (15)...	76,905
1884CC.....	9,925
1884S......	124,250
1885 (65)...	253,527
1885S......	228,000
1886 (60)...	236,160
1886S......	826,000
1887 (80)...	53,680
1887S......	817,000
1888 (72)...	132,996
1888O......	21,335
1888S......	648,700
1889 (45)...	4,485
1889S......	425,400
1890 (63)...	58,043
1890CC.....	17,500
1891 (48)...	91,868
1891CC.....	103,732
1892 (72)...	797,552
1892CC.....	40,000

EAGLES

Date and Mint Mark	Quantity Minted
1892O......	28,688
1892S......	115,500
1893 (55)...	1,840,895
1893CC.....	14,000
1893O......	17,000
1893S......	141,350
1894 (43)...	2,470,778
1894O......	107,500
1894S......	25,000
1895 (56)...	567,826
1895O......	98,000
1895S......	49,000
1896 (78)...	76,348
1896S......	123,750
1897 (69)...	1,000,159
1897O......	42,500
1897S......	234,750
1898 (67)...	812,197
1898S......	473,600
1899 (86)...	1,262,305
1899O......	37,047
1899S......	841,000
1900 (120)..	293,960
1900S......	81,000
1901 (85)...	1,718,825
1901O......	72,041
1901S......	2,812,750
1902 (113)..	82,513
1902S......	469,500
1903 (96)...	125,926
1903O......	112,771
1903S......	538,000
1904 (108)..	162,038
1904O......	108,950
1905 (86)...	201,078
1905S......	369,250
1906 (77)...	165,497
1906D......	981,000
1906O......	86,895
1906S......	457,000
1907 Liberty head. All kinds (74)..	1,203,973
1907S Liberty	210,500
1907D Liberty	1,030,000
1907 Indian, reg.	239,406
1907 Indian, wire edge, periods	500
1907 Indian, rolled edge, periods.....	42
1908 No motto	33,500
1908 Motto (116)......	341,486

EAGLES

Date and Mint Mark	Quantity Minted
1908D No motto.....	210,000
1908D Motto	836,500
1908S Motto	59,850
1909 (74)...	184,863
1909D......	121,540
1909S......	292,350
1910 (204)..	318,704
1910D......	2,356,640
1910S......	811,000
1911 (95)...	505,595
1911D......	30,100
1911S......	51,000
1912 (83)...	405,083
1912S......	300,000
1913 (71)...	442,071
1913S......	66,000
1914 (50)...	151,050
1914D......	343,500
1914S......	208,000
1915 (75)...	351,075
1915S......	59,000
1916S......	138,500
1920S......	126,500
1926.......	1,014,000
1930S......	96,000
1932.......	4,463,000
1933.......	312,500

DOUBLE EAGLES

Date and Mint Mark	Quantity Minted
1849........	1
1850........	1,170,261
1850O......	141,000
1851........	2,087,155
1851O......	315,000
1852........	2,053,026
1852O......	190,000
1853........	1,261,326
1853O......	71,000
1854........	757,899
1854O......	3,250
1854S.......	141,468
1855........	364,666
1855O......	8,000
1855S.......	879,675
1856........	329,878
1856O......	2,250
1856S.......	1,189,750
1857........	439,375
1857O......	30,000
1857S.......	970,500
1858........	211,714
1858O......	35,250
1858S.......	846,710

[249]

DOUBLE EAGLES

Date and Mint Mark	Quantity Minted
1859	43,597
1859O	9,100
1859S	636,445
1860	577,670
1860O	6,600
1860S	544,950
1861	2,976,453
1861O	5,000
1861S	768,000
1862	92,133
1862S	854,173
1863	142,790
1863S	966,570
1864	204,285
1864S	793,660
1865 (25)	351,200
1865S	1,042,500
1866 (30)	698,775
1866S	842,250
1867 (50)	251,065
1867S	920,750
1868 (25)	98,600
1868S	837,500
1869 (25)	175,155
1869S	686,750
1870 (35)	155,185
1870CC	3,789
1870S	982,000
1871 (30)	80,150
1871CC	14,687
1871S	928,000
1872 (30)	251,880
1872CC	29,650
1872S	780,000
1873 (25)	1,709,825
1873CC	22,410
1873S	1,040,600
1874 (20)	366,800
1874CC	115,085
1874S	1,214,000
1875 (20)	295,740
1875CC	111,151
1875S	1,230,000
1876 (45)	583,905
1876CC	138,441
1876S	1,597,000
1877 (20)	397,670
1877CC	42,565
1877S	1,735,000
1878 (20)	543,645
1878CC	13,180
1878S	1,739,000
1879 (30)	207,630
1879CC	10,708
1879O	2,325
1879S	1,223,800
1880 (36)	51,456
1880S	836,000
1881 (40)	2,260
1881S	727,000
1882 (40)	630
1882CC	39,140
1882S	1,125,000
1883 (40)	40
1883CC	59,962
1883S	1,189,000
1884 (71)	71
1884CC	81,139
1884S	916,000
1885 (77)	828
1885CC	9,450
1885S	683,500
1886 (106)	1,106
1887 (121)	121
1887S	283,000
1888 (102)	226,266
1888S	859,600
1889 (41)	44,111
1889CC	30,945
1889S	774,700
1890 (55)	75,995
1890CC	91,209
1890S	802,750
1891 (52)	1,442
1891CC	5,000
1891S	1,288,125
1892 (93)	4,523
1892CC	27,265
1892S	930,150
1893 (59)	344,339
1893CC	18,402
1893S	996,175
1894 (50)	1,368,990
1894S	1,048,550
1895 (51)	1,114,656
1895S	1,143,500
1896 (128)	792,663
1896S	1,403,925
1897 (76)	1,383,261
1897S	1,470,250
1898 (75)	170,470
1898S	2,575,175
1899 (84)	1,669,384
1899S	2,010,300
1900 (124)	1,874,584
1900S	2,459,500
1901 (96)	111,526
1901S	1,596,000
1902 (114)	31,254
1902S	1,753,625
1903 (158)	287,428
1903S	954,000
1904 (98)	6,256,797
1904S	5,134,175
1905 (92)	59,011
1905S	1,813,000
1906 (94)	69,690
1906D	620,250
1906S	2,065,750
1907 Liberty (78)	1,451,864
1907D	842,250
1907S	2,165,800
1907 Flying eagle, MCMVII	11,250
1907 Flying eagle, 1907	361,667
1908 No motto	4,271,551
1908 Motto (101)	156,359
1908D No motto	663,750
1908D Motto	349,500
1908S Motto	22,000
1909 (67)	161,282
1909D	52,500
1909S	2,774,925
1910 (167)	482,167
1910D	429,000
1910S	2,128,250
1911 (100)	197,350
1911D	846,500
1911S	775,750
1912 (74)	149,824
1913 (58)	168,838
1913D	393,500
1913S	34,000
1914 (70)	95,320
1914D	453,000
1914S	1,498,000
1915 (50)	152,050
1915S	567,500
1916S	796,000
1920	228,250
1920S	558,000
1921	528,500
1922	1,375,500
1922S	2,658,000
1923	566,000
1923D	1,702,000
1924	4,323,500
1924D	3,049,500
1924S	2,927,500
1925	2,831,750

DOUBLE EAGLES		DOUBLE EAGLES		DOUBLE EAGLES	
Date and Mint Mark	Quantity Minted	Date and Mint Mark	Quantity Minted	Date and Mint Mark	Quantity Minted
1925D	2,938,500	1927	2,946,750	1930S	74,000
1925S	3,776,500	1927D	180,000	1931	2,938,250
1926	816,750	1927S	3,107,000	1931D	106,500
1926D	481,000	1928	8,816,000	1932	1,101,750
1926S	2,041,500	1929	1,779,750	1933	445,500

COINAGE FIGURES FOR ALASKA A.R.R.C. TOKENS OF 1935

Cent	5,000
Five Cents	5,000
Ten Cents	5,000
Twenty-five Cents	3,000
Fifty Cents	2,500
One Dollar	2,500
Five Dollars	1,000
Ten Dollars	1,000

COINAGE FIGURES FOR HAWAII

1847 Cent	100,000
1883 Ten Cents	250,000
1883 Twenty-five Cents	500,000
1883 Fifty Cents	700,000
1883 Dollar	500,000

INDEX

African Head Cent (Connecticut)....... 27
Alaska, ARRC Tokens................ 229
Arrows, at Date....................... 10
Arrows at Date, Half Dimes............ 92
Arrows at Date, Dimes............. 95, 96
Arrows at Date, Quarter Dollars... 104, 106
Arrows at Date, Half Dollars..... 119, 121
Atlee, James F.................... 24, 39
Auctori Connec Cents (Connecticut).... 27
Auctori Plebis Token.................. 47

Baldwin & Co. (Private Gold)..... 211-212
Baltimore, Lord (Maryland)............ 17
Bar Cent............................. 43
Barber Dimes ("Morgan") 1892-1916 97-98
Barber Quarter Dollars ("Morgan")
  1892-1916......................... 107
Barber Half Dollars ("Morgan")
  1892-1915..................... 122-123
Barry, Standish Threepence
  (Baltimore, Md.).................. 42
Bechtlers, The, Christopher and
  August........................ 9, 191-193
Bermuda Islands (Sommer Islands)..... 13
Bibliography—
  Early American Coins and Tokens.... 57
  Half Cents......................... 62
  Cents, Large....................... 77
  Half Dimes......................... 93
  Quarter Dollars................... 109
  Half Dollars...................... 124
  Silver Dollars.................... 135
  Commemorative Coins............... 186
  Private Gold.................. 188-225
Birch, Robert, Engraver............ 8, 58
Birch Cents.......................... 58
Bishop, Samuel (Connecticut).......... 27
Bit (Fractional Spanish Coin).......... 5
Bit (Nova Constellatio Pattern)....... 36
Blake & Agnell.................. 209-210
Blake & Co......................... 210
Bland-Allison Act, 1878............ 11-12
Bland Dollars (Liberty Head or
  Morgan Type) 1878-1921...... 134-135
Booby Head Cent, 1839................ 75
Brasher, Ephriam, Doubloons....... 39-40
Brenner, Victor B. (Designer of
  Lincoln Cent)..................... 82
Britannia (1787 Cent)................ 24
Broome, Samuel (Connecticut)......... 27
Buel, Abel (Die-sinker Connecticut).... 27
Buel, Abel (Fugio dies).............. 56
Buffalo Nickels (Indian Head)
  1913-1938....................... 87-88

California Gold................. 194-225
California Fractional Gold........... 218
Callender, Joseph (Mass.)............ 31
Carolina Elephant Tokens.......... 44-45
Carolina Gold (Bechtler)....... 9, 191-193
Castorland Medal.................... 51
Cent, Confederate.................. 227
Cent, 1804, Restrike................. 67
Cent, 1864, L on Ribbon, How to
  Locate............................ 81
Cent, Silver Center............... 8, 58
Cents, Large 1793-1857........... 62, 78
Cents, Copper-Nickel (White Cents)
  1856-1864....................... 79-80
Cents, Flying Eagle 1856-58.......... 79
Cents, Indian..................... 80-81
Cents, Lincoln................... 82, 84

Cents, Shell-Case Copper 1944........ 83
Cents, Steel 1943.................... 83
Chalmers, J., Silver Tokens
  (Annapolis, Md.)................ 5, 42
Charlotte, No. Car. Branch Mint....... 9
Chase, Salmon P.................. 10, 84
Cincinnati Mining & Trading Co.
  (Private Gold)................... 205
Civil War Tokens................... 226
Clark, Gruber & Co. (Private Gold)222-223
Clinton, George, Cent (New York)..... 25
Coinage, Gratuitous.................. 12
Coinage, First Regular................ 8
Coinage, Subsidiary................... 9
Colorado Gold Pieces............ 222-223
Comet Variety 1807 Cent.............. 68
Commemorative Coins, General
  Information...................... 163
Commemorative Gold............. 184-186
  Grant Memorial................... 186
  Lewis and Clark Exposition....... 184
  Louisiana Purchase Exposition.... 184
  McKinley Memorial................ 186
  Panama-Pacific Exposition........ 184
  Philadelphia Sesquicentennial.... 186
Commemorative Silver........... 163-183
  Alabama Centennial............... 167
  Albany, N. Y., Charter........... 179
  American Independence, Sesqui-
    centennial of.................. 170
  Antietam, Battle of.............. 182
  Arkansas Centennial.............. 174
  Boone, Daniel, Bicentennial...... 173
  Bridgeport, Conn., Centennial.... 178
  California Diamond Jubilee....... 169
  California-Pacific Exposition.... 175
  Cincinnati Music Center.......... 177
  Cleveland Great Lakes Exposition. 176
  Columbian Exposition............. 164
  Columbia, S. C., Sesquicentennial. 180
  Connecticut Tercentenary......... 174
  Delaware Tercentenary............ 181
  Elgin, Ill., Centennial.......... 179
  Fort Vancouver Centennial........ 170
  Gettysburg, Battle of............ 181
  Grant Memorial................... 168
  Hawaiian Sesquicentennial........ 171
  Hudson, N. Y., Sesquicentennial.. 175
  Huguenot-Walloon Tercentenary.... 168
  Illinois Centennial.............. 165
  Iowa Centennial.................. 183
  Isabella Quarter................. 164
  Lafayette Dollar................. 165
  Lexington-Concord Sesquicentennial. 169
  Long Island Tercentenary......... 177
  Lynchburg, Va., Sesquicentennial. 179
  Maine Centennial................. 166
  Maryland Tercentenary............ 172
  Missouri Centennial.............. 167
  Monroe Doctrine.................. 168
  New Rochelle, N. Y............... 182
  Norfolk, Va., Bicentennial....... 181
  Old Spanish Trail................ 176
  Oregon Trail Memorial............ 170
  Panama-Pacific Exposition........ 165
  Pilgrim Tercentenary............. 166
  Providence, R. I., Tercentenary.. 176
  Roanoke Island, N. C............. 182
  Robinson-Arkansas Centennial..... 180
  San Francisco-Oakland Bay Bridge. 180
  Stone Mountain Memorial.......... 169
  Texas Centennial................. 172

[252]

INDEX — *Continued*

	Page
Vermont Sesquicentennial	171
Washington, Booker T.	183
Washington-Carver	184
Wisconsin Centennial	177
York County, Maine, Tercentenary	178
Condition of Coins	2
Confederate Half Dollar and Cent	226-227
Confederatio Cents	39
Connecticut Cents (Auctori Connec.)	27-30
Continental Dollar, 1776	35
Conway, J. J. & Co. (Private Gold)	224
Cooley, Col. William	23, 24
Copper Co. of Upper Canada Token	48
Cox, Albion (New Jersey)	33
Dahlonega, Ga., Branch Mint	9
Decimal Ratio System	7, 35
Designs, Law Concerning Change of	12
Dimes	93-99
Dimes, Liberty Seated 1837-1891	95-97
Dimes—Barber ("Morgan") 1892-1916	97-98
Dimes, "Mercury" Head	98-99
Dimes, Roosevelt	99
Disme, 1792	58
Dollar, Origin of	123
Dollar, 1804 (Authenticity)	129
Dollars, Gold, 1849-1889	138-139
Dollars, Gold (Calif.)	218
Dollars, Silver, Liberty Seated 1840-1873	133
Dollars, Silver, Liberty Head, Bland, or Morgan Type 1878-1921	134-135
Dollars, Silver, Peace Type 1921-1935	136
Dollars, Patterns (Gobrecht) 1836-1839	131-132
Dollars, Silver, Report for 1805	123
Dollars, Trade	137
Drapery from Elbow, Half Dimes	91
Drapery from Elbow, Dimes	95
Drapery from Elbow, Quarters	103
Drapery from Elbow, Half Dollars	116
Dubosq & Co. (Private Gold)	210-211
Dudley, Benjamin (Nova Constellatio)	6, 35
Dunbar & Co. (Private Gold)	213
Eagles ($10 Gold Pieces) 1795-1933	154-158
1873, Law of	11
Elephant Tokens	44-45
English-American Colonies, Coins and Tokens	13-22
Excelsior Cents (New York)	25
Feuchtwanger, Dr. Lewis	85
Five Cent, Nickel	86-89
Five Cent, Silver	89, 90-93
Five Cent, Shield Type 1866-1883	86
Five Cent, Liberty Head 1883-1913	86-87
Five Cent, Indian or Buffalo Type 1913-1938	87, 88
Five Cent, Jefferson Type	88, 89
Flying Eagle Cent 1858, Large and Small Letters	79
Fifty Dollar Gold (Private)	199-201, 203, 217, 219
Five Dollar Gold Pieces, Half Eagles, 1795-1929	145-153
Florida Token	49
Four Dollar Gold (Stellas)	144
Fox Variety Cent (N. J.)	34

	Page
Franklin, Benjamin—Fugio Cents	56-57
Franklin Press Cent	50
Free Coinage	7
French Colonies	38
Fugio Cents	56-57
George III—Immune Columbia	38
George III—Indian Cent (New York)	26
Georgia Gold (Reid)	9, 189-190
Georgia Gold (Bechtler)	9, 191-193
Georgius Triumpho Token	46
Gloucester Token	40
Goadsby, Thomas (N. J.)	33
Gobrecht, Christian	125, 131-132
Gold, Historical Significance	138
Gold Standard	11
Gold Standard Act	12
Gold Surrender Order	12
Gold Dollars 1849-1889	138-139
Gold, $2.50	140-143
Gold, Three Dollars	143-144
Gold, Stella, $400 Patterns	144
Gold, Five Dollars	145-153
Gold, Ten Dollars	154-158
Gold, Twenty Dollars	158-162
Gold, Private	188-225
Good Samaritan Shilling	17
Goodrich, John (Connecticut)	27
Granby Coppers (John Higley)	41
Half Cents	59-62
Half Dime (LIBEKTY Variety) 1800	91
Half Dimes	90-93
Half Dimes, Liberty Seated	91-93
Half Disme 1792	8, 58
Half Dollars	110-122
Half Dollars, Liberty Seated	116-119
Half Dollars, Barber ("Morgan")	120
Half Dollars, Liberty Standing	121-122
Half Dollars, Confederate	226-227
Half Dollars, Gold	218
Half Eagles 1795-1929	145-153
Hamilton, Alexander	7, 57
Hard Time Tokens	225
Harmon, Reuben Jr.	23-24
Hawaii, Coins and Tokens	228
Hercules Head Cent (Connecticut)	28, 29
Hibernia—Voce Populi Token	50
Hibernia Coins, William Wood	21-22
Higley, John Coppers (Granby, Connecticut)	41
Hillhouse, James (Connecticut)	27
"Hogge Money" (Sommer Islands)	5, 13
Hopkins, Joseph (Connecticut)	27
Horned Bust Cent (Connecticut)	29
Hull, John (Mass. Colonial Silver)	14
Humbert, Augustus (U. S. Assayer)	197
Immune Columbia Cents 1785	38
Immune Columbia Cents—Vermont Obverse	38
Immunis Columbia Cent (New Jersey)	33
Immunis Columbia Cent (New York)	26
Indian—George III Cent (New York)	26
Indian Head Cents	80-81
Indian Head (Buffalo) Nickels	87-88
Indian Head Quarter Eagle	143
Indian Head Half Eagles	153
Indian Head Eagles ($10)	157-158
Ingots, California Gold	195, 212

[253]

INDEX — *Continued*

	Page
Janus Copper 1776 (Mass.)	31
Jefferson, Thomas	6, 9, 10, 129
Jenks, Joseph	14
Kellogg & Co. (Private Gold)	216-218
Kentucky Cent (Kentucky Triangle)	47
Kentucky, Myddleton Tokens	47
James King of William & Co.	212
Kohler, F. D. (Calif. State Assayer)	209
Laughing Head Cent (Connecticut)	29
Lesher Dollars	225
LIBEKTY Variety, 1800 Half Dime	91
Liberty Head Dollars (Bland or Morgan)	134-135
Liberty Head Nickels	86-87
Liberty Seated Half Dimes	91-93
Liberty Seated Dimes	95-97
Liberty Seated Quarter Dollars	103-106
Liberty Seated Half Dollars	117-122
Liberty Seated Dollars	131-133
Liberty Standing Quarter Dollars	108
Liberty Standing Half Dollars	123-124
LIHERTY, Cent Variety 1796	64
Liverpool Half penny	52
London Token (Elephant)	45
Lord Baltimore (Maryland)	17
Mark (Nova Constellatio Patterns)	6, 36
Maryland (Lord Baltimore)	17
Massachusetts & California Co. (Private Gold)	206
Massachusetts, Colonial Silver	14-17
Massachusetts 1787-8 Cents and Half Cents	31-32
Massachusetts Tokens and Patterns	31
"Mercury" Head Dimes 1916-1945	98
Meyers & Co.	195
Miners Bank (Private Gold)	206-207
Mint, Location of First	7
Mint Mark "P" (Silver Five-Cent Pieces)	89
Mintage of U. S. Coins	232-251
Mints and Mint Marks	231-232
Moffat & Co. (Private Gold)	196-204
"Morgan" Dimes (Barber)	97-98
"Morgan" Quarter Dollars (Barber)	107
"Morgan" Half Dollars (Barber)	122-123
Morgan Dollars (Liberty Head or Bland Type)	134-135
Morgan, George T	134
Mormon Gold Pieces	220-221
Morris, Gouverneur	6, 37
Morris, Robert	6, 36
Mott Token	43
Motto In God We Trust	84
Mould, Walter (New Jersey)	33
Moulton, William (New Hampshire)	22
Mutton Head Cent (Connecticut)	29
Myddleton Tokens	47
Newby, Mark (St. Patrick) Halfpence	18
New England (N. E.) Shillings, etc	14
New England Elephant Token	44
New England Stiver	49
New Hampshire Cent	22
New Jersey (Mark Newby) Halfpence	18
New Jersey Cents	33-34
New York (Nova Eboracus-Neo Eborac)	24-27
New Yorke Token	48
Nickel, First Use of	10
Nickel, Three Cents	85

	Page
Nickel, Five Cents	86-86
Non Virtuti Vici Cent (New York)	25
Norris, Grieg & Norris (Private Gold)	195
North American Token	49
North Wales Halfpenny	55
North West Token	48
Nova Caesarea Cents (New Jersey)	33
Nova Constellatio Coppers	36-37
Nova Constellatio Patterns (Silver)	6, 36
Nova Eborac Cents (New York)	26-27
Oak Tree Shilling, etc	15-16
Oregon Exchange Co. (Private Gold)	218-220
Ormsby, J. S. (Private Gold)	207
Pacific Co. (Private Gold)	208
Parsons, John & Co. (Private Gold)	223-224
Peace Dollars 1921-1935	136
Perkins, Jacob (Mass.)	31
Philippines	230-231
Piece of Eight	4
Pillar Dollar	4
Pine Tree Copper 1776 (Mass.)	31
Pine Tree Shillings, etc	16
Pitt Tokens	50
Platt, Jeremiah (Connecticut)	27
Postage Currency	10
Pratt, Bela Lyon (Indian Quarter and Half Eagles)	143, 153
Private or Territorial Gold	188-225
Proof Coins	187
Quantities Minted U. S. Coins	232-251
Quarter Dollars	100-109
Quarter Dollars, Liberty Seated	103-106
Quarter Dollars, Barber Type	107
Quarter Dollars, Liberty Standing	108
Quarter Dollars, Washington Head 1932 to date	109
Quarter Dollars, Gold	218
Quarter Eagles	140-143
Quarter Eagle, "CAL" on Reverse 1848	141-142
Quarter Eagle, Indian Head	143
Quint (Nova Constellatio Patterns)	6, 36
Ratio, Gold and Silver	8, 11
Reid, Templeton (Private Gold)	9, 189-190
Rhode Island Ship Token	51
Rittenhouse, David	7
Roosevelt, Franklin D., Dimes	99
Roosevelt, Theodore (Mottoes)	158
Rosa Americana Coins (William Wood)	18
Saint Gaudens, Augustus, Eagles and Double Eagles	157-158, 161-162
St. Patrick (Mark Newby) Half Pence	18
Samaritan Shilling	17
Sanderson, Robert (Mass. Colonial)	14
Schultz & Co. (Private Gold)	213
Serpent Head Cent (New Jersey)	34
Shield Nickels	86
Ship Halfpenny	52
Silly Head Cent 1839	75
Silver Center Cent	8, 57, 58
Silver Certificates	12
Silver Composition Five Cents	89
Silver Dollars	125-136
Somers, Sir George (Sommer Islands)	13
Sommer Islands (Bermudas)	5, 13
Spanish Milled Dollar (Piece of Eight)	Frontispiece, 123

[254]

INDEX — *Continued*

	Page
States, Coinage of	6, 22-34
Stellas, $4.00 Gold Patterns	144
Stiver, New England	49
Subsidiary Coinage	9
Talbot Allum & Lee Cents	43-44
Ten Dollar Gold Pieces (Eagles)	154-158
Territorial or Private Gold	188-225
Three Cent, Nickel	85
Three Cent, Silver	90
Trade Dollars 1878-1885	137
Twenty Cent Pieces	11, 99
Two- and One-Half Dollar Gold Pieces (Quarter Eagles)	140-143
Two-Cent Pieces	84
United States Assay Office (Humbert)	197-204

	Page
VDB on Lincoln Cents	82
Vermont Coppers	23-24
Virginia Halfpenny, Shilling	46
Voce Populi—Hibernia Token	50
Voce Populi, Georgius Triumpho	46
Voigt, Henry (Silver Center Cent)	8
Wampum	5, 14
Washington, George	5, 6, 8
Washington Head Quarter Dollars	109
Washington Pieces 1783-95	51-55
Wass, Molitor & Co. (Private Gold)	214-216
White Cents (Copper-Nickel) 1856-1864	79-80
"Wildcat" Banks, Notes of	9
Willow Tree Shilling, etc	15
Witherle, Joshua (Mass.)	31
Wood, William Rosa Americana and Hibernia Coins	18-22

The following numismatic magazines are obtainable by subscription. They are published monthly:

The Numismatist (Published by the American Numismatic Association. Single Copy 50¢.)
Box 577
Wichita 1, Kansas

Numismatic Scrapbook Magazine
(Single Copy 50¢)
7320 N. Milwaukee Ave.
Chicago, Ill.

Hobbies Magazine
(Has a coin section, Single copy 35¢)
1006 S. Michigan Ave.
Chicago, Ill.

COIN FOLDERS

A Convenient Method for Housing Your Collection

Made by Whitman

SIZE FOLDED
5¾" x 7½"

Made in two tones of blue ... printed in black and silver, giving a brilliant "Jewel Case" effect to your coin collection.

COMPLETE LIST OF STYLES

Large Cent—1793 to 1825
Large Cent—1826 to 1857
Indian-Eagle Cents—1856 to 1909
Lincoln Head Cent—1909 to 1940
Lincoln Head Cent—Starting 1941
Cents—Plain, no printing

Half Dime—1794 to 1873
Shield Type Nickel—1866 to 1883
Liberty Head Nickel—1883 to 1913
Buffalo Nickel—1913 to 1938
Jefferson Nickel—Starting 1938
Nickels—Plain, no printing

Bust Type Dime—1796 to 1837
Liberty Seated Dime—1837 to 1862
Liberty Seated Dime—1863 to 1891
Barber Dime—1892 to 1916
Mercury Head Dime—1916 to 1945
Roosevelt Dime—Starting 1946
Dimes, Plain, no printing

Liberty Seated Quarter—1838 to 1865
Liberty Seated Quarter—1866 to 1891
Barber Quarter—1892 to 1905
Barber Quarter—1906 to 1916
Liberty Standing Quarter—1916 to 1930
Washington Head Quarter—1932 to 1945
Washington Head Quarter—1946 to 1959
Washington Head Quarter—Starting 1960
Quarters—Plain, no printing

Liberty Seated Half Dollar—1839 to 1850
Liberty Seated Half Dollar—1851 to 1862
Liberty Seated Half Dollar—1863 to 1873
Liberty Seated Half Dollar—1873 to 1891
Barber Half Dollar—1892 to 1903
Barber Half Dollar—1904 to 1915
Liberty Standing Half Dollar—1916 to 1936
Liberty Standing Half Dollar—1937 to 1947
Ben. Franklin Half Dollar—Starting 1948
Halves—Plain, no printing

Morgan Dollar—1878 to 1883
Morgan Dollar—1884 to 1890
Morgan Dollar—1891 to 1897
Morgan Dollar—1898 to 1921
Peace Dollars—1921 to 1935
Dollars—Plain, no printing

Half Cent—1793 to 1857
Silver Three Cent—1851 to 1873
Two Cent — Nickel Three Cent — 1864 to 1889
Type Coins, Small Denominations
Type Coins, Large Denominations
20th Century Type Coins

CANADA

Large Cents—1858 to 1920
Small Cents—Starting 1920
Silver Five Cents—1858 to 1921
Nickels—Starting 1922
Dimes—1858 to 1936
Dimes—Starting 1937
Quarters—1858 to 1910
Quarters—1911 to 1952
Quarters—Starting 1953
Halves—1870 to 1910
Halves—1911 to 1936
Halves—Starting 1937
Silver Dollars—1935 to 1957
Silver Dollars—Starting 1958
Cents and Half Cents—Newfoundland, New Brunswick, Nova Scotia and Prince Edward Island
Newfoundland 5¢—1865 to 1947
New Brunswick 5-10-20¢—1862 to 1864
Newfoundland 10¢—1865 to 1947
Newfoundland 20-25¢—1865 to 1919
Newfoundland 50¢—1870 to 1919
Quarters—Plain, no printing
Halves—Plain, no printing
Type Coin Collection
Dollars—Plain, no printing

GREAT BRITAIN

Farthings—1860 to 1901
Farthings—1902 to 1936
Farthings—1937 to 1956
Halfpennies—1860 to 1901
Halfpennies—1902 to 1936
Halfpennies—Starting 1937
Pennies—1860 to 1880
Pennies—1881 to 1901
Pennies—1902 to 1929
Pennies—Starting 1930